PROBLEMS IN THE PHILOSOPHY OF SCIENCE

STUDIES IN LOGIC

AND

THE FOUNDATIONS OF MATHEMATICS

NORTH-HOLLAND PUBLISHING COMPANY
AMSTERDAM

PROBLEMS IN THE
PHILOSOPHY OF SCIENCE

*Proceedings of the International Colloquium
in the Philosophy of Science, London, 1965,
volume 3*

Edited by

IMRE LAKATOS
Reader in Logic, University of London

ALAN MUSGRAVE
Lecturer in Logic and Scientific Method, University of London

1968

NORTH-HOLLAND PUBLISHING COMPANY
AMSTERDAM

PRINTED IN THE NETHERLANDS

PREFACE

This book constitutes the third volume of the Proceedings of the 1965 International Colloquium in the Philosophy of Science held at Bedford College, Regent's Park, London, from July 11th to 17th 1965. The Colloquium was organised jointly by the British Society for the Philosophy of Science and the London School of Economics and Political Science, under the auspices of the Division of Logic, Methodology and Philosophy of Science of the International Union of History and Philosophy of Science.

The Colloquium and the Proceedings were generously subsidised by the sponsoring institutions, and by the Leverhulme Foundation and the Alfred P. Sloan Foundation.

The members of the Organising Committee were: W. C. Kneale (Chairman), I. Lakatos (Honorary Secretary), J. W. N. Watkins (Honorary Joint Secretary), S. Körner, Sir Karl R. Popper, H. R. Post and J. O. Wisdom.

The Colloquium was divided into three main sections: *Problems in the Philosophy of Mathematics*, *The Problem of Inductive Logic*, and *Problems in the Philosophy of Science*. The full programme of the Colloquium is printed in the first volume of the Proceedings.

This third volume of the Proceedings, *Problems in the Philosophy of Science*, contains revised, and at times considerably expanded, versions of fourteen of the eighteen papers presented in this field at the Colloquium. Some members of the Colloquium, in most cases participants in the debates, were invited to submit comments based on the revised versions of the papers, to which the authors of the papers replied.

The Editors wish to thank all the contributors for their kind co-operation. They are also grateful to Miss Phyllis Parker for her conscientious secretarial and organisational help.

THE EDITORS

London, August 1967

CONTENTS

SCEPTICISM, THEOLOGY AND THE SCIENTIFIC REVOLUTION
IN THE SEVENTEENTH CENTURY

RICHARD H. POPKIN

University of California, San Diego

It has now become so much a part of our *Weltanschauung* that
religion impeded the rise of modern science, and that modern
science liberated the world from the clutches of a monolithic,
superstitious, intolerant, anti-scientific, all controlling Church. The
battle was joined in the years between Copernicus and Galileo;
Galileo was the heroic martyr, and as Galileo died, Newton was
born, and 'God said, Let Newton be! and All was light' [1]. From
Condillac and Condorcet to Lecky, Lange, Andrew White and
Bertrand Russell we have been regaled with horror tales concerning
the warfare of theology and science, with stories of Galileo and
the Inquisition, Servetus burned by Calvin, Uriel da Costa forced
to commit suicide, Spinoza excommunicated from the Synagogue,
down to poor Mr. Scopes in Tennessee, arrested for trying to teach
evolution [2]. By now, I think it is time to reexamine this part of
our mythology and to try to delineate what kind of war between
religion and science did, or might have taken place in the seventeenth century, who won, and what the victory signified then and
means to us now.

---

[1] Alexander Pope's epitaph for Sir Isaac Newton.

[2] Cf. Etienne Bonnot de Condillac, *Cours d'études pour l'instruction du
Prince de Parme*, livre xx, ch. iv; Antoine–Nicolas de Condorcet, *Sketch
for a Historical Picture of the Progress of the Human Mind*, trans. by June
Barraclough, New York, 1955, esp. 8th, 9th and 10th stage; William E. H.
Lecky, *History of the Rise and Influence of the Spirit of Rationalism in
Europe*, New York, 1955; Frederick A. Lange, *The History of Materialism*,
London, 1957, esp. Book i, sec. 2–4; John M. Robertson, *A Short History of
Freethought Ancient and Modern*, ii, 3rd ed., London, 1915; Bertrand Russell,
Religion and Science, London, 1947; and Andrew D. White, *A History of
the Warfare of Science with Theology in Christendom*, New York, 1960.

The tone of my introduction indicates that I am somewhat dubious of the official account. White, Russell and others have joined together a potpourri of cases, miscellaneous data, and lop-sided interpretations of some events to make a shocking picture of religious bigotry versus the noble spirit of free scientific inquiry. Descartes' departure for Holland in 1618 is attributed to his need to escape the Church in order to pursue his mathematical and physical investigations. The 1624 ban on teaching non-Aristotelian physics in Paris (actually directed against alchemists) is assumed to have been strictly enforced against the new scientists. The condemnation of Galileo is assumed to have represented a view accepted and held by all Churchmen everywhere. The pro-religious views stated and published by Gassendi, Galileo, Descartes, Pierre Bayle and others are assumed to be necessary camouflage to avoid persecution and censorship. The rigid censorship conditions that existed in France around 1750 are assumed to be the normal state of affairs throughout the seventeenth century. The Spanish Inqui-sition is assumed to be the norm for religious institutions every-where at the time. Spinoza's excommunication is assumed to repre-sent the usual reaction of organized religion to new ideas [1].

Well, obviously the situation was more complex. Local con-ditions varied greatly, and at various periods Church support or Church opposition occurred. The Copernican theory was taught at Salamanca before Galileo started arguing for it in Italy. The new physics was promulgated in France by Mersenne, Gassendi and Pascal while the ban on non-Aristotelian physics was on the books. Galileo's mechanics was published by Mersenne right after the former's condemnation. Church groups, especially the Oratorians and the Jansenists taught Cartesian physics even through the period in the 1670's when Descartes' views were condemned. The Index, French government censorship, etc. accomplished little in impeding the publication and diffusion of the new science, and very often Church authorities and institutions promoted the new science and the new scientists. Galileo, up to 1632, was a good friend of the

---

[1]   See, for instance, the accounts in the works of Lange, Lecky, Russell, and White mentioned in n. 2, p. 1.

Pope and of other leading Churchmen. Descartes' career was launched by Cardinal Bérulle. The Royal Society was started and led by a group of Anglican bishops. I submit that if one wanted to make the effort, one could assemble at least as impressive a case that religious institutions fostered, encouraged and developed the new science in the seventeenth century, as that they opposed and hindered it.

Part of the problem involved is the ambiguity of what constitutes the religious side and what the scientific one. Are the professors of mathematics and physics the latter, and the professors of theology the former? Who gets to count Father Mersenne, Father Gassendi, Father Torricelli, and the scientific genius and religious fanatic, Blaise Pascal? Which side has to count the physics professor who, when asked by Descartes why he didn't teach Cartesian physics instead of that Aristotelian drivel, replied, that if we taught your physics, we'd need new textbooks?

What it meant in 1600, or 1650 to be scientific and what it meant to be religious is very hard to define precisely, and I think the attempt to do so would show the classifications overlapping to a large extent. One solution, which I think is also part of *our* mythology, is to count on the scientific side those people who regardless of occupation or affiliation *actually* held modern scientific and irreligious views, and who saw the new science as the opponent of religious orthodoxy. But who are these people? Well, it is assumed that Father Gassendi, Galileo, Descartes, Bacon, etc. must have seen what we see, and hence that they must have been secret atheists no matter how much religious cant they uttered and wrote to please the authorities. If we could read between the lines (as all good scholars do anyway) and read their unwritten works, we would find a multitude of secret atheists, conducting a war of science against religion, liberating mankind and overthrowing Christianity. All sorts of people are supposed to have been secret atheists – Machiavelli, Bodin, Arentino, Pomponazzi, Montaigne, Charron, Gassendi, Pope Leo X . . .[1]. But how does one ascertain

---

[1]   All of these cases are discussed at length in Pierre Bayle's *Dictionnaire historique et critique.* In his article on Leo X, Bayle seriously examines the **evidence** about whether that Pope was an atheist. See *Dictionnaire*, art. 'Leon X', remarks 'O', 'P' and 'Q'.

what someone believed 300 or 400 years ago, beyond what that person said he believed? The data about who was accused of atheism in the seventeenth century is interesting but inconclusive. As Kristeller, D. C. Allen and Popkin have argued [1], 'atheist' was a pejorative term, used with as much accuracy as 'communist' is in Southern California today. The nastiest thing one could say about an opponent was that he was an atheist. Father Garasse, in his enormous McCarthy-like attacks on the freethinkers of the early seventeenth century, claimed that Luther and Calvin were atheists [2]. Father Hardouin, in his work, *The Atheists Detected*, detected that Descartes, Malebranche and Arnauld were atheists [3]. Arnauld, another one with a nose for secret atheism, saw right away that Bishop Huet was an atheist [4]. Mersenne made the impressive claim that in 1625 there were 50 000 atheists in the city of Paris alone (the then estimated population of Paris was 50–60 000) [5]. Mersenne did not indicate if he was counting his friends Hobbes, Gassendi, Grotius, Herbert of Cherbury, etc. Pierre Bayle, who was fascinated with the possibility of secret atheists (and was accused of being one himself) looked into all the reputed cases, and came to the conclusion Kristeller and I have, that, in the modern sense of atheist – that is, someone who denies that there is any super-natural being or force that guides or controls

---

[1]   Paul O. Kristeller, 'El mito del ateísmo renacentista y la tradición francesa del librepensamiento', *Notas y Estudios de Filosofia* **4**, (1953), pp. 1–14; Don Cameron Allen, *Doubt's Boundless Sea*, Baltimore, 1964, esp. ch. 1; and R. H. Popkin, *The History of Scepticism from Erasmus to Descartes*, Assen and New York, 1964, esp. chs. v and vi.

[2]   Father François Garasse, *La Somme Theologique des veritez capitales de la Religion Chrétienne*, Livre i, Paris, 1625.

[3]   Father Jean Hardouin, *Athei detecta*, and *Reflexions importantes qui doivent se mettre à la fin du Traité intitulé Athei detecti*, in *Opera varia*, Amsterdam, 1733.

[4]   Antoine Arnauld, *Oeuvres de Messire Antoine Arnauld*, iii, Lausanne, 1775–1783, Lettres 830, 833, 834, and 847.

[5]   Marin Mersenne, *Quaestiones in Genesim*, Paris, 1623, col. 671. The background of Mersenne's estimate is discussed in Robert Lenoble, *Mersenne ou la naissance du mécanisme*, Paris, 1943, pp. 171–175; and *Correspondance de Marin Mersenne*, i, ed. by De Waard, Pintard, Rochot, Paris, 1945, pp. 133–134.

the universe, or who denies any special spiritual status to the Judeo-Christian tradition – there were no atheists before the 1650's. When Bayle wrote a history of modern atheism in his article on Spinoza, he could find no identifiable atheistic individuals between David of Dinant (thirteenth century) and Spinoza [1]. (Recently I have become a little dubious of my own view, since there is some evidence that secret atheism may have developed among some of the Spanish Jews forced to embrace Catholicism. But, if so, these possible secret atheists had little influence on modern science until the mid-seventeenth century.) [2]

Rather than trying today to pick apart the strains of the alleged history of the warfare of science and theology, and to question the facts and interpretations on which White, Lecky, Russell and others base their case, I should like to offer an alternative picture of what may have happened. By-and-large, my suspicion is that the period from Copernicus to Newton is dominated by a war amongst the theologians, with the scientists only occasionally entering in, or being caught in the struggle. The riskiest occupation from 1500 onward was that of a theology professor. It really mattered what one said. The death rate from burning, torture, incarceration, etc. among theologians far exceeds that among scientists. (In fact it is hard to find many scientists before the twentieth century who really got killed for their scientific views, and not for either religious or political ones.) The great Servetus, whose scientific contribution was enormous, was burned solely for a fine point in theology, his denial of the doctrine of the Trinity. As has been said, Calvin killed him for a misplaced adjective, when Servetus prayed to the son of the Eternal Father, and not to the Eternal Son of the Father [3]. The heresy hunters of the Inquisition were primarily concerned with catching secret Jews, secret Muslims and

[1] Bayle, *Dictionnaire*, art. 'Spinosa, Benoît', Rem. A.

[2] At least it seems plausible that some of those forcibly converted in the fifteenth and sixteenth centuries may have come to the conclusion that their new unwanted religion was false, and may have generalized from that to denying all religions.

[3] On Servetus' case, see Roland H. Bainton, *Hunted Heretic : the Life and Death of Michael Servetus 1511–1553*, Boston, 1960.

Lutherans, but not scientists *per se* [1]. (In Spain and Portugal a good many scientists were persecuted, but far fewer than the number of theologians, and almost always the scientists were persecuted as Judaizers, as Lutherans, or as mystics.) In a world in which priests were boiled in oil in Holland, or jailed in England, Protestants slaughtered in France, religious views obviously mattered in a way that scientific ones did not. In a world full of radical religious innovators, much in the style of Southern California today, one could speak of the hunted heretic, but hardly of the hunted scientist. Most scientists died of old age or medical malpractice, unless they combined their scientific work with religious interpretations as did Agrippa von Nettesheim and Giordano Bruno. Archbishop Carranza, the primate of Spain, spent thirteen years in solitary confinement awaiting trial for the most picayune theological deviations [2], while Galileo's case was handled with dispatch and simple abjuration. I say 'simple abjuration' since all he had to do was say that he recanted, whereas in normal Spanish Inquisition cases people would rot in dungeons for years, then be asked to recant without being told what the crime was, then be tortured to see if they really had recanted, then be forced to name all the heretics they knew and to give evidence against them, and *then* the inquisitional authorities would decide the proper punishment before the individual could be reconciled with the Church. The punishments ranged from banishment, economic ruin, massive scourging and prison terms, to death by garrotting for their sincere repentance. (A *negativo*, i.e. an unrepentant heretic, was burned alive) [3].

In a world so dominated by theological controversies and the vicious and violent suppression of alleged unorthodoxy (though

---

[1]　See the types of heretics persecuted by the Spanish Inquisition in Henry C. Lea, *A History of the Inquistion in Spain*, New York, 1907. Vols. III and IV contain Book VIII on 'Spheres of Action', in which the main classes of victims are Jews, Moriscos (Moslems), Protestants, Mystics, Sorcerers.

[2]　On Archbishop Carranza's case see Lea, II, pp. 45–87; and Marcelino Menéndez Pelayo, *Historia de los Heterodoxos*, II, Madrid, 1946, Lib. IV, cap. VIII, pp. 1–59.

[3]　See Lea, II, Book VI, 'Practice', pp. 457–586.

unorthodoxy was rampant in both the Catholic and Protestant worlds, especially where the civil authorities were not easily excited about minor religious differences), the scientists, that is, those studying nature, only, I believe, get involved in the religious wars when their efforts directly relate to some theological point, or when they inadvertently or deliberately antagonize some theologians. There is an age-old tension between man's natural curiosity about his world and the acceptance of the religious traditions of his society. Intellectuals have, as far back as we have written records, caused difficulties in the easy acceptance of mythologies or religions by confronting these traditional views with information or reasonable beliefs that do not seem to fit. A major dynamic force in Western intellectual history has been the continuing effort to harmonize religious belief with new conditions, new data, and new theories. Hillel's Academy and the Talmudic schools that followed from it, developed a powerful technique for adaptation of the Jewish heritage through unending re-interpretation of a fixed revealed text. Geniuses from the days of Rabbi Akiba and Johannan ben Zakkai to Raschi, Maimonides and the Gaon of Vilna managed to harmonize almost all relevant findings with the Divine Message, and succeeded in channelizing the most creative intellectual endeavors into this crucial stabilizing effort. In the Christian world a similar type of exegesis and interpretation developed, and became a major preoccupation of the Church Fathers and of the medieval universities. After all, the *Sentences* of Peter Lomabard are a way of listing the problems to be reckoned with in making the Bible, the tradition, the rational, and the observable world fit together. The endless number of commentaries on the *Sentences* testify to the highly developed technique, and its continuing success. It was only when Maimonides and the Latin Averroists touched the raw nerve of the process of reconciling reason and faith that a shock wave ran through the intellectual world. Maimonides pointed out that no matter how much reconciling one did, one might still have to choose between reason and religion. The rabbis who opposed him, like Rabad of Posquières [1], saw that Maimonides had exposed

---

[1] On him see Isadore Twersky, *Rabad of Posquières. A twelfth century Talmudist*, Cambridge Mass., 1962.

the tension between the two worlds too forcefully, and for seven centuries Jewish intellectuals have been trying to digest and accept Maimonides. Latin Averroïsm posed the possibility that something might be true theologically and false scientifically. All the genius of the high Middle Ages, of the Thomists, the Scotists, the Ockhamites, went into achieving a satisfactory reconcilation and separation of religion and science, sufficiently satisfactory to last until the sixteenth century, when Europe was overwhelmed with new data and new and old theories.

When Copernicus, Tycho Brahe and Kepler broke down the accepted Ptolemaic astronomy, and replaced the Alphonsine tables with the Rudolphine, they saw no real problem in reconciling their theories and their data with Christian theology. Copernicus, in the preface, shows that he knew all the accepted rationales. He knew how to distinguish carefully the role of mathematical and astronomical theorizing from theology, and to show that a better understanding of nature could only help in appreciating God's achievement and His Message. He also knew how to interpret scriptural statements that apparently conflict with the data, by considering them as allegorical, symbolical, metaphorical and so on. Kepler, in his mystical Kabbalistic frenzy, could see his monumental vision of the mathematization of Nature as bringing him closer to knowing God and His Message. Kepler could, like Galileo, ridicule the pompous conservative academicians, who confused the Scholastic physics and astronomy they taught with Scripture. Galileo, in his letter to the Grand Duchess, carried on the accepted harmonization procedures. Scripture tells us how to go to Heaven, not how the Heavens go. Scripture is not a text on physics or astronomy. When Scripture stated that Joshua commanded the sun to stand still, it can be interpreted as speaking in ordinary language, not that of technical science [1].

---

[1]   Cf. Copernicus' dedicatory preface to Pope Paul III in *De Revolutionibus Orbium Coelestium* (see also Osiander's preface); Kepler's 'Proem' to *The Harmonies of the World* and Galileo's *Letter to the Grand Duchess Christiana*. In the latter work, Galileo cites with approval the view of Cardinal Baronius 'That the intention of the Holy Ghost is to teach us how one goes to heaven, not how heaven goes', in *Discoveries and Opinions of Galileo*, trans. and ed. by Stillman Drake, New York, 1957, p. 186.

What I am suggesting is that the Copernican theory when presented was only one additional item for intellectuals to harmonize with the accepted religious tradition. The Copernicans did just about what previous theorists had done. The authorities do not seem to have gotten upset or excited. The University of Salamanca taught the Copernican theory in the 1590's [1]. Father Tommaso Campanella, in his defense of Galileo, showed how all the apparent counter-evidence in the Bible, and in the Church Fathers, could be handled by traditionally acceptable exegetical techniques [2]. Originally only people like Martin Luther found the Copernican theory upsetting, I suspect, because of his biblical fundamentalism which differs greatly from the more flexible Catholic modes of scripture interpretation. When Bruno turned up with his pantheistic interpretation of the Copernican theory, he proposed, with grim results, a theological heresy of high order, not a scientific one.

I shall not here attempt to deal in detail with the Galileo case, because I think its involuted intrigues and twists and turns belong more to the history of Church politics than to the development of a conflict between religion and science. Galileo and Campanella certainly showed how Copernicism could be reconciled with Christianity, and twenty years earlier or twenty years later they might well have gotten the Church authorities to accept their view (as these authorities did in the nineteenth century). The condemnation of Galileo for holding the specific Copernican thesis that the earth moves definitely looks like a conflict of religion with science. However, I submit that the condemnation had very little immediate effect on the development of modern science. In the long run, it may mark the point at which the Church in Italy, Spain, Portugal and Poland stopped encouraging scientific activity, and moved gradually towards a more and more rigid Scholasticism. In the short run, almost all of the 'new scientists' continued holding their Copernican views. Mersenne, Gassendi, Pascal and hosts of others, though good Catholics, remained good Copernicans. Galileo made

---

[1]   Menéndez Pelayo, *Historia de los Heterodoxos*, p. 361.

[2]   Thomas Campanella, *The Defense of Galileo, Mathematician of Florence*, trans. by Grant McColley, in *Smith College Studies in History*, XXII, Nos. 3–4, 1937.

no effort to make a big issue of the matter. He did not flee to Holland where he could have boldly denounced his forced re-cantation. Instead he retired, wrote, and received such visitors as Hobbes and John Milton, both of whom accepted his theory. Mersenne's vast correspondence, with practically all of the modern scientists of the day, indicates that Descartes alone took the condemnation seriously, and decided not to publish *Le Monde*, since it differed from the Church's view. But pious Father Mersenne helpfully got Galileo in more trouble by publishing his *Mechanics* and agitating for the acceptance of this non-Aristotelian mechanistic physics [1].

In theory, I contend, there was nothing in the Copernican theory to produce a war between religion and science. Judeo-Christianity as a religious view does not seem committed to any particular theory of celestial motions and the Copernican system or Ptolemaic one can be handled by anyone who has studied Pilpul or has read a good Catholic exegete like Juan Maldonado.

Further, I similarly contend that there was no reason why the next major ingredient of the scientific revolution, the mechanistic interpretation of Nature should have caused a conflict. The me-chanistic thesis, in embryo in Kepler and Galileo, was fully stated by Mersenne, Gassendi, Descartes and Pascal (all practicing Catho-lics). Gassendi, a priest until his death, started his career teaching anti-Aristotelianism and scepticism at Aix. In the 1620's when he met Mersenne, he began to develop his new version of Epicurean atomism, and spent the rest of his life working out his materialistic atomism. Father Mersenne from 1625 onward became a one man society for the advancement of science, advocating the mechanistic view, the mathematization of nature, writing the new textbooks, encouraging everyone with mechanistic tendencies, and beating down the alchemists, numerologists, etc. He arranged for the publication of the works of Galileo, Hobbes, Herbert of Cherbury, Descartes and others. He kept everybody informed of the latest data and the latest theories [2]. Pascal, in his brilliant work on the

---

[1] See the various letters about the case in Mersenne, *Correspondance*, III.

[2] On Gassendi and Mersenne, see Popkin, *History of Scepticism*, chs. V

vacuum and atmospheric pressure, shredded the Aristotelian conception of nature, especially the contention that Nature abhors a vacuum, and showed how a wide range of phenomena about liquids and pressures could be comprehended under mechanical laws. Descartes offered a new metaphysics to justify interpreting Nature as a vast machine, and all the parts therein, including biological organisms, as small machines and Hobbes extended the mechanistic thesis to man and society.

With all of this occuring in the period 1625–1650, there were howls and hoots from some of the Aristotelian physics professors and some of the mossback theologians, but there was also a widespread acceptance of mechanism by avant-garde intellectuals. The Augustinians, both Catholic and Calvinist, very quickly became adherents of the 'new science' since its determinism and materialism coincided with their view of the natural world, which could only be activated by God. The Jansenists in the Oratory and Port-Royal became the leading advocates of Cartesian physics in France. Father Bernard Lamy, Oratorian, was the major popularizer of the new science well into the eighteenth century. Recently when I was reviewing a new study on Lamy, I feared that I found a real case of religion versus science with regard to physics, since Lamy was hounded out of his professorship at Angers for teaching Cartesian physics. The documents show however that it is a case of religion versus religion, that the Jesuits were fighting Cartesianism, the Oratorians defending it. The Oratorians, one of the most pious orders, can hardly be accused of irreligious scientific activity [1]. In their greatest theoretician, Father Malebranche, the new science and Augustinian theology were welded into a magnificent theodicy.

In England, liberal Anglicans, like Bishop John Wilkins, the founder of the Royal Society, became the advocates of the 'new science'. Wilkins was the first to popularize Galileo's work in England, and then encouraged that of Boyle and Hooke. For

---

and VII, Lenoble, *Mersenne*, and Bernard Rochot, *Les travaux de Gassendi sur épicure et sur l'atomisme, 1619–1658,* Paris, 1944.

[1] On Lamy's case, see François Girbal, *Bernard Lamy, Étude biographique et bibliographique,* Paris, 1964, esp. chs. VII and VIII, and sec. III. My review is in the *Journal of the History of Philosophy* 3 (1965), pp. 279–280.

Wilkins and his theological cohorts, the study of nature in mechanistic terms enhanced one's knowledge, understanding and appreciation of God, since, as Scripture says, 'the firmament showeth His handiwork' [1].

Thus Mechanism, even in its most materialistic and deterministic form was no shock to many theologians. The problem of harmonizing it with Christianity was handled in various ways, two principle ones being joining it to an Augustinian theology, or coupling it with a scepticism about metaphysical knowledge and a fideistic acceptance of religion. Descartes, the Jansenists, and Malebranche followed the first course, and found their theology unacceptable to Church authorities, and the application of their physics to religion scandalously heretical. (Cartesianism was actually condemned because of the results of explaining transsubstantiation in terms of Cartesian physics. If the essence of matter is extension, and if each physical object is defined by its extensional properties, how can a little wafer be changed into the body of Christ?) The crushing of Jansenism and Calvinism in France drove Cartesianism underground or into exile. This conflict can hardly rank as one between science and religion, but was rather a theological and political struggle, in which the Augustinians lost, not because of their scientific views but almost entirely because of their religious ones, and the political conflicts these engendered. Louis XIV, having sapped the strength of the Jansenists and Calvinists, then tried to encourage new scientific activity by the remaining intellectuals.

The *modus vivendi* between mechanism and religion that was more acceptable in the seventeenth century was that offered by the sceptics. Gassendi and Mersenne both developed a theory of the 'new science' as the constructive result of a complete scepticism about the possibility of gaining genuine (i.e. necessarily true) knowledge of the nature of reality. Using the arguments of Sextus Empiricus and modern sceptics like Sanches, Montaigne and Charron, they contended that man seemed to have no reliable data,

---

[1]   On Wilkins see Henry G. Van Leeuwen, *The Problem of Certainty in English Thought, 1630–1690*, The Hague, 1963, ch. III; and Richard S. Westfall, *Science and Religion in Seventeenth Century England*, New Haven, 1958.

criteria or faculties for attaining knowledge about the real world. However, instead of this leading to a depressing negative conclusion, they insisted that it should make one realize that we can gain a useful and important type of information about the world of appearances. We can develop an empirical science apart from any metaphysics, which can be considered as a hypothetical system describing the sequences and relations found in the phenomenal world, and predicting future sequences and relationships. Such a system can be useful, and can provide us with a guide to living, while we are deprived of any knowledge of reality. Gassendi's atomism was set forth as the best such hypothetical system available. It is a model that enables one to connect appearances, describe their sequences in terms of mechanical laws and predict the future course of observable events. This model can be judged, not in terms of whether it is a true picture of reality, but in terms of whether its predictions can be verified, and whether they provide a pragmatically useful guide for dealing with human problems. In Gassendi's final presentation of his system in his *Syntagma*, he began with an analysis of the nature of knowledge, indicating its limits, then he stated his physics. No section on metaphysics occurs in the work at all. Gassendi's Epicureanism is never offered as a materialistic theory of reality, but only as a way of dealing with appearances. And, the new physics, both for Gassendi and Mersenne, is in no way incompatible with religion. Religious knowledge is gained by faith and revelation, and is not open to scientific questioning or sceptical doubting. However, science can help explain how certain revealed events take place. Hence, Mersenne was interested in a hydraulic explanation of the source of all the water at the time of the Flood, and the Gassendists offered an atomic account of transsubstantiation which was much more acceptable than Descartes' [1].

The sceptical reconciliation of mechanism and faith was quite successful in many quarters during the seventeenth century. Contrary to the claim in Lange's *History of Materialism* that

---

[1] On Gassendi's and Mersenne's 'constructive' or 'mitigated' scepticism, see Popkin, *History of Scepticism*, ch. VII,

'Gassendi did not fall a victim to theology, because he was destined to fall a victim to medicine' [1], there is practically no evidence of organized religious opposition to his views. He had his opponents, of course, but he remained a practicing priest, and was the Royal Professor of Mathematics in Paris. He was never charged with heresy for all his Epicurean works. In the latter half of the century his theories were at least as popular as Descartes', and many of the Jesuits who fought to suppress Cartesianism as heretical, offered Gassendism as a better theory. Father René Rapin, famous for his defense of Aristotle against the moderns, actually argued that in physics no genuine knowledge beyond appearances and hypotheses is possible. Therefore, he claimed Aristotle was as wrong in this area as any other metaphysician. But Gassendi, Boyle and other such scientists, Rapin considered stupendous, because they have taught us more about the phenomenal world in the last 60 years than we learned in the previous 1600 [2]. Gassendi's physics died not from religious opposition, but from lack of results [3]. And when the Royal Society scientists, accepting a similar sceptical interpretation of the new physics, began pouring forth results, laws about the phenomenal world – Hooke's, Boyle's and Newton's – Gassendism was soon replaced by Newtonian physics.

Probably the strongest presentation of the sceptical interpretation of mechanism as part of a religious view is that of Pascal, both in his achievements and in his writings. In his studies on the nature of the vacuum and on the theory of atmospheric pressure, Pascal pointed out the hypothetical-probabilistic nature of scientific reasoning. He showed that no finite amount of evidence would ever constitute a demonstration of a truth about Nature, although just one crucial experiment could disprove a theory, if it showed that a logical deduction from the theory was contrary to fact [4].

---

[1]   Lange, *History of Materialism*, I, p. 269.

[2]   On Rapin, see R. H. Popkin, 'The traditionalism, modernism and scepticism of René Rapin', *Filosofia* 63 (1964), pp. 3–16.

[3]   Cf. Alexandre Koyré, 'Gassendi: le savant', in Centre International de Synthèse, *Pierre Gassendi, sa vie et son œuvre, 1592–1655*, Paris, 1955, pp. 59–70.

[4]   Blaise Pascal, 'Réponse de Blaise Pascal au très bon Révérend Père

The best that man could accomplish was to find the hypothesis which best fitted with the facts known at a given stage in the world's history [1].

Pascal explained in *De l'esprit géométrique et de l'art de persuader* and in the *Pensées* (both works written in the last years of his life, when religion was the focus of his interests), why man was unable to attain complete knowledge by natural means. In the former work, the discussion of the nature of an axiom system, Pascal asserted that such a system was always limited by the fact that one could always raise the sceptical problem, viz. what evidence is there that even the clearest and most certain axioms are true? Man's rational nature is such that he will constantly raise this problem undermining every proposed axioms system, and he will introduce doubts over and over again about the greatest human rational and natural accomplishments. The only way these doubts could be overcome, according to Pascal, was by the acceptance of principles known by instinct and intuition, and not by reason. 'The heart has its reasons that reason knows not of' [2].

In the climatic *pensée* concerning scepticism and faith, Pascal stated at the beginning that even the fundamental appeal to instinct and intuition as the basis for accepting first principles can be seriously challenged by the sceptics, 'since, not having any certitude apart from faith as to whether man is created by a good God, by an evil demon, or by chance, it is in doubt whether these principles that are given to us, are true, or false, or uncertain, depending upon our origin.' Then Pascal developed the tension between natural belief and scepticism – each fighting the other and undermining the other, with man caught helplessly in their combat – 'Nature confounds the Pyrrhonists and the Academicians, and reason confounds the Dogmatists. What will you then become,

---

Noel' in *Oeuvres complètes*, New York, 1963: 'pour faire qu'une hypothèse soit évidente, il ne suffit pas que tous les phénomènes s'en ensuivent, au lieu que, s'il s'ensuit quelque chose de contraire à un seul des phénomènes, cela suffit pour assurer de sa fausseté.' (p. 202).

[1]   Pascal, 'Préface sur le traité du vide', *Oeuvres complètes*, pp. 230–232.

[2]   Pascal, 'De l'esprit géométrique et de l'art de persuader', *Oeuvres complètes*, pp. 348–359; and *Pensées* 277 and 282 (Brunschvicg numbering).

a man, who seeks to know what is your actual condition by means of your natural reason? You cannot flee from one of these sects, nor subsist in any of them.' In the *Pensées* the solution offered is 'Hear God' [1]. But in *De l'esprit géométrique* a more mundane solution was proposed, that of constructive scepticism, namely that of doing the best that one can, in the light of the human predicament, by following a limited rather than an ideal geometrical method. Terms should be defined until the clearest possible ones have been found. Principles that are most indubitable according to our natural beliefs should be used as a starting point. Then, one should proceed carefully and methodically, and draw conclusions from these definitions and principles, while realizing the conditional truth value of what is thereby demonstrated, since its certitude depends upon human natural capacities and abilities [2]. In his earlier work *Préface sur le traité du vide*, Pascal had claimed that the situation is even worse with regard to 'all matters in which the proof consists in experiments and not in demonstrations', since here 'no universal assertion can be made except by general enumeration of all the parts or of all the different cases', and that such an enumeration is always restricted by the extent and reliability of man's experience [3].

Thus, according to Pascal, the rational and natural examination of man's intellectual accomplishments leads to the conclusion that 'Pyrrhonism is the truth' [4], in an ultimate sense, until we receive God's Revelation. But, even in man's state of misery without God, he is capable of attaining certain and useful mathematical and scientific knowledge.

Pascal was certainly not a scientist at war with religion, and the difficulties he encountered in having his calculating machine and his theory of the vacuum accepted can be much better accounted for as part of the normal and usual human resistance to new ideas than by supposed religious obscurantism [5]. The suppression of the

---

[1]   Pascal, *Pensées* 434.

[2]   Pascal, 'De l'esprit géométrique et de l'art de persuader'.

[3]   Pascal, 'Preface sur le traité du vide', *Oeuvres complètes*, p. 232.

[4]   Pascal, *Pensées* 432.

[5]   Cf. Pascal, 'Lettre dédicatoire à Monseigneur le Chancelier sur le sujet

Provincial Letters is part of the war within the religious camp, and Pascal, as a leading spokesman for Jansenism, was obviously open to attack on this score from the Church.

The serious conflict between theology and science developed, I believe, not from the rise of Copernican astronomy or mechanism, but from the application of new data and new scientific concepts to Judeo-Christianity. One such kind of conflict was that involved in explaining Mysteries and Miracles in terms of seventeenth century science. Transsubstantiation was a most serious problem for the Catholic Cartesians, though, of course, not for the Protestant ones. However the more dramatic cases develop from the attempt to comprehend key events in Biblical history in terms of modern science. The flood, and the descendance of all of mankind from Noah and his family provided serious difficulties when examined in the light of new geographical, anthropological, meteorological data, and mechanistic physics. Mersenne and Pascal, among others, had tried to explain how 40 days and 40 nights of rain could provide enough water to inundate the entire Earth so that even the highest mountains could be covered. Even with the false estimate that the top of the highest mountain was one and one-half miles up, not enough water was available. Medieval rabbinical accounts had obtained more water by claiming that an enormous sphere of water surrounded the Earth, and that God dropped that in too, along with the rain. But, alas, modern astronomy eliminated that source of supply. Problems also developed in determining the requisite size of the Ark in the light of all the newly discovered species of which there had to be two on board. The problems of food supply, animal husbandry (to prevent the rabbits from multiplying *ad infinitum*) added to the difficulties of a modern comprehension of what had happened. The discovery of people in the most isolated parts of the Earth further complicated matters, since presumably those people must have wandered from Mount Ararat across oceans and wildernesses. The differences in peoples, their cultures, histories,

de la machine nouvellement inventée par le sieur B.P. pour faire toutes sortes d'opérations d'arithmetique . . .'; 'Réponse . . . au Père Noel'; 'Lettre de Pascal à M. Le Pailleur au sujet du Père Noel, Jésuite'.

chronologies, etc. also posed the problem of how they could all be descendants of Noah, and yet look and be so different. In the first half of the seventeenth century, theories offering more water, (underground springs, geysers, etc.), localizing the Flood to the Near East, or just to Palestine, in changing the shape of the earth (due to the weight of all that water) were presented to harmonize the Scriptural account and the new science [1]. Scholars like Rabbi Menasseh ben Israel of Amsterdam (the 'discoverer' of the news that the Indians were the Lost Tribes) [2] and Archbishop Ussher (who calculated the data of Creation as 4004 BC, and thereby gained a full 5 % more time over the Hebrew calender for all of the events) [3] made valiant efforts to reconcile with the Bible the data obtained by the explorers. And, at just about the same moment that Menasseh ben Israel and Ussher had reconstructed man's history from Noah to the world of 1650, in a possible chronology, and with conceivable migrations to put people in China, Polynesia, America, etc., the whole enterprise of reconciling Scripture and the new science was blown apart by a mad genius, Isaac La Peyrère (Pereira), who, I believe, really set off the warfare between theology and science.

Pereira, a Portuguese Jewish refugee from Bordeaux, raised as a Calvinist, was the secretary of the Prince of Condé, and a good friend of Gassendi, Grotius, and many other avant-garde thinkers in Paris. After a trip to Denmark, he wrote two important scientific works, on Iceland and on Greenland, giving the best geographical, anthropological, sociological and historical accounts of those lands available at the time. From 1643 onward, he advanced a strange Messianic theory, that of two Messiahs, one for the Gentiles (who turned up around the year 1) and the other for the Jews, who would soon turn up. The second Messiah would bring about the culmination of Judeo-Christian history. Before he came it was

---

[1] On the background of these problems connected with Noah and the Flood, see Don Cameron Allen, *The Legend of Noah*, Urbana, 1963.

[2] This thesis is set forth in Menasseh ben Israel's *Esperanza de Israel*, originally published in 1650, last published Madrid 1881.

[3] See James Ussher, *The Annals of the Old and New Testament*, London, 1658.

necessary for all the Jews and Christians to unite, and to reconquer Palestine so that His throne would be available in Jerusalem. So, Pereira advocated that Louis XIV drop all other activities, and join forces with the Jews to get David's Holy City ready for the great event [1].

Besides this apocalyptic vision, Pereira had another bombshell, his theory that there were people before Adam, and hence that Judeo-Christian biblical history was only a part of the world's history. In 1655 he published his work on the pre-Adamites. His arguments develop from a rather far-fetched interpretation of a passage in *Romans*, and then proceed to utilize what was to become the crucial data, facts about America, China, Greenland, etc. Mexican, Chinese and Eskimo history all showed that there were people in those cultures long before 4004 BC. The calendars indicated human beings as far as at least 50 000 BC!! Unless one adopted the pre-Adamite theory, it would be impossible to convert the infidels, since they knew that the Bible did not represent *their* history. So, Pereira offered a theory of the independent origin of different cultures, the local occurrence of the Flood, the derivation only of Judeo-Christians from Noah, etc. [2]. The appearance of his work produced an enormous shock, and the first reaction was to

---

[1]   On Pereira, see R. H. Popkin, 'Isaac La Peyrère (Pereira)', *Encyclopedia of Philosophy*, forthcoming; Bayle, *Dictionnaire*, art. 'Peyrère, Isaac de'; and David R. McKee, 'Isaac de la Peyrère, a precursor of eighteenth-century critical deists', *Publications of the Modern Languages Assn.* **59** (1944), pp. 456–485. Pereira's two-messiah theory appears in his *Le Rappel des Juifs* (n.p. 1643).

[2]   La Peyrère, Isaac, *Men before Adam, or A Discourse upon the twelfth, thirteenth, and fourteenth Verses of the Fifth Chapter of the Apostle Paul to the Romans, By which are prov'd that the first Men were created before Adam.* Latin ed. 1655, English, London 1656. 'Moreover from this Tenet which asserts men to have been before *Adam*, the History of Genesis appears much clearer, and agrees with itself. And it is wonderfully reconciled with all profane Records, whether ancient or new, to wit, those of the *Caldeans*, *Egyptians*, *Scythians*, and *Chinensians*; that most Ancient Creation which is set down in the first of *Genesis* is reconciled to those of *Mexico*, not long ago discovered by *Columbus* . . . Again, by this Position, Faith and right Reason are reconciled, which suffers us not to believe that the world had so late an infancy . . .', p. 22.

save the appearances by jailing Pereira and suppressing his book. He was imprisoned in Brussels, and as an adroit courtier soon discovered that if he converted to Catholicism and recanted, all would be well. So, he went to Rome, gave the Pope his apologies, blamed his pre-Adamite theory on his unfortunate Calvinist up-bringing, and all was well [1]. The Pope offered him a post, but Pereira decided to return to France, to join the pious Oratory, and devote his life to pious study. At the Oratory, Bayle reports, he was always writing books which his superiors intended to burn as soon as the author died, and he lived a happy life, participating in the high society of Paris. Bayle's informant concluded, 'La Peirera was the best man in the world, the sweetest, who tranquilly believed very few things' [2]. The British Museum has one of the only remaining copies of one of his last works, a French translation of the Bible, which was suppressed by the time it got to Leviticus 14. In it, Pereira, starting in the first chapter of *Genesis*, proceeded to explain in the notes that there is a madman who holds that there were people before Adam, and then he gave the evidence for this thesis, the kind of evidence that was to shatter the harmo-nization of religion and science [3]. His last work, which was not published, contains a new version of his two-Messiah theory, in which the Judeo-Christians could at least have the comfort that their private world was about to come to a happy ending, even if this was no longer the core or focus of a comprehension of the entire universe [4].

Pascal tried in the *Pensées* to dismiss Pereira as a crank [5], and Bishop Huet tried, in his *Demonstratio Evangelica*, to trivialize Pereira's views by offering a kind of Leibnizian theory of religious history, namely that every culture is independent, but mirrors the same basic religous truths. According to Huet, Judeo-Christianity

---

[1]   La Peyrère, *Apologie de La Peyrère*, Paris, 1663.

[2]   Bayle, *Dictionnaire*, art. 'Peyrère', Rem. G.

[3]   (La Peyrère, Isaac), *La Livre de la Genèse* (n.p. 1671).

[4]   This work is mentioned by Father Richard Simon, in *Lettres choisies*, Amsterdam, 1730, Lettre IV. See letters 1–3 for Simon's discussions with Pereira. The manuscript is at Chantilly. I am planning to publish it.

[5]   Pascal, *Pensées* 651.

is the best mirror in that it has all the names of the crucial figures spelled correctly, while the others have a Moses figure, a Christ figure, a Mary figure, but with bizarre names [1].

It was Pereira's two disciples, Spinoza and Richard Simon who were to develop his theory and his method to the point where Judeo-Christianity was a subject for scientific study and evaluation, not something to be harmonized with the results of scientific study. In the Amsterdam of Spinoza's day, if we take Uriel da Costa's alleged autobiography [2] (as well as other indications) at face value, there was a real religious ferment in the Jewish community because most of its members were forced converts to Christianity who had grown up in Spain, Portugal, Italy, France, the Levant and the New World, and who had come to Amsterdam to practice Judaism freely. Many had no training in Jewish practices and beliefs, some, like Da Costa, (formerly a priest in Portugal) had their own versions of Judaism. A very recent study by Professor Révah has shown that Spinoza's rejection of Judaism is dateable within a few weeks. In this period, right after the appearance of Pereira's work on the pre-Adamites (1655) and Pereira's one and only visit to Holland, a couple of teachers in Jewish private schools in Amsterdam, who were friends of young Spinoza, started raising problems about the historical accuracy of the Bible [3]. Spinoza apparently developed this approach, and soon found all sorts of questions in addition to those about Adam, Noah, the Flood, etc. His *Tractatus-Theologico-Politicus*, probably drafted originally in 1656–57 as an answer to his expulsion, challenged the entire Judeo-Christian conception of the world. Spinoza challenged the Mosaic authorship of the Pentateuch, the historicity of the Bible, the possibility of

---

[1]   Pierre–Daniel Huet, *Demonstratio Evangelica*, 3rd ed., Paris, 1690.

[2]   Uriel da Costa, *Exemplar Humane Vitae*, originally published as an appendix to Philip van Limborch's *De Veritate Religionis Christianae, amica collatio cum erudito Judaeo* (Isaac Orobio de Castro), Gouda, 1687. It appears in Da Costa, *Die Schriften des Uriel Da Costa*, ed. Carl Gebhardt, Amsterdam, 1922.

On the development of Da Costa's views, see I. S. Révah, 'La religion d'Uriel da Costa', *Revue de l'Histoire des Religions* 161 (1962), pp. 45–76.

[3]   I. S. Révah, 'Aux origines de la rupture spinozienne', *Revue des Études Juives* 3 (cxxiii) (1964), pp. 359–431.

miracles, and so on [1]. In fact, the *Tractatus* is almost the complete inversion of Pascal's apologetic argument in the *Pensées*. Starting in the *Tractatus*, and then developing it in the *Ethics*, Spinoza set forth a complete rationalistic conception of the world, in which everything including, or especially, the Judeo-Christian conception of the world, can be understood in terms of a deterministic, mechanistic science. Spinoza provided a metaphysics in which Judeo-Christianity was only one major example in the history of human stupidity, to be understood, in terms of a mechanistic psychology, as a kind of superstition due to fear [2]. The new science for Spinoza was a way of seeing the entire world *sub specie aeternitatis*. It did not have to be reconciled or harmonized with religion. Rather religion was to be understood and rejected as a serious picture of the world by it. The rational criteria of mathematics were to be applied to religion, and then it would be seen that there was more certitude in science and mathematics than in the Bible, and that historical religion was just the result of man's superstitious nature which impeded true and adequate comprehension of the world. Hence, Spinoza had provided an ontological base for a real war between science and theology, by showing how religious data could be examined and judged scientifically. It is interesting in terms of Spinoza's role in making it possible or conceivable to apply scientific analyses to alleged supernatural data, that it was only after Spinoza died, that the famous secret work, *The Three Impostors* (concerning, namely, Moses, Jesus and Mohammed) turns up, often entitled, *L'Esprit de M. Spinoza* [3]. The plot of the work is mentioned much earlier, but apparently without the Spinozistic outlook, no one really knew what to offer as the contents. The conception of Moses, Jesus and Mohammed as im-

---

[1]   Baruch de Spinoza, *Tractatus-Theologico-Politicus*, esp. chs. i–xv.

[2]   Spinoza, *Ethics*, Appendix to Book i.

[3]   *On De Tribus Impostoribus*, its history and its possible authors, see D. C. Allen, *Doubt's Boundless Sea*, Appendix, pp. 224–243; and Gerhard Bartsch, ed. *De Tribus Impostoribus*, Berlin, 1960, 'Einleitung', pp. 5–38. (The Latin text and a German translation appear in this edition.) There are manuscripts of the work with the title, 'L'Esprit de M. Spinoza' in Copenhagen, Leiden and elsewhere.

postors really required an anti-supernaturalistic theory of the universe before it could be written.

If Spinoza provided the metaphysic for a war of science against religion, Pereira's other disciple, Father Richard Simon provided the method – the scientific study of the Bible. Simon, the greatest Bible scholar of the seventeenth century, was a fellow Oratorian and close friend of Pereira. He knew all of the languages, documents, and background details relevant to Biblical studies. He started out in typical French Counter-Reformation style to undermine the Calvinist claim that religion is based on Scripture alone. He questioned whether anyone could ascertain what Scripture actually said. Do we possess an accurate copy? Can we, at this late date, tell what Hebrew and Greek words of ancient times really meant? Is even the earliest known Hebrew or Greek text the Word of God, or is it some human being's version of what God said? [1]

Simon accepted and reinforced Spinoza's denial of the Mosaic authorship of the Torah, and advanced an even more shocking thesis – namely that the Bible, as we know it, is a compilation of the work of public scribes from around 800 BC onward, and that the text that we possess is based on copies of copies of copies, containing all sorts of variants.

The text of the *New Testament*, Simon argued, is in even worse shape, since Jesus told the Apostles to go out and preach, not to sit down and write. As a result, the text was only written down decades later, in a language different from what Jesus or the Apostles spoke. This text has been copied and copied, and all sorts of errors and variants have crept in.

The *Vulgate*, St. Jerome's Latin version, Simon regarded as a fifth century attempt to establish an accurate text by comparing the Greek, the Hebrew, the Syriac, the Coptic, and other versions. St. Jerome, according to Simon, did the best he could. He consulted

---

[1] On Richard Simon, see Jean Steinmann, *Richard Simon et les origines de l'exégèse biblique*, Paris, 1960; A. Bernus, *Richard Simon et son histoire critique du Vieux Testament*, Lausanne, 1869; Henri Margival, *Essai sur Richard Simon et la critique biblique en France au XVIIe siècle*, Paris, 1900; and Louis I. Bredvold, *The Intellectual Milieu of John Dryden*, Ann Arbor, 1959, esp. pp. 98–107.

with rabbis. He studied the Biblical quotations in the early Church Fathers. He compared the Hebrew and the Greek *Old Testament* texts. He did what was possible, and established the best text for his time. But now in the seventeenth century with all sorts of additional data, such as Erasmus' evidence that the line in *John* stating the doctrine of the Trinity was a late interpolation, such as the evidence from Greek Church texts of early interpolations, such as the Jewish evidence concerning early practices and beliefs; a critical study of the Bible is needed.

Simon's higher criticism, the commencement of modern Biblical studies, first appeared in his *Critical History of the Old Testament* (1678) [1]. It was suppressed by Bossuet when it was in galley proofs. It was followed by another immediately suppressed work the *Critical History of the New Testament* [2], which was followed by a series of banned works on the history of the editions and translations of the Bible. The final culmination of Simon's efforts was a banned new French translation of the Bible.

Simon's fantastic erudition could and did drown all opposition in a sea of problems. But, as his opponents, Catholic and Protestant alike, saw, Simon had opened a Pandora's Box. If all of these problems were taken seriously, could God's message to man be found? On the basis of just a few of these problems, Spinoza had asserted that there was no message, and that human reason was the only judge of all truth. Simon insisted that he did not accept Spinoza's conclusion. The central problem, he contended, was to find *the* message. But this could only be done after it had been realized that what we possessed was a *human* version that had grown up over many centuries of *human* history. Then we would have to apply the best scholarly techniques and the latest scientific findings to the version of the message we possessed in order to try to figure out what must have been the original formulation. His opponents saw that if Simon were ever taken seriously, we would be lost in a scepticism about any and all points involved in the

---

[1] Richard Simon, *Histoire critique du Vieux Testament*, Paris, 1678, 1st English ed. 1682.

[2] RichardSimon, *Histoire critique du texte du Nouveau Testament*, Rotterdam, 1689.

Judeo-Christian conception of the world. Whether intentional or not, Simon had made scientific examination the measure of Judeo-Christianity.

Simon's Protestant contemporary, the great sceptic Pierre Bayle, carried this development a step farther by portraying over and over again the ridiculousness and immorality of religion when considered rationally and scientifically (especially Old Testament accounts, such as those dealing with the sex life of Abraham and Sarah and Ham's debauchery on the Ark) [1]. Although Bayle kept insisting that his aim was fideistic, to show that religion can only be based on faith, and that human reason is unable to make sense of any aspect of the world apart from faith, he succeeded in providing future generations with what Voltaire called 'the Arsenal of the Enlightenment' and in engendering a genuine scepticism about truth, merits, or importance of Judeo-Christianity [2]. It is in the eighteenth century that a full-scale war of science against religion really occurs, when the anti-supernaturalistic metaphysics of Spinoza is transformed into a pure materialism, the Biblical scholarship of Simon is transformed into a scientific means of challenging every basic historical claim of Judeo-Christianity and the scepticism of Bayle is transformed into a way of ridiculing any and all aspects of religion. The optimists of the Enlightenment could now claim that the application of Newtonian science to religion (as in Hume's *Natural History of Religion,* and in the many works of Anthony Collins and D'Holbach on Judaism and Christianity) had shown that religion was passé, and that everything could be understood and resolved scientifically. Religion and morality could now become subjects for serious scientific study. The supernaturalistic hypothesis was no longer needed and man could be studied as a machine. The intellectual rout of the harmonizers

---

[1]   See for example, Bayle's articles in the *Dictionnaire* on Abimelech, David, Eve, Ham and Sarah.

[2]   Bayle's fideistic claim is made throughout the *Dictionnaire.* See, for example, article Pyrrho, Rem. Band C, and the 3rd clarification. On Bayle, see introduction by R. H. Popkin to Pierre Bayle, *Historical and critical dictionary (Selections),* Indianapolis, 1965; and Elisabeth Labrousse, *Pierre Bayle,* I and II, The Hague, 1963–64.

and reconcilers of religion and science by the eighteenth century enthusiasts of Enlightenment has created, I believe, the mythology we now live with. Much of the religious side was turned into a bitter camp of anti-scientists, suspecting the worst from each further scientific development. The religious groups within Catholicism and Protestantism that had done so much to foster and support the 'new science' in the seventeenth century, now were faced with an implacable foe that they had helped to spawn. After the Enlightenment, it could be claimed that reasonable, decent people were now too enlightened to have either the ignorant innocence of the simple believer, or the supposed malicious sophistication of the religious chieftains. The latter were now seen as a malevolent group who out of a desire for personal power and gain prevented the rise of science and the progressive amelioration of the problems of mankind. (After all, what other motives could have led to their being religious leaders?) The scientific explanations of Comte, Marx, Nietzsche, Freud, etc. about the religious side have given us an elaborate picture of the enemy, still always ready to do more diabolical work against humanity unless the scientists are always on guard. As Dewey, Russell and Huxley have portrayed the matter, the religious camp fought to preserve its bastions. In the seventeenth and eighteenth centuries, it lost the physical and chemical world to the scientists, in the nineteenth it lost the biological one, and in the twentieth it is now losing the psychological and sociological ones, and then, nothing will be left. This picture may be comforting, but as I have tried to suggest it is far from accurate or adequate. And in so easily accepting it we may well be losing much of our seventeenth century legacy that is incisive and valuable to us today.

From the beginning of the Enlightenment, when traditional Judeo-Christianity was routed, until the present, modern science and technological change have obviously developed with an ever-increasing rapidity. This has resulted in an inundation of data, theories, and inventions. The Divine revenge for the Enlightenment seems to be another Flood, this time lasting not just 40 days and nights, but apparently with no end in sight – unless an atomic holocaust stops the mad pursuit for more and more and more information about the cosmos. The Bible tells us, in the story of the Tower of Babel, that the Lord put a temporary stop to inordinate human curiosity by creating multiple languages and thereby chaos among men. We now have more and more technical languages, and branches of branches of branches of various sciences. We are being drowned in data bleeping to us from outer space (as in the case of the now almost pre-historic American satellite that keeps bleeping, and will do so for a 1000 years, with data nobody wants anymore). We have a technological crisis in dealing with all the data, storing it, retrieving it, finding ways of getting still more, and so on [1].

There are constant optimistic reports that *The Answer* is just about to be found. There are similar optimistic reports that religion is just about to disappear. But after two centuries of such news, it has somewhat the hollow ring of the US communiqués from Viet-Nam announcing that another small escalation will bring peace, freedom, justice, etc.

The scientific domination of religion and ethics, that is, the examination and evaluation of these domains in solely scientific terms, has sapped them of any status or stature from which they could provide us a focus or guide for what we are doing. By now, three centuries after Pereira and Spinoza launched the war of science against religion, we have so many doubts about faiths, supernatural or secular, that it is extremely difficult to accept them as final answers. (And yet, it is the twentieth century's allegedly scientific, secular faiths that have really done the most fantastic damage to human beings, and that have actually killed people for their scientific beliefs.) We may well be in the situation Pierre Bayle described at the end of the seventeenth century, of knowing too much to be sceptical, and too little to be dogmatical. The warfare has also obviously cost us our innocence. But, perhaps we are now far enough removed from it so that we can begin to seek a *modus vivendi*. Perhaps, through a new examination of the history we

---

[1]   And *Jeremiah* 31 : 37 states, 'Thus saith the LORD; If heaven above can be measured, and the foundations of the earth searched out beneath, I will also cast off all the seed of Israel for all that they have done, saith the LORD.'

accept, of how science conquered religion, and a recognition of the roles played by scepticism, and the application of scientific standards and methods to evaluating religion in this struggle, rather than the arid repetition of Enlightenment and nineteenth century versions of what was supposed to have happened, we can better understand our present, and better appreciate and profit from the contributions of our past. The solution offered by Richard Simon, had it been accepted by both sides with good grace and good faith, might have avoided the conflict in the first place. If the scientific examination of the Judeo-Christian tradition and the mitigated sceptical interpretation of the new science had been accepted as one of man's best ways of comprehending his world, and seeking the meaning of his traditions, no war might have occurred. However, the Church immediately turned its back on Simon, hounded him out of his jobs, banned all his books, reduced him to a priest and scholar at large, refusing his data and his quest for a continuous historical reinterpretation and reevaluation of the still significant core of the religious traditions. The new materialists and Spinozists accepted his techniques, but changed the aim from one of seeking the authentic meaning of the religious documents as religious ones, to that of rejecting them as having any value. Had Simon's road been accepted, there would have been no need for the shock of a Rabbi Jacobs or a Bishop of Woolwich today. But, as Simon's religious opponents feared, if they accepted his scientific investigation and reevaluation of religion, they could not be sure of what, if anything, would remain.

The Vatican Council of today, and the liberal Protestants are still wrestling with this problem, trying to determine what is left after the warfare of science and theology, trying to assess what the science of religion launched by Pereira, Spinoza and Simon has left as the religious content of religion.

DISCUSSION

B. A. O. WILLIAMS: *Science and theology in the seventeenth century.*

I agree with Professor Popkin that we have suffered, and still suffer, from a distorted account of the relations of religion and science in the seventeenth century, an account particularly propagated by the Enlightenment. There are, however, one or two points in his paper that remain obscure to me, and which I should like, very briefly, to comment upon.

Popkin himself remarks, near the beginning of his paper: 'Part of the problem involved is the ambiguity of what constitutes the religious side and what the scientific one'. He goes on to ask 'Are the professors of mathematics and physics the latter, and the professors of theology the former?' and he shows that to identify the two sides in these terms would certainly be unsatisfactory – too many of the advocates of the new science were, unsurprisingly, themselves divines. Again, we shall not get very far if we seek to identify the 'scientific side' with some body of convinced atheists; Popkin is no doubt right in saying that there were extremely few convinced atheists at this period, and the most prominent supporters of the new science were not among them.

These points are certainly important in discouraging any simple Enlightenment-style picture of a confrontation between non-religious scientific workers on the one hand, and non-scientific theologians on the other. However, these same points seem to me also to put difficulties in the way of construing Popkin's own thesis, or at least one version that he gives of his thesis. He says that we should see the seventeenth century disputes as essentially disputes between theologians and theologians, rather than as disputes between theologians and scientists. But if, as he has shown, there is the difficulty about identifying theologians and scientists as such, he himself has not left it too clear what the difference between these two sorts of dispute is.

However, there is probably no need to put the point in terms

of the groups involved at all. Popkin's thesis can be taken to be
one about the grounds of the disputes, rather than about the
identity of the disputants: the thesis being that what caused the
trouble were excursions into theology which were associated with
the new science, rather than the doctrines of the new science itself.
As he puts it, 'The scientists . . . get involved in the religious wars
when their efforts directly relate to some theological point, or when
they inadvertently or deliberately antagonise some theologian.'
This formulation, however, does not remove the difficulty in interpreting these disputes, but rather focusses it; for the problem
now becomes, what count as efforts directly relating to a theological point? How far could the new science go before it antago-
nised some theologian?

One precaution obviously has to be taken in trying to answer
this question: not to approach it from the point of view of purely
logical relations between religious and physical doctrines, saying,
for instance, that there is no *intrinsic reason* why Catholic theology
and the new science should have conflicted. For, first, theology
is not a purely timeless conceptual structure, and if now Catholic
theology can live moderately happily with physics, this may not
reflect the degree of its commitments in the seventeenth century,
but, rather, later adjustments. Second, the historical question
about the disputes is not about what the logical relations and
commitments were, but (to the extent that this can be distinguished) what people took them to be; and if we are asking
whether the disputes could have been avoided, we must be asking
whether, granted the historical background, people could have seen
the relations between the two fields in such a way that dispute
could have been avoided.

Popkin's answer seems to be that they could have done: that
the pieces were already on the board which could have been re-
arranged into a more harmonious pattern. In particular, he stresses
the point that there were established ways out, available both to
theologians and to scientists. He does not entirely convince me,
however, of the essential point: that these were ways out which
everyone who was in, or on the edge of, a theological dispute could
prudently, plausibly or with good conscience have taken. Thus

he discusses very interestingly one possible way of reconciling mechanism and Christianity by means of an Augustinian theology, and remarks that the eventual condemnation of extreme Augustinianism was on religious and theological grounds, rather than on grounds of the Augustinians' scientific views. But this seems to miss the point. *If* such Augustinian theology was theologically objectionable – and I leave aside the question of how far its condemnation was even theological in origin – then *that* theology was not a way, for the orthodox, of reconciling Christianity and mechanism.

Popkin's approach here seems to depend, to some extent, on not taking theology and theological differences very seriously, an attitude (as he recognises) not notably characteristic of the earlier seventeenth century. He mentions the condemnation of Cartesianism because of its consequences for transsubstantiation. This he presumably regards as a clear case of opposition to the 'new science' on grounds of its theological, rather than its scientific doctrines. But it is really not at all clear how much turns on this contrast; if Cartesian physics had unfortunate consequences for transsubstantiation, and neither the physics nor the theology could be lightly modified in these respects, then there existed a reason, in the eyes of the theologian, for supposing that physics to be false and worthy of condemnation. Of course to object to physics on these grounds is a different thing from objecting to it because it did not explain the empirical phenomena; but this is just to say that the opposition in question is theological and not scientific opposition to the 'new science', which is agreed by all, including the Enlightenment caricaturists.

Popkin mentions possible ways out in the case also of Copernicanism. In particular, there was the way of representing the heliocentric theory as a predictive device or a purely geometrical representation of the motions, on the lines of Bellarmine or of Osiander's preface to *De Revolutionibus Orbium Coelestium*. But one clearly cannot regard these devices just as possible routes, neutrally available, for avoiding the conflict; for the question of whether these devices were acceptable was, or became, precisely one of the questions at the heart of the conflict. The fact, to which Popkin refers, that Catholic (as distinguished from Lutheran) opposition to Copernicanism was slow to arise, and broke out seriously more or less with the case of Galileo, is surely connected with the fact that Galileo's interest in the question was in its dynamical significance, and hence with the issue of 'real motion', and not in issues of predictive accuracy and the economical representation of the data of positional astronomy. It was no good, as Bellarmine found, advising Galileo to stick to the 'predictive device' story; he thought – rightly – that there was more to be said. The onus lay rather on the other side, not to regard *this* issue as one 'directly relating to some theological point'. As Galileo himself put it, in the famous note written in his own copy of the *Dialogues*;

> 'Take note, theologians, that in your desire to make matters of faith out of propositions relating to the fixity of the Sun and Earth you run the risk of eventually having to condemn as heretics those who would believe the Earth to stand still and the Sun to change position – eventually, I say, at such a time as it might be physically or logically proved that the Earth moves and the Sun stands still.'

If this, most notorious, case presents us with an involvement of the new science in theological territory, it is only because the theologians had extended their territory so as to include the proper concerns of the new science. It may well be more obscure in this case than in some others why the theological territory should have been regarded as extending so far; but at a crucial time it was so regarded, and Popkin's account of the situation does not basically remove or reinterpret this fact.

There is one last point that I should like to mention in connection with Popkin's thesis that it was not the scientific doctrines of the new science as such that caused the theological opposition. When in 1640, Descartes sent Mersenne the *Meditations*, he sent also a letter in which he said that while this work was not about physics, it contained his physical doctrines implicitly in its metaphysics; but he preferred Mersenne not to make this known, since if people got to know that it implicitly refuted Aristotelian physics, they would be opposed to it, but if they could assimilate the metaphysical views first, this would in fact prepare them for an easier acceptance of the physical theory later on. What Descartes anticipates here is opposition to his physical, rather than his metaphysical or theological, doctrines; and hence his attempt, very characteristic of his self-conscious prudence, to use the latter as a cloak for the former. Perhaps the opposition that Descartes anticipated was merely the opposition of academic conservatism, rather than anything specifically theological. But this was a world in which academic conservatives, and theologians, were usually the same people, and academic conservatives would be expected to invoke theological arguments and possibly theological authority. This being so, it seems, once more, less than realistic to insist that the new science need not, as such, have run into theological trouble. That non-theological objections in this age, turned so rapidly into theological ones, and that scientific arguments so readily touched on theological points, were surely the sort of facts that the Enlightenment, however crudely, had in mind.

A. MOMIGLIANO: *The greater danger – science or biblical criticism?*

My friend Professor Popkin combines two different theses in his paper. One is that there was no serious clash between science and theology in the seventeenth century; the other is that the real clash happened between biblical history and the new historical and geographical knowledge, especially of the East.

I am not competent to express an opinion on the first thesis. I should only like to remark that perhaps more research needs to be done on seventeenth-century public opinion before dismissing 'l'affaire Galilée' as irrelevant. For instance, the members of the Peiresc circle, which Professor Popkin knows so well, were deeply disturbed by the trial of Galileo. As Peiresc wrote in 1634: 'L'acte rendu contre Galilée fera bien, je m'asseure, parler du monde à son tour, quelque part que ce puisse estre' [1]. In his caricature of

---

[1] Unpublished letter quoted by Cecilia Rizza, *Peiresc e l'Italia*, Torino 1965, p. 220.

Galileo's trial Cyrano de Bergerac wrote some years later: 'Vous le forcerez bien à dire que la lune n'est pas un monde; mais il ne le croira pas pourtant . . . il vous dira bien qu'il croit; mais il ne croira pas pour cela' [1].

As regards the second thesis, I am glad to be able to support it as far as my knowledge goes. Some independent research had persuaded me, even before I read Popkin's illuminating pages, that I. La Peyrère (Pereira) was a key figure in the theological and historical controversies of the late seventeenth and early eighteenth centuries. As I tried to show in my papers [2], Vico develops in the *Scienza Nuova* (1725) a theory intended to refute, *inter alia*, La Peyrère's and Spinoza's arguments against the Bible. In order to defend the historical value of the Bible, Vico draws a sharp line between profane and sacred history. The poets who provide evidence for the earliest profane history (for instance Homer) cannot be taken literally, whereas the Bible is literally true. There cannot be a real conflict between the language of unreason which characterizes the heroic ages of profane history and the language of reason which is the very essence of the Biblical text. Vico's famous theory of the heroic ages is primarily an answer to La Peyrère and Spinoza. Other research [3] has proved that La Peyrère was known in Giannone's circle and raised serious difficulties for the believer in the Bible.

I am less happy about Popkin's final contention that 'had Simon's road been accepted, there would have been no need for the shock of a Rabbi Jacobs or a Bishop of Woolwich today'. First of all, I am not sure that I understand what it is that connects Richard Simon with the Bishop of Woolwich, though I can well see the relevance of R. Simon to Rabbi Jacobs. Anyway, hypothetical history is here made even more questionable by the assumption that 'Simon's road' – that is, the critical study of the Bible – is a central problem of our intellectual world.

R. Simon lived in a world in which history was one thing and

---

[1]   *L'Autre Monde*, ed. Leo Jordan, 1910, p. 172.

[2]   *Rivista Storica Italiana* 77 (1965), pp. 773–790; *History and Theory* 5 (1966), pp. 3–23.

[3]   G. Ricuperati, *Rivista Storica Italiana* 77 (1965), pp. 602–638.

natural sciences were another. His analysis of the Biblical texts was unrelated (or only very vaguely related) to any discovery in the natural sciences. Similarly, La Peyrère's pre-Adamites owed nothing to Galileo's theories [1]. Today history and the natural sciences have in common, to say the least, the immense territory of prehistoric anthropology. What the modern student of the Bible can say about the evolution of religious ideas is nothing in comparison with what biology and prehistory have revealed about the past of the human species. Contemporary theologians have to make sense of God in a world in which Bible criticism is only a tiny fraction of the body of knowledge which has changed our outlook in religious matters. No doubt the critical approach to the Bible of the Tübingen school was a significant factor in undermining traditional religious beliefs in the nineteenth century. It may also be argued that the Modernist crisis within the Catholic Church in the first decade of this century was a consequence of the new approach to the Bible. But in the nineteenth century it was the theory of evolution that presented itself to educated people as incompatible with Jewish and Christian dogmas. In the present century biology, psychology, sociology, historical materialism, comparative anthropology have variously combined to produce a picture of human nature and human history that is a challenge to any theologian. To the best of my knowledge, today few theologians (and not the most influential) are mainly concerned with the consequences of Bible criticism. As I have said, I am not competent to

---

[1] La Peyrère was very interested in astronomy and, no doubt, vaguely felt that there was some basic incompatibility between astronomy as he knew it and theology as he read it: see the telling episode of a dispute between a theologian and a 'mathematicus' in *Pre-Adamitae*, ed. 1655, pp. 216–217. But his argument against the traditional notion that Adam was the first man (and not, as he thought, the first ancestor of the Jews) was not founded upon any scientific data. He mainly relied on the well known incompatibility between American, Babylonian and Egyptian systems of chronology on the one side and the traditional Judaeo-Christian system of chronology on the other. He also observed that Oriental nations would not have been able to gather the astronomical knowledge they possessed within the span of time allotted to them by the Judaeo-Christian interpreters of the Bible.

decide whether Popkin has underrated the gravity of the conflict between science and theology in the seventeenth century. But I feel certain that he has underestimated the impact of biological and prehistoric research on the theological situation of the twentieth century.

R. H. POPKIN: *Reply.*

Professors Momigliano and Williams raise some interesting points about my paper. As Professor Williams states, it is not enough for me to contend that there were not sufficient logical grounds for a conflict between religion and the new science in the early seventeenth century. One must also consider the problem in its historical context, where theologians did in fact find religious and theological objections to some of the findings of the new science. I did not intend to deny that some conflicts did occur. I was challenging the traditional picture given us from the Enlightenment onward of a clash between groups rigidly opposed to the new science and of the heroic new scientists bringing us out of the world of medieval ignorance and superstition by finding out what the world is really like in opposition to the superstitious beliefs being enforced on mankind by the Christian authorities. In theory, I believe that there was no need for a clash, since Judeo-Christianity does not entail any particular scientific picture of the world, and since some ways of reconciling the new science with traditional religion were available – the hypothetical, predictive interpretation of the new science, an Augustinian interpretation of mechanistic physics, and the coupling of a scepticism about any metaphysical interpretation of the world with a positivistic–pragmatic interpretation of the new science. Williams rightly points out that in the context of seventeenth century history not all of these available solutions managed to avoid conflict and condemnation as theologically unorthodox. On the whole, I would argue that for most of the seventeenth century, they did provide ways of harmonizing the new science with the Judeo-Christian tradition, and that the development of science proceeded amazingly well, quite often with

Church encouragement and through the efforts of people anxious to hold on to both religious convictions and the new scientific outlook. The occasions where serious conflict occurred, I would argue, were theoretically avoidable, though in practice, due to the *dramatis personae* and local conditions, they, in fact, were not avoided. I doubt that the Augustinian mechanistic solution of the Cartesians would have been condemned were it not for the Jansenist controversy and the political and theological struggles this engendered between the Jesuits and the followers of any aspect of Jansenism.

Williams is incorrect in suggesting that I do not take the theological issues involved seriously. In fact, I do. I do not feel that it is up to me to offer the Church advice as to what is orthodox and what is not, but it seems to me as an outsider that the overall view of the Augustinian–Cartesian mechanists could have been accepted as a way of interpreting the new science. The application of the Cartesian theory to explaining transsubstantiation indicated that Cartesian physics might not be able to deal satisfactorily with this question. At this point several ways of adjustment were possible, such as saying that the new physics does not deal with miracles and mysteries, without leading to a real conflict. And I believe that the actual conflict that occurred between the Augustinian–Cartesian mechanists and the Church authorities in France is better understood in terms of the theological wars and the politics of the time than in terms of religion trying to suppress science.

The Galileo 'case', which I tried to minimize, is of course symbolically the most important. I argued that the case and Galileo's 'recantation' did not significantly impede the development of mechanistic physics. There were many conservatives in the academic and theological ranks who tried hard before, during, and after the case, to oppose innovators, but I think this was part of a continuous problem, and not one peculiar to developments in the seventeenth century. Momigliano points out that there is evidence that some people were disturbed by the Galileo affair, but the people he cites, Peiresc and Cyrano de Bergerac, were not however at all inhibited in their advocacy of mechanistic physics. I think we need a detailed examination of the impact of the Galileo affair to see what actual effect the condemnation had on scientific work and scientific thinking in the period. As I indicated, it certainly did not stop Fathers Gassendi and Mersenne, and the Catholic religious fanatic, Blaise Pascal, from continuing their researches along purely mechanistic lines.

My main line of argument was that the real clash between religion and science arose from the application of techniques, attitudes, and findings of the new science to the content of the Judeo-Christian tradition, starting with the work of Isaac La Peyrère. I am most happy to find that so eminent a scholar as Momigliano shares my view that La Peyrère was a key figure in the period. Both Momigliano's studies on the relation of Vico's theories and La Peyrère's, and an edition I am preparing of La Peyrère's final version of his *Rappel des Juifs*, may establish La Peyrère's crucial role in seventeenth century thought. (And I believe that La Peyrère was much more in the movement of the new scientists than Momigliano is willing to grant.)

I think that Momigliano misunderstands an unclear phrase of mine, that of 'Simon's road', which I suggested as the best path for finding a way of reconciling meaningful and vital aspects of the Judeo-Christian tradition with the findings of modern science. I did not intend 'Simon's road' to be just what it was for Father Richard Simon, that is, scientific and critical study of the Bible, but more generally the application of scientific and critical tools to the complex of views and beliefs involved in the Judeo-Christian tradition *in order to* find a significant content for modern man. Simon tried to do this in terms of seventeenth century information. As Momigliano indicates, the problem has become very much more complicated because of the development of our information about man, his nature and his history, in the last three hundred years. It is my belief that the *kind* of problem involved in seeking a present day formulation of a meaningful and valuable message for mankind in the Judeo-Christian tradition is the same as it was in Simon's day. In detail the twentieth century problem is far more complicated because of what we now know about man, nature and history. This, however, does not mean that the attempt, in our day, to reconcile science and religion by following 'Simon's road' in its twentieth century form, is either insignificant or futile. Personally, I believe it is one of the most important things we have to do – to see if we can still find a meaningful message for mankind in whatever elements of the Judeo-Christian tradition are still valid for us today. And I think this must be done in terms of a full awareness of what we have learned about our situation through the various sciences and history, and by applying the techniques, methods and findings of these fields to the materials of the Judeo-Christian tradition. Probably in each generation we shall have to face this task anew as the frontiers of our knowledge and understanding change. For each generation, the task will probably be monumental. But, in view of the tremendously vital role that the Judeo-Christian tradition has played in shaping our natures and destinies, and because there is as yet no really viable alternative source of guidance as to why we are here and what we are supposed to do about it, I personally feel that we have no choice but to try over and over to meet the challenge, and to try to put the scientific, moral and religious pieces of our puzzle together again in one harmonious whole. Fortunately many theologians are now trying, following a modernized 'Simon's road', to find a new solution, and we can only hope that some will succeed. I personally believe they will only if they are fully cognizant of modern scientific developments, and if they employ these to explore and reinterpret the traditional information about man's contact with the Divine. The seventeenth century struggles on this score may well provide guidance for the twentieth century ones, but the twentieth century struggles will certainly have to be carried on in twentieth century terms. The mitigated sceptical interpretation of modern science has again become acceptable. If this can now be coupled with a modern Simonian scientific study of the religious traditions, we may gain a new major perspective for comprehending our cosmos. I hope in future studies to be able to contribute in this venture.

In closing, I want to thank Professors Momigliano and Williams for making me think out some of the implications of what I said, and for making me clarify my views.

THEORIES OF DEMARCATION BETWEEN SCIENCE AND METAPHYSICS

W. W. BARTLEY, III

University of Pittsburgh

'I state my case, even though I know it is only part of the truth, and I would state it just the same if I knew it were false, because certain errors are stations on the road to truth.'

ROBERT MUSIL, *Notebooks* [1]

1. Man is by nature a confused animal. And his rationality, his politics, his science, are confused attempts to cope with his confusion. It should then hardly be surprising that the history of his thought is fraught with unintended and unwanted consequences of ironical character, children of the marriage of an unpredictable future and an unfathomable present. This is as true as it is anywhere in that part of philosophy which I call the theory of rationality or of evaluation. In some earlier essays I have tried to mitigate the effects of some of these unwanted results and to repair those aspects of whatever theories of rationality happened to lead to them. In particular, I tried to combat those parts of traditional theories of rationality which forced their advocates to the sceptical and fideistic conclusion that rationality is logically so limited that rationality is in fact impossible [2]. But that is a long story in itself.

---

[1]   Quoted in the Foreword to *The Man Without Qualities*, I, Secker and Warburg, London, 1961, p. xii.

[2]   See my book *The Retreat to Commitment*, Alfred A. Knopf, New York, 1962 and Chatto and Windus, London, 1964, or revised version in German *Flucht ins Engagement*, Szczesny Verlag, Munich, 1964, and my essay 'Rationality versus the theory of rationality', in Mario Bunge, ed., *The Critical Approach to Science and Philosophy*, The Free Press, New York, 1964. See also Hans Albert, 'Probleme der Theoriebildung', in *Theorie und Realität*, J. C. B. Mohr, Tübingen, 1964; 'Die Idee der kritischen Vernunft',

Whilst conducting the investigations just mentioned I was aided by some of the philosophical ideas of Sir Karl Popper. It therefore came as a surprise to me to discover that the continuation and improvement of my work forced me to reject some parts of Popper's philosophy which he and his disciples regard as fundamental. This essay has the modest aim of stating some of my differences with his ideas. I shall discuss one irony-impregnated episode in the theory of rationality, where attempts were made to deal decisively with problems of rational evaluation of claims by means of 'criteria of demarcation'. In particular, I shall sketch some historical and theoretical criticisms of Popper's falsifiability criterion of demarcation between science and nonscience, a theory which he has offered – in opposition to what he takes to be logical positivism – to unravel what he describes as one of the two fundamental problems of philosophy [1]. Making his priorities even plainer, Popper has written that the problem of demarcating science from nonscience is the central problem of the theory of knowledge; and in his *Conjectures and Refutations* he has described the solution to the problem of demarcation as the '*key* to most of the fundamental problems of the philosophy of science' [2]. It is, then, with some

in *Club Voltaire*, I, Szczesny Verlag, Munich, 1964, and 'Tradition und Kritik', in *Club Voltaire*, II, 1965. See also H. P. Duerr, 'Rechtfertigungs-freier Kritizismus? Zur Theorie der Vernunft', *Forum Academicum*, Heidelberg, May–June 1966; H. P. Duerr, 'Pankritischer Rationalismus: Bemerkungen zur Metakritik', *Forum Academicum*, Heidelberg, July 1966; H. P. Duerr, 'Nachtrag zur "Kopernikanischen Wende" der Epistemologie', in *Forum Academicum*, Heidelberg, November 1966, pp. 32–33. See also the comments by Helmut F. Spinner, Howard K. Davis, W. Ackermann, K. Kowalski, A. Mittermaier, W. Nemeth, J.-P. Lacroix, Morton White, Eberhard Braun, and others in 'Leser-forum', *Forum Academicum*, Heidelberg, November 1966.

[1] K. R. Popper, *Conjectures and Refutations*, Basic Books, New York, 1962, p. 254. Such remarks account for the title of Popper's early unpublished work: 'Die beiden Grundprobleme der Erkenntnistheorie'.

[2] K. R. Popper, *Conjectures and Refutations*, op. cit., p. 42. But see also *The Logic of Scientific Discovery*, Basic Books, New York, 1959, p. 51, where Popper writes that 'the main problem of philosophy is the critical analysis of the appeal to the authority of experience'. Earlier in *The Logic of Scientific Discovery*, on p. 15, Popper had written: 'the central problem

sense of expectancy that one learns that Popper believes that he himself, in his critique of logical positivism, has solved this important problem. And it is with some disappointment that one discovers, on reflection, that his assessment of his achievement is incorrect.

2.   Before turning to criticize Popper's theory of demarcation, I wish to record my agreement with part of the inspiration that doubtless underlies his theory of demarcation: namely, that a sound characterization of science, a 'definition of the idea of empirical science', as he puts it in *The Logic of Scientific Discovery* (p. 39), could be very important, and that, moreover, a critical examination of logical positivism would be necessary before any satisfactory characterization of science could be given.

For some time two strident motifs of our intellectual life have been the efforts of scientists and non-scientists to come to terms with one another, and the efforts of scientists to state just what it is that makes what they do scientific. Any number of questions depend on the results of such efforts: Is there any reasonably sure way to distinguish between a scientific and a non-scientific theory? What are the limits of scientific activity? Are these also the limits of rational activity? If there are any legitimate areas of non-scientific activity, where do these belong and how are they to be discussed and assessed? Such questions rise in almost any intellectual activity that has even the remotest link with science. Even in literature and art the distinction between scientific 'descriptive meaning' and 'emotive meaning' set the pattern and problems for a good part of a generation of criticism. Again, in that highly introspective field of psychoanalysis such methodological questions have risen repeatedly in its effort to leap from myth to science in a half-century. The same is true of the social sciences and of history; half the world is more or less ruled ideologically by Marx's 'scientific history', which many thinkers in the other half – such as Popper – dismiss as highly unscientific. And that other half

---

of epistemology has always been and still is the problem of the growth of knowledge'. Since all these problems are closely related, the looseness of Popper's account of priorities should not be taken too seriously.

has its own problems about history: are Toynbee's methods scientific? How far? And in what respects? His critics are themselves divided on such issues.

The point is, of course, that all these – as well as other activities like religion, philosophy, the various social sciences – have a tendency to characterize themselves by contrast to and in comparison with 'the sciences'. Thus a prior understanding of the nature of science has, for other disciplines, become a kind of prerequisite of self-knowledge. And by and large, it has been the positivist characterization of science or 'empiricism' that has been most widely accepted, even when some wider positivistic claims have been vigorously denied. Consequently, if it should happen that the positivist conception of science were shown to be unsatisfactory, half the disciplines in the academic curriculum would, one supposes, quite literally suffer what some psychologists describe as 'crises of identity'. If these various traditions and disciplines do understand themselves in terms of their conceptions of one another, confusion or revolution in one field – and especially in philosophy of science – might have serious repercussions for the rest.

3.   Theories, including not only the scientific and other theories just mentioned, but also philosophical theories such as theories of rationality and theories of demarcation, are in my view as in Popper's *guesses*, hopefully but not necessarily 'stations on the road to truth'. One of many jobs the philosopher may usefully perform is to explore the ways in which these theories, these guesses, may be subjected to the maximum amount of criticism without hampering the creativity needed to put better guesses in their places.

By contrast to Popper, I believe that his falsifiability criterion of demarcation is relatively unimportant, at least for purposes of evaluation and criticism. And I shall argue that if the problem of the demarcation between science and nonscience is taken in Popper's sense, the problem of demarcation is an unimportant problem. Moreover, the importance lent to the falsifiability criterion and the demarcation problem by Popper and others distorts his thought and is largely responsible, among other things, for the misunderstandings and controversies between him and the members of the Vienna Circle, as well as more recent philosophical thinkers. Since these controversies have, for better or for worse, influenced much recent philosophical thinking, a reinterpretation of them may be useful [1].

4.   That Popper intended his falsifiability criterion of demarcation to deal with the problem of the rational evaluation of hypotheses, with the judgement of their acceptability, there can be little doubt. Popper's interest in the problem of demarcation was kindled by the practical problem of deciding whether a theory was acceptable. He writes of 'degree of corroboration' as 'degree of acceptability' [2]. And his polemic against the application of the probability calculus to the evaluation of scientific hypotheses, his own development of a calculus of 'content', his theory of basic statements which one decides to accept, and his discussions of 'verisimilitude', can only be understood as part of a program intended to help sift the good from the bad, the acceptable from the unacceptable scientific theories, as part of a theory of evaluation. Viewing the scientist's task as that of judging theories, Popper reports that the group of philosophers to which he belongs replace 'the Humean problem of 'reasonable belief' by the problem of the reasons for accepting or rejecting scientific theories' [3]. The logical analysis of scientific knowledge, he stresses, is concerned with 'questions of *justification or validity*' [4].

When one attempts to evaluate Popper's solution to the problem

---

[1]   I should like to acknowledge my thanks to J. O. Wisdom, Avrum Stroll, David Rynin, Stephen Kresge, I. C. Jarvie, Hans Albert, and Joseph Agassi for their helpful comments and suggestions on an earlier draft of this paper.

[2]   *Logic of Scientific Discovery*, op. cit., p. 309.

[3]   Ibid., p. 22.

[4]   Ibid., p. 31. There are many such passages in Popper's writings. But it should be mentioned that there is one curious passage where Popper, in the course of narrating his intellectual autobiography, appears to give a different impression. On page 33 of *Conjectures and Refutations*, op. cit., he writes: 'The problem which troubled me ... was neither, "When is a theory true?" nor "*When is a theory acceptable?*" My problem was different. I wished to distinguish between science and pseudo-science.'

of demarcation in the light of his aim, however, one encounters some difficulties. For in its present form, Popper's theory of demarcation is not quite coherent.

Under the same rubric – the problem of demarcating science from nonscience – Popper deals with several problems which should be sharply separated. The *first problem of demarcation* is that of demarcating those theoretical statements which are not – *even when regarded with the most critical scrutiny* – subject to *empirical* argument or refutation. Those theoretical statements which *are* subject to empirical refutation or falsification, by the production of an empirical counter-example, are called scientific. An example would be: 'All orbits of heavenly bodies are ellipses', which could be falsified by the discovery of a heavenly body which did not orbit in an ellipse. To be demarcated from such scientific statements are others which could not be falsified by any empirical counter-example, and are therefore nonscientific. Examples might be: 'There exists a fountain of youth', and 'For every mental illness there exists an effective cure'. Even in their theoretical contexts, presumably, these statements cannot be falsified by empirical arguments. No possible empirical report could falsify such statements, provide counter-examples to them, unless these statements were first incorporated into theoretical contexts which would render them testable.

Popper's *second problem of demarcation* is different. Popper also wishes to exclude from science theories (often theories which claim or aspire to scientific status) which have built-in devices for avoiding or deflecting critical arguments – empirical or otherwise. Examples which Popper himself adduces are Freud's psychoanalysis, Adler's individual psychology, and Marxism. In order to understand how these theories might deflect criticism, imagine that someone presented a criticism of Freudian or Marxist theory. Both of these theories include – at least in some formulations – the assumption that ideas may be causally reduced or explained genetically. So, apologists for such views may, in the first instance, point to the sexual disposition of the critic, or – in the second instance – to his economic origins and status, in order to *explain away* the criticism. An uncritical Freudian could for example invoke the theory of resistances or of the censor to try to discredit the objections of a critic on the ground, say, that he had not been analyzed and was, because of his own repressions, resisting the 'obvious truth' of Freudian theory. A similar strategy might be taken by a Marxist by appealing, for instance, to the 'bourgeois background' of his critic, which would explain his 'vested interest' in criticizing Marxism. Popper's critical comments on the various forms such strategies may take, and on how to avoid them, are quite valuable [1]. A good way to learn how to heighten criticism is indeed to study how it may be reduced, evaded, or avoided. Until one has brought to light and exposed to criticism various hidden, often unconscious, stratagems that work against criticism, one can hardly expect to be in a position to recommend effective ways of eliminating or circumventing their effects. This is one reason why the study of the history of religion, or of, say, the history of astrology, is as important to the methodologist of science as is the study of the history of science itself.

I have said that Popper's remarks on this type of 'criticism-reducing strategy' are quite valuable. That is true; but they occasionally need qualification. For instance, there is nothing intrinsically wrong about invoking a theory of the character of the theory of resistances. It may well be true, as many psychologists have argued, that consciousness is so recent an acquisition of human nature, and still in so frail a state, that resistance may easily be aroused when the existence of an unconscious is argued. Pointing out this possibility, then, need not necessarily be a criticism-reducing strategy; it is an important part of the psychological theories in question, and to discount it just because it can be misused would be itself uncritical.

5. Now it is possible that theories which contain such built-in devices for deflecting criticism may also be nonscientific in Popper's first sense. But these two senses of 'nonscientific' do not necessarily

---

[1] See for instance *The Logic of Scientific Discovery*, op. cit., p. 42 and sec. 20. In this connection see also Jerzy Giedymin's discussion of 'dictatorial strategies' in his paper 'A generalization of the refutability postulate', *Studia Logica* **10** (1960), pp. 97–110.

go together, despite Popper's frequent identification of them in his writings. I shall argue that whereas the second kind of demarcation is indeed relevant to the problem of the evaluation of theories, the first kind of demarcation has little evaluatory importance, even though it is the first kind that Popper stresses, particularly in *The Logic of Scientific Discovery*. It is not being suggested that empirical tests are irrelevant in evaluation; what I am saying is, that the question whether any particular theory is testable (or 'refutable') in Popper's first sense is not very important in evaluating it – even if we grant the moot point that it is usually possible to say whether and under what circumstances a particular theory is testable. If my argument is correct, Popper's famous maxim – 'Irrefutability is not a virtue but a vice' – is simply untrue of the first category, however true it may be, in a different sense of 'irrefutable' (or 'unfalsifiable') of the second. This is my first point, which I shall explain in the next section.

My second, perhaps more important, point – which I shall begin to explain at once – is that although the problem of spotting theories which have built-in devices for avoiding criticism (that is, theories which are unfalsifiable in the *second* sense) is indeed relevant to the problem of evaluating theories, it is not a problem that should be called a problem of demarcation between science and nonscience. And for similar reasons there is no point to following Popper in calling a method which avoids these stratagems 'the empirical method' (*Logic of Scientific Discovery*, pp. 41–42). Such a method may be especially common in the empirical sciences; but 'the critical attitude' is hardly restricted to them. Of course, when such stratagems appear in theories, such as versions of those of Freud, Adler, and Marx, which *purport* to be especially scientific, it seems apt to label them pseudo-scientific [1]. Nonetheless, such stratagems for weakening criticism can arise in or out of science –

---

[1] In his essay, 'The nature of scientific problems and their roots in metaphysics', published in *The Critical Approach*, op. cit., p. 197, Joseph Agassi also observes correctly that Popper's characterization of science requires reformulation. But Agassi goes on, I think incorrectly, to remark that Popper's demarcation between science and pseudo-science needs no amendment.

in ethics, metaphysics, politics, theology, and elsewhere. So their presence or absence is no barometer of scientific or of nonscientific character. The presence of such stratagems in a metaphysical theory may, for example, enable that theory to deflect a non-empirical argument just as deftly as it deflects an empirical argument. An ethical theory, to take another example, is not necessarily scientific or empirical or acceptable, or even virtuous, if these stratagems are absent; nor is it pseudo-scientific if they are present [1]. Ethics, in particular, is often characterized by nonempirical arguments; and yet an ethical system may well contain many devices for deflecting criticism. For example, it may contain a theory about the *nature* of moral theories which entails that reforming them is immoral, impossible, or rationally arbitrary. Such a theoretical component can certainly weaken the effect of criticism on the theory. Again, it might be noted correctly that while ethical theories are never empirically verifiable there are some theoretical contexts in which they conflict with synthetic scientific statements. This can occur for example in contexts where ' "ought" implies "can" ' is agreed to apply to persons [2]. In such situations ethical statements may be criticized by synthetic statements of physical impossibility. Yet this does not render ethical statements scientific – or synthetic. Metaphysical and ethical theories, in short, may also be interpreted as explanatory or programmatic guesses which are subject to nonjustificational criticism [3]. Although the 'manner

---

[1] Thus Popper is wrong (in *Logic of Scientific Discovery*, p. 84), in writing that 'Only in the case of systems which would be falsifiable if treated in accordance with our rules of empirical method is there any need to guard against conventionalist stratagems'.

[2] Statements containing 'ought' imply statements containing 'can', if they do, when the subject of the 'ought' is a person. One can say that *things* or 'life' ought to be different even if alternatives are impossible. Here 'ought' would not imply 'can'.

[3] I use 'non-justificational criticism' in the sense given in 'Rationality versus the theory of rationality', op. cit., and *The Retreat to Commitment*, op. cit. There are several different ways in which one statement has been regarded as bearing a critical relationship to another statement. On one hand, it may provide a counter-example to that theory – as a statement of the existence of a black swan contradicts the statement that all swans

of exposing to falsification, in every conceivable way, the system to be tested' (*Logic of Scientific Discovery*, p. 42) may well be characteristic of the empirical method, it is not characteristic of the empirical method alone. 'The *distinguishing* characteristic of empirical statements', is not, as Popper claims, 'their susceptibility to revision' [1].

In brief, an important evaluatory problem is not to demarcate scientific from nonscientific theories but to demarcate critical from uncritical theories or from theories that are protected from criticism – particularly pseudo-critical theories. One might, if useful, call a pseudo-critical theory which purported to be scientific a pseudo-scientific theory. But in this broader context the demarcation of science and nonscience is, *per se*, unimportant.

6. Since these remarks are directed to Popper's views, it should be kept in mind that he quite explicitly denies that he regards 'science' as exhaustive of legitimate claims [2]. Nonetheless his writings occasionally suggest that he regards metaphysics as at best a necessary evil; he frequently uses the maxim: 'Irrefutability is not a virtue but a vice'. It might be argued that Popper has in his later work begun to emphasize metaphysics more. This is so; but his remarks are confusing just because he has retained the old slogans along with the new emphases, and failed to state explicitly

---

are white. This can be nonjustificational criticism provided that the refutation is not regarded as conclusive. Or it may refuse to endorse it in the sense that the statement under criticism cannot be derived logically from the criticizing statement. This can be justificational criticism. Logically speaking, such lack of derivability need not be important: the fact that one theory cannot be derived from another does not mean that it contradicts it logically; the two may be logically independent. Such lack of derivability becomes important when the criticizing statement is given some sort of special epistemological status: when, for example, it is considered the test of truth or rationality from which all true or rational statements must be derivable. Such an approach would be required for instance by any comprehensive attempt to separate the rational from the irrational by demarcating the true from the false.

[1] *Logic of Scientific Discovery*, p. 49, my italics.
[2] See for instance *Logic of Scientific Discovery*, op. cit., p. 19, p. 38.

how and why his ideas have changed. For example, it is interesting
to compare the final sentence of his article 'What is dialectic?',
published in *Mind* in 1940, with the final sentence of the revised
version of this article that appears in *Conjectures and Refutations*
(1962). In the 1940 version, Popper writes: 'The whole development
of dialectic should be a warning against speculative philosophy.
It should remind us that philosophy must not be made a basis
for any sort of scientific system and that philosophers should be
much more modest in their claims. *For their task*, which they can
fulfil quite usefully, *is the study of the methods of science*' [1]. In the
revised 1962 version, which appears in *Conjectures and Refutations*,
Popper writes: 'The whole development of dialectic should be a
warning against the dangers inherent in philosophical system-
building. It should remind us that philosophy must not be made
a basis for any sort of scientific system and that philosophers should
be much more modest in their claims. *One task which they can fulfil
quite usefully is the study of the critical methods of science* [2]. The
difference between these two quotations is profound and illuminating. Although Popper was never a positivist he was clearly
more positivistically inclined and anti-metaphysical in the 1930's
than he is today. Here I do not mean by 'positivistically inclined'
that he shared their main ideas, but that he took them (and their
programmatic statements) so seriously. It would be interesting to
study the development of Popper's thought from the 1930's to
the present.

In the previous section, I indicated my disagreement with

---

[1]   K. R. Popper, 'What is dialectic?' *Mind* N.S. **49** (1940), p. 426; my
italics.

[2]   K. R. Popper, 'What is dialectic?' ch. 15 of *Conjectures and Refutations*,
Basic Books, New York, 1962, p. 335; my italics. See also the introduction
to the English translation of *The Logic of Scientific Discovery*, where (p. 20)
Popper reports that the group of philosophers to which he belongs 'does
not confine itself to the study of the language of science, or any other
language, and it has no such chosen philosophical method. Its members
philosophize in many different ways, because they have many different
problems which they want to solve; and any method is welcome to them
if they think that it may help them to see their problems more clearly,
or to hit upon a solution, however tentative.'

Popper's suggestion that irrefutability is a vice even when it appears in the first class of nonscientific statements. I should like to explain and strengthen that remark by noting that in many contexts empirically irrefutable theories are highly desirable – even more desirable than empirical tests. If one's aim is to maximize criticism of existing views, it is by and large *more* important to have some alternative theory or explanation, scientific or not, which *conflicts* with the currently most popular account of the matter to be explained, than it is to have what appears to be an empirical refutation or counter-example to the reigning theory. This point has been made by several writers; it was first presented, to my knowledge, by Joseph Agassi, and has been developed in a most interesting way by Paul Feyerabend, in an attack on the idea that a plurality of theories represents a preliminary stage of knowledge which will at some time in the future be replaced by 'The One True Theory' [1]. As Agassi puts it [2], much original scientific research 'tends to begin with hypotheses which have a low degree of testability or are not testable at all'. Advocating what he calls 'theoretical pluralism', Feyerabend argues – giving as an example Einstein's utilization of the kinetic theory in the calculation of the statistical properties of Brownian motion, leading to the refutation of the phenomenological second law of thermodynamics – that the very production of a refuting fact will often depend on the prior invention of an alternative to the theory to be refuted. He goes on to suggest that a good empiricist 'will not rest content with the theory that is in the center of attention and with those tests of the theory which can be carried out in a

---

[1]   See Agassi's doctoral thesis, 'The function of interpretations in physics,' University of London Library, 1956, unpublished. See also Joseph Agassi, 'Sensationalism', *Mind*, January 1966, and 'The nature of scientific problems and their roots in metaphysics', op. cit. For P. K. Feyerabend, see 'How to be a good empiricist – A plea for tolerance in matters epistemological', *Delaware Studies*, p. 37; 'Materialism and the mind-body problem', *The Review of Metaphysics*, September 1963, pp. 49–66; 'Problems of empiricism', in *Beyond the Edge of Certainty*, ed. R. G. Colodny, Prentice-Hall, New York, 1965, esp. sec. 9; and 'A note on the problem of induction', *The Journal of Philosophy* 11 (1964), pp. 349–353.
[2]   'The nature of scientific problems', op. cit., p. 99.

direct manner. Knowing that the most fundamental and the most general criticism is the criticism produced with the help of alternatives, he will try to invent such alternatives. It is, of course, impossible at once to produce a theory that is formally comparable to the main point of view and that leads to equally many predictions. His first step will therefore be the formulation of fairly general assumptions which are not yet directly connected with observations; this means that his first step will be the invention of a new metaphysics' [1].

Feyerabend adds that the function of such alternatives is that 'they provide means of criticizing the accepted theory in a manner that goes beyond the criticism provided by a comparison of that theory with the "facts". However closely a theory seems to reflect the facts, however universal its use, and however necessary its existence seems to be to those speaking the corresponding idiom, its factual adequacy can be asserted only *after* it has been confronted with alternatives . . . The function of unusual *metaphysical* ideas is defined accordingly: they play a decisive role in the criticism and in the development of what is generally believed and "highly confirmed", and they must therefore be present at any stage of the development of our knowledge' [2]. Feyerabend might have added that facts not previously noticed, or facts previously regarded as trivial or irrelevant, may suddenly leap into importance when an alternative theory is produced, even if that theory is itself metaphysical.

All of this does not mean, of course, that whenever there is a conflict between a metaphysical theory and a scientific theory, that the scientific theory is to be overruled! Nor can one go to the other extreme, as J. O. Wisdom appears to have done, to suggest that in such a conflict the metaphysical theory is to be jettisoned [3]. I doubt that any general rule can be given for deciding;

---

[1] Feyerabend, 'How to be a good empiricist', op. cit., p. 37. See also 'Theoretischer Pluralismus – Philosophie ohne Dogma', by Helmut F. Spinner, in *Die Ampel*, Mannheim, July 1966.

[2] Feyerabend, 'Problems of empiricism', op. cit., p. 150.

[3] J. O. Wisdom, 'The refutability of "irrefutable laws" ', *British Journal for the Philosophy of Science*, February (1963), pp. 303–306.

but if one's general aim is to maximize criticizability, one might allow as a 'rule of thumb' that a new, severely tested theory of high content should generally overrule an old highly developed metaphysical framework with which it conflicts, but that an old highly tested scientific theory should not be allowed to preclude serious consideration of a new, as yet undeveloped, metaphysics [1].

However this may be, arguments like those of Agassi and Feyerabend can be used to support my contention that to regard metaphysical theories as at best a necessary evil, whose irrefutability is a vice, is to reduce rather than to enhance criticism by (1) discouraging the invention of such theories, and (2) causing these vague new theories to be knocked out before they have been developed in sufficient detail to illustrate their power – or lack of it. Thus, in general, the question whether a theory is irrefutable or nonscientific in Popper's first sense does not materially contribute, and may often be irrelevant, to the question of its desirability, acceptability, rationality, legitimacy, seriousness, interest (to all of which problems Popper's theory of demarcation was directed).

Once it has been agreed, as has been done by Popper, that not all metaphysical views are illegitimate, that some may be valuable – rather than their all sharing the ultimate disreputability of 'meaninglessness' – and that a deductive logical relationship can obtain between some synthetic metaphysical and scientific statements, any attempted demarcation criterion between metaphysics in this sense and nonmetaphysical scientific views loses most of its value as a means of evaluating theories. Rather, what now become needed are more general criteria, applicable to the whole range of logically interrelated claims – metaphysical, scientific,

---

[1] Compare Popper's *Logic of Scientific Discovery*, pp. 53–54: 'Once a hypothesis has been proposed and tested, and has proven its mettle, it may not be allowed to drop out without "good reason". A "good reason" may be, for instance: replacement of the hypothesis by another which is better testable.' See also P. K. Feyerabend, 'Realism and instrumentalism', in *The Critical Approach*, op. cit., p. 283. Feyerabend argues against what may be called Popper's 'retention principle' in 'Problems of empiricism', op. cit., pp. 148 ff.

theological, ethical – which help sift theories of dubious interest from those which deserve further discussion.

We cannot even tell from the falsifiability criterion alone whether closer study of a particular theory is the *concern* of empirical science. I mention this because Popper has written that his 'business . . . is . . . to formulate a suitable characterization of empirical science, or to define the concepts 'empirical science' and 'metaphysics' in such a way that we shall be able to say of a given system of statements whether or not its closer study is the concern of empirical science' [1]. Elsewhere, Popper has written: 'Those (theories) which are non-testable are of no interest to empirical scientists. They may be described as metaphysical' [2]. If my argument is correct, the closer study of a metaphysical system of statements, or simply of a system of statements which is not obviously falsifiable, may well be in the interest of empirical science and of important interest to empirical scientists in furthering the criticism of some current doctrine of empirical science. Consequently, the falsifiability criterion does *not*, to repeat, inform one whether a given system of statements deserves the closer study of empirical science. Popper's description of the proper concern of scientists is simply incorrect.

7. If an example is required of the way in which considerations other than empirical testability can play a more important role than empirical testability in deciding one's view of, or one's evaluation of, some theory or a conflict between two theories, one might usefully examine, and perhaps even solve, Nelson Goodman's famous problem of grue emeralds. In *Fact, Fiction and Forecast* [3], Goodman describes a hypothetical situation in which all emeralds examined before a certain time t are green. He then introduces a special artificial predicate, 'grue', which applies to all things examined before t just in case they are green but to other things just in case they are blue. Thus, at time t we have, for each evidence

[1] *Logic of Scientific Discovery*, op. cit., p. 37.

[2] *Conjectures and Refutations*, p. 257.

[3] Nelson Goodman, *Fact, Fiction and Forecast*, Harvard University Press, Cambridge, 1955, pp. 74 ff.

statement asserting that a particular emerald is green, a parallel evidence statement stating that that emerald is grue. So whatever has confirmed the statement that all emeralds are green will also confirm the statement that all emeralds are grue. This is of course a variant of the possibility, well known from the works of Hume, that the next instance may indeed be different. Goodman claims that 'we are well aware which of the two incompatible predictions is genuinely confirmed', but searches unsuccessfully for a *definition* of the difference between 'lawlike' or 'projectible' and 'non-lawlike' or 'non-projectible' properties which could provide a basis for sorting the correct statement from the incorrect, to demarcate the good statement from the bad one.

I do not know how Popper himself would solve this problem, but I imagine that a Popperian approach would be rather like this. To attempt a decision on the basis of confirmation theory, which would involve an inductive logic, would be impossible because an inductive logic is impossible; to attempt a decision on the basis of a definition of 'lawlike' or 'projectible' character of predicates would be Cartesian or 'essentialistic', not empirical, despite the fact that an empirical study of the actual history of the predicates in the language may be required to discover which is 'better entrenched'. Rather, what is needed is a crucial experiment between these two theories which would falsify at least one of them. But no crucial experiment of an empirical character is possible before time t. Therefore one must wait for time t.

Such an approach would be interesting, but it would hardly satisfy Goodman, even if he accepted, as I take it is not the case, Popper's assumptions about the impossibility of an inductive logic. Rather, I fancy that what Goodman really wants is some explanation of why it happens that *even before* time t we do not take seriously the claim that 'All emeralds are grue' ('we are well aware which of the two incompatible predictions is genuinely confirmed . . .'). At the risk of seeming simple-minded, I venture that the explanation is simple. The reason we do not take seriously the 'whacky hypothesis' that all emeralds are grue has little to do with the evidence at our disposal. We do not take it seriously because there simply is no problem in mineralogy to which it

responds. Whether we take seriously a whacky, highly counterintuitive hypothesis is a contingent matter, depending neither on
an analysis of the 'predicates' used in the hypothesis, nor on our
psychological dispositions, nor on our past experience, nor on the
degree to which certain predicates are 'entrenched', but rather on
the question whether the odd or whacky hypothesis in question
is directed to an existing intellectual problem, scientific or otherwise. Theories do not arise in a vacuum; they arise in situations
where some problem exists, and where some attempt is being made
to solve it. The grue hypothesis appears odd, implausible, unacceptable *not* because of the peculiarity of the properties used,
which are surely no more peculiar than the ideas of mass, force,
and simultaneity as they occur in Einstein's theories – 'peculiarity'
being defined by reference to the properties used in late nineteenth-
century Newtonian theory. Take the idea of mass for instance.
In Newtonian theory mass is a property of an object, independent
of its behaviour in coordinate systems. Whereas in relativity
theory, mass is a relation, involving relative velocities, between
an object and a coordinate system.

One might add another *prima facie* 'whacky' hypothesis about
emeralds to illustrate further the context and problem dependence
of our theories. Suppose one said: 'All emeralds are young'. The
proverbial 'man in the street' would hardly pause to listen further.
And the sophisticated philosopher, if he paused to listen, would
probably do so with the surprised expectation that he was actually
witnessing a 'category mistake' like 'Socrates is identical'. It would
probably take a quite alert mineralogist to recognize that 'All
emeralds are young' is true. If we think comparatively in terms
of the geological age of stones, emeralds are young – and diamonds
are old [1]. But we need this context in order to respond intelligently
to such a statement.

In sum, we fail to take seriously hypotheses like 'All emeralds
are grue' because we are not informed of any problem towards the
solution of which both 'All emeralds are green' and 'All emeralds
are grue' are directed. On the other hand, we do take seriously
Einstein's theory – which is at least as queer and unintuitive –

---

[1] I owe the example of young emeralds and old diamonds to Agassi.

because it was posed as a solution to certain problems which Newtonian theory appeared unable to solve. Einstein's general theory of relativity, it might be noted, was taken very seriously long before its 'time t'. It had been around several years before it could be tested seriously in the famous crucial experiment conducted by Sir Arthur Eddington at Principe, off West Africa, on May 29, 1919. And that it could be tested as soon as that was due to a quite exceptional coincidence. Writing of his famous experiment, Eddington muses:

'In a superstitious age a natural philosopher wishing to perform an important experiment would consult an astrologer to ascertain an auspicious moment for the trial. With better reason, an astronomer to-day consulting the stars would announce that the most favourable day of the year for weighing light is May 29. The reason is that the sun in its annual journey round the ecliptic goes through fields of stars of varying richness, but on May 29 it is in the midst of a quite exceptional patch of bright stars – part of the Hyades – by far the best star-field encountered. Now if this problem had been put forward at some other period of history, it might have been necessary to wait some thousands of years for a total eclipse of the sun to happen on the lucky date. But by strange good fortune an eclipse did happen on May 29, 1919' [1].

Another example of a theory which had to wait for a serious test is Einstein's photoelectric equation of 1905. It was not until 1916 that Robert A. Millikan was able to obtain experimental data sufficiently precise to test the photoelectric equation. Yet, fitting in as it did with Planck's quantum hypotheses, Einstein's photon theory was given immediate attention.

8. So far, we have been discussing the acceptance of theories. I should, however, like at least to raise the question whether the

[1] Sir A. S. Eddington, *Space, Time and Gravitation : An Outline of the General Relativity Theory*, Cambridge University Press, 1920, Cambridge, p. 113. The relevance of this example is of course independent of R. H. Dicke's important criticisms of general relativity theory. See for reference R. H. Dicke and H. M. Goldenberg, 'Solar oblateness and general relativity', *Physical Review Letters*, 27 February, 1967.

whole issue of the acceptability of a theory or explanation is really
as important as is often thought. What is more important in en-
hancing criticism of current theories is to have an informed
knowledge of many different theories and explanations, and *to
entertain them* or *to conjure with* them. When I use these words I
mean them in the sense of 'enjoy' or 'play with' theories or explanations – where no suggestion is made that the play will have a
happy ending in which one of them must win. To give an example:
one of the outstanding examples of metaphysical controversy in
this century has had to do with just those warring psychological
schools of Adler, Jung, Freud, behaviourists, neo-Freudians, and
so on, which Popper has referred to in a hyper-critical and sometimes even patronizing way. The doctrines of all these schools
doubtless have some bit of truth to them; all of them are, it appears,
false; all of them are difficult to test experimentally; none of them
is acceptable. Yet, deep awareness of – conjuring with – all of
them can heighten one's understanding and sensitivity to particular
human situations and interrelations, and one's ability to assess
the possible consequences of one's actions and participation in such
situations. Whether these theories are true, or scientific in Popper's
sense, or not, an intimate familiarity with them can enhance one's
critical prowess; and such familiarity is more important than
acceptance of any of them. This is only one example; similar things
could be said of rival cosmological theories. But the example is
an apt one: for one can hardly understand or assess Popper's
social theory, as presented in *The Poverty of Historicism* and elsewhere, without some knowledge of the thought of Alfred Adler,
whose influence on Popper was very deep, however vigorously they
may have disagreed on certain points.

Of course, in addition to this institutionalized entertainment
(and indeed part of it) an up-to-date knowledge of the problem-
situation in the field is needed – by which is meant that one needs
to know what problems are current and to what criticisms, non-
empirical as well as empirical, the rival hypotheses have been
subjected. It would be encouraging to think that we might even
be able to achieve an objective estimate of what I would call the
'degree of problematicality' of a theory, based on a report of its

problematical aspects. Such an estimate would of course be quite different from its 'degree of testability', and perhaps more valuable even if we assume that the latter may be obtained [1]. And it would, unlike degrees of corroboration and corroborability, be applicable to metaphysical, ethical, and philosophical theories as well as to scientific theories. But I should think that any attempt to formalize such a 'degree of problematicality' would be made in vain.

9. I should now like to turn to some brief historical remarks. In a footnote to *The Logic of Scientific Discovery* (p. 55, n. 3), Popper reports that 'In an as yet unpublished work ... I have tried to demonstrate that the problems of both the classical and the modern theory of knowledge (from Hume via Kant to Russell and Whitehead) can be traced back to the problem of demarcation, that is, to the problem of finding the criterion of the empirical character of science.'

Popper's historical hypothesis is interesting, but I doubt that it is true. Although it would be wrong to deny that such a problem of demarcation has played an important role historically, Popper overemphasizes its importance. Most theories of demarcation have been the result of science's occasional claim to omnicompetence, which put it in the role of challenger, combined with the failure of attempts to solve the problem of induction. The latter failure meant that scientific challenges could be rebuffed by clever opponents, and the rationality, let alone the omnicompetence, of *science* thereby cast in doubt. Given this situation, demarcational attempts have entered philosophical discussion in two chief ways, which I by no means suggest are exhaustive, since the history of the philosophy of science is a quite unexplored region.

(A)   Where the demarcation between science and nonscience is considered the chief method of evaluation and exclusion, of sorting the good theories from the bad. This has been a common tactic of justificational or verificational empiricism, whether science was regarded as the repository of legitimacy, or empirical character,

---

[1]   Agassi has cast doubt on the practical importance of degrees of testability in his brilliant article: 'Scientific problems and their roots in metaphysics', op. cit., p. 199.

or reducibility, or as marking the boundaries of possible human knowledge, or perhaps as marking the boundaries of meaningful speech.

(B) Where a demarcation between science and nonscience is regarded – whether by scientists and philosophers or their alleged opponents – as an effective means of preventing the claims of science from conflicting with some other area of human interest recognized as legitimate, such as metaphysics or – most commonly – religion. One often finds in religious theory demarcational criteria to determine (1) what is endorsed by religious authority; (2) what is prohibited by religious authority; (3) issues on which religious authority is neutral. Unlike science, religious theories have rarely claimed evaluational omnicompetence; but they have often wanted protection from the possibility of scientific challenge. I shall cite two comparatively uncontroversial examples, both of which Popper has himself discussed. One beautiful example of the importance of demarcation criteria in battles between scientific and religious world views may be found in the controversy between Abel Rey and Pierre Duhem, over the latter's instrumentalistic conception of scientific theories, which led to Duhem's essay 'Physics of a believer' [1]. Duhem regarded metaphysics as explanatory and certainly legitimate, but within the province of religious authority. Physical theory, on the other hand, was on his view not explanatory, but classificatory, and made no truth claims. Another interesting but rather more complicated example is to be found in Robert Cardinal Bellarmino's attitude to the theories of Copernicus and Galileo, stated in his famous letter to Father Antonio Foscarini of 12 April 1615.

---

[1] Originally published in the *Annales de Philosophie Chrétienne*, 77th Year, 4th Series, I, (Oct. and Nov. 1905), and in *Revue de Métaphysique et de Morale*, 12 (July 1904). Duhem's article is republished in English translation as an appendix to Duhem, *The Aim and Structure of Physical Theory*, Princeton University Press, Princeton 1954. For Bellarmino's, letter, see *Le Opere di Galileo Galilei*, XII, Barbera, Firenze, 1902. Item 1110*, pp. 171–172. For Bellarmino's letter do not consult the partial translation of it in K. R. Popper, 'Three views concerning human knowledge', in *Contemporary British Philosophy*, ed. H. D. Lewis, George Allen and Unwin, London, 1956, p. 358, which omits a crucial passage.

10. The two sorts of demarcational effort discussed (A and B) have in fact usually had the consequence of reducing rather than heightening criticism. Positivistic attempts to use empirical reducibility as a sufficient strategy of criticism, as Popper has put it: 'far from defeating the supposed enemy metaphysics, in effect presented the enemy with the keys of the beleaguered city' [1]. Their criteria of evaluation were both too narrow and too wide: they excluded intuitively acceptable views, such as Newton's and Einstein's theories, and included intuitively unacceptable views. And often such failures led to instrumentalistic (or 'conventionalist') conceptions of science – which in turn admirably suited the purposes of theologians and others who wished to circumscribe the domain of science, since scientific instrumentalism did in effect allow theological doctrines to avoid clashing with scientific theories.

Whatever the ironies resulting from these attempts at demarcation, it is apparent that Popper's theory does not even fit their *aims,* and consequently the question arises whether his so-called criterion of demarcation is even in the tradition of theories of demarcation. He has repudiated instrumentalism and is far from wanting to aid theology or other concerns in isolating themselves from the possibility of clashing with science; and he has effectively criticized positivistic and other attempts to employ verificationist reductionism as a sufficient evaluatory device. However, whether one judges Popper or the positivists closer to the tradition depends on what aspect of the tradition one is emphasizing. Popper is, for instance, in the tradition of Kant and Duhem in so far as all three tried to separate science from metaphysics, however different their reasons for doing so may have been, without *decrying* metaphysics.

11. What, then, it might be asked, has Popper done? I have sketched a general assessment of his work elsewhere [2]. In this more limited context his achievement is twofold:

(1) Popper destroyed the evaluational program of the early logical positivists, by showing that their answer to their demarcational problem was radically inadequate. But to do this is not

---

[1] *Conjectures and Refutations*, op. cit., p. 254.

[2] 'Rationality versus the theory of rationality', op. cit,

tantamount to answering the main problem of the logical positivists or even to speaking to it. Both Popper's arguments and the positivists' views were doubtless intended to heighten criticism. And in both cases the result of this intended heightening of criticism was expected to be a sorting out of competing views, some sort of sifting of 'good' views from 'bad' ones. The device the positivists chose, particularly in their earlier writings, had however the unhappy consequence of in fact working against the criticism of theories rather than heightening it, as remarked above. But their chief aim was clear: to wipe out nonsense and to put a final end to philosophical, metaphysical controversy [1]. The fact that the positivists wanted to name all and only those claims which were reducible to sense experience 'scientific' claims is almost incidental.

Popper's criterion did not on the whole work against, i.e., diminish, criticism; and to that extent it was successful. On the other hand, it did not achieve the radical sort of sifting which the positivists wanted. And this makes it more understandable why the positivists, even when they could accept the gist of Popper's objections, were not sufficiently satisfied with his 'solution' to 'their problem' to abandon their attempts to achieve a device – through meaning analysis – for a more radical sifting. The positivists stuck to meaning analysis in part because Popper's criterion was insufficient to get rid of long-winded nonsensical-appearing claims and other illegitimate theories. Popper showed that the specific kind of meaning analysis in which the early positivists engaged could not generally succeed, but he did not show that *no* metaphysical statements could be dealt with in such a way; Popper did not, for instance, show that *no* traditional metaphysical doctrines were analogous to category mistakes, only that *not all* were. It was, then, not unreasonable on the part of some positivists to suppose that *some* kind of meaning analysis might be useful in criticizing such views – and I think they are right.

In sum, Popper and the positivists were – largely unwittingly – concerned with rather different problems and quite different general

---

[1]   See for instance Moritz Schlick, 'The turning point in philosophy', in *Logical Positivism*, ed. A. J. Ayer, George Allen & Unwin, Ltd., London, 1959.

aims. The positivists still wanted some way to spot nonsense; but Popper's falsifiability criterion was not sufficient to sort out the rational from the irrational *meaningful* theories – let alone sort out the meaningful from the nonsensical [1].

(2) In the course of battling with the positivists Popper did present an excellent resolution of one form of the problem of induction – which surely has been a fundamental philosophical problem. By 'problem of induction' is meant here, that of indicating the relationship between theoretical statements of universal form and observational statements. Popper's well-known view is that, although there is no verifying relationship between an observational statement or finite collection thereof and a universal statement of scientific theory, there may be a falsifying relationship; and moreover, an asymmetry exists between the verification and the falsification of a law which preserves the possibility of a logical relationship between the two and which, when analyzed, discredits attempts to obtain an 'inductive logic'. As a corollary of this theory, Popper stressed that observational reports were themselves dispositional, or theory-impregnated, and thus also subject to revision.

There are, of course, anticipations of Popper's general approach: to give a few examples, in the work of William Whewell, as Joseph Agassi and Sir Peter Medawar have pointed out; and in the work

---

[1] Some confirmation for the view that Popper and the positivists were concerned with different problems may be found in Rudolf Carnap's reply to his critics, printed in *The Philosophy of Rudolf Carnap*, P. A. Schilpp, ed. La Salle, Open Court, 1963, where Carnap reports that his and Popper's theses 'concern entirely different problems', and that he only became aware of this after reading Popper's contribution to *The Philosophy of Rudolf Carnap*, 'The demarcation between science and metaphysics'. I think Carnap is basically correct on this point, although I cannot accept the details of his outline of his and Popper's differences. Moreover, adding to the confusion, it must be noted that Popper's first discussion of demarcation, in 1933, was directed towards the views championed in the early days of logical positivism; and as Carnap indicates in his autobiography, these views were modified radically between 1932 and 1936, partly as a result of Popper's criticisms. Compare Carnap's 'The elimination of metaphysics through logical analysis of language', 1932, reprinted in *Logical Positivism*, op. cit., and Carnap's 'Testability and meaning', *Philosophy of Science*, October 1936 and January 1937.

of C. S. Peirce, as David Rynin has remarked. I have even discovered some very Popperian utterances in the writings of the Viennese novelist Robert Musil, who had written his thesis at the University of Berlin on the philosophy of Mach. But whatever the antecedents may be, one must appreciate Popper's solution if only for the sharply focused, systematic, and highly effective way in which he is able to handle the problem. Curiously, however, Popper's clarification of the nature of the relationship between theory and observation somewhat diminishes the importance of that relationship. For the *critical* relationship between empirical fact and theory has been *most* important historically because of the assumption that experience is the *source* of *all* knowledge. Where this assumption is dropped, as it is in Popper's theory, the problem of stating the critical relationship between empirical fact and theory diminishes in general importance.

If I do not accept, for the reasons indicated in this paper, Popper's solution to the 'problem of demarcation', by the same token I do not believe that the solutions to the problems of induction and of demarcation are as closely connected as Popper has argued they are. This is not to say that they are not connected; for in so far as they are both taken to be part of the broader problem of providing a critical analysis of the role of experience in shaping our ideas, they clearly are related. I can agree with Popper's remark that the 'problem of induction is only a . . . facet of the problem of demarcation' (*Conjectures and Refutations*, p. 54), but not with his view (same reference) that it is an 'instance' of the same problem – if that means that to solve the one is to solve the other.

The later development of Popper's thought, and the generalization and application of his ideas outside science, have rendered his discussion of demarcation obsolete. Popper suggested to the positivists that the problem lies not in the demarcation of the meaningful from the meaningless, but in the demarcation of the scientific from the nonscientific. I suggest to Popper that the problem lies not in the demarcation of the scientific from the nonscientific but in the demarcation of the rational from the irrational, the critical from the uncritical.

J. O. WISDOM: *Refutation by observation and refutation by theory.*

Dr. Bartley was dealing with three topics: (1) whether the solution to the demarcation problem offered by Sir Karl Popper was correct; (2) whether it was important; (3) a question to do with Freud and others.

The first one, on the demarcation problem, I was surprised didn't occupy the centre of the stage just now, because I would have thought that all Popperians would agree that there was something needing adjustment in the solution of the problem, which intuitively seems broadly right and highly significant.

I would like to outline very briefly what seems to me slightly defective and what seems to me is needed to be added. What Popper did in his early work was to provide a method of discriminating general empirical statements from metaphysical statements according to whether they are refutable or not by observational means.

True, he has always been concerned with criticism in general or any form of refutation, but refutation by observation was his special study.

Now not so very long ago I chanced on a method of refutation, and I produced a very little paper discussing statements that appear in science but are not refutable by observational means. For example consider 'Energy appears at all levels' or 'There are continuous values for energy'. This is a consequence of classical physics, although it is not something you would find in books on physics. Now you can't refute this: if you didn't find continuous levels of energy, you would think it was perhaps because you hadn't been very successful in looking for them. But there is a method of refuting this possibility, not by observational means, but in a totally different way. For example take the wave-equation and derive eigen-values of the energy from it. Now, if quantum physics is testable, if it is tested, and if it is not refuted, i.e. if

65

it is corroborated, you have a theory which has a consequence that refutes this statement. Thus our statement, which is not refutable by observation, can be refuted by a theory. Hence empirical theories are, in Popper's manner, observation-refutable; certain others may be theory-refutable.

When I published that, one of the near Popperians was very excited, and said 'this refutes Popper'. I said 'I don't think so; he has always been concerned with refutability in the large, though in the *Logik der Forschung* he was concerned exclusively with refutability by observation. He may have thought for a time that this was the only form of refutability, but would surely never have objected to other forms of it if they could be found'.

We may now regard science as made up of the following: first of all general empirical statements which are refutable by observation; and secondly it contains statements which are not observation-refutable and which are therefore metaphysical, and these may be theory-refutable. The two together seem to me to make up the corpus of science. Specifically we should note one other type of statement, a presupposition of a content statement, such as absolute space in Newtonian theory, which is refutable, not by observational means, but by the general theory of relativity. Thus it seems to me that one can draw a demarcation line very near to where Popper drew it, not exactly in the same place, though in spirit the same.

Now, to turn to the second topic, why the issue is important: it does seem to me to connect with the question of rationality or, as I prefer to put it, with the question how you are going to decide whether some general claim made about the world is acceptable or not.

Now to connect this with Bartley's last topic to do with Freud and Marx and other views of this sort. Here I thought that Bartley followed Popper too closely in taking these things to be irrefutable. Popper has spoken of them as irrefutable, and I have never quite understood why for the following two reasons: one can't tell *a priori* that a theory is irrefutable as a rule (of course sometimes the form of the statement will tell you, but this is not very common). Usually you have to have considerable inspiration to find a method of testing a theory at all, and until you have found one you may think it is untestable and irrefutable, until some method of testing turns up. So you cannot tell *a priori* that, say, a Freudian theory or any other is untestable. Now Bartley seems to accept it that that kind of theory is untestable and irrefutable, but none the less he thinks it is very useful. Well, I would myself think it was entirely useless if it was untestable and irrefutable: and one of the most important things one has to seek to do is to find methods of testing such theories. If you take enough trouble over it, it is I think sometimes possible to devise tests for them – indeed I have managed to force several of such theories to a test. Before a test has been thought of, all we can say of an untested Freudian theory is that it may be untestable or it may be testable, and that it is not as yet part of empirical science.

Untestable theories may stimulate you – even stimulate you into developing a theory that may be testable – of course they can be useful in this way. But I am not here concerned with these utilities.

J. GIEDYMIN: *Empiricism, refutability, rationality.*

An account of the development of Karl Popper's ideas would indeed be a fascinating story, as would be an account and analysis of the anticipations of some of his and of related ideas by other philosophers. In this latter respect Professor Bartley's list of examples, including W. Whewell and C. S. Peirce, might be further extended; for example, Jan Łukasiewicz in an essay entitled 'On the creative nature of science' published in 1912 [1] and apparently unknown outside Poland, gave an interesting criticism of the idea of induction, dismissed inductive logic as impossible, and proclaimed that the principal aim of science was not to 'collect' or 'reproduce' facts but to explain facts and regularities, that the pattern of such explanations was deductive, and that explanatory hypotheses

---

[1] In later editions the title was altered to 'On science'; in the recent English edition of J. Łukasiewicz's *Elements of Mathematical Logic*, Pergamon Press-PWN, an appendix of the original edition entitled 'On inferences in the natural sciences' and dealing with induction was omitted altogether.

were not 'induced from observations' but were conceived in creative acts of imagination. His criticism of the logical-empiricist 'elimination of metaphysics' was known from his other pre-war writings, lectures, etc.

Both these subjects await a historian. Meanwhile Bartley offers us an account of his reception of and critical reaction to some of Popper's ideas. In what follows I want to comment on several claims made either explicitly or implicitly by Bartley, namely, on the claims that: (1) it is not true that irrefutability is always a 'vice' and never a 'virtue'; (2) empirical character and content, e.g. in the sense of refutability and degree of refutability as defined in *Logik der Forschung*, is inessential in the evaluation or acceptance of hypotheses; (3) the distinction between empirical-scientific and other statements becomes uninteresting once the role of non-empirical statements in the development of science is taken into account; (4) there were two distinct but confused problems and criteria of demarcation in *Logik der Forschung*; and (5) empiricists proposing various criteria of demarcation between empirical-scientific and non-empirical or non-scientific statements have overlooked a more important problem – that of demarcating rational from irrational procedures.

1. *Is irrefutability always a vice?* It is argued in Bartley's paper (e.g. pp. 47, 51) that non-testable and in this sense 'metaphysical' theories frequently play an important role in the development of science, since often they are the only alternatives to the accepted, well-confirmed theories and so form the only basis for criticizing the latter. From this Bartley draws the conclusion: "If my argument is correct, Popper's famous maxim 'Irrefutability is not a virtue but a vice' is simply untrue of the first category [of statements which are irrefutable because they do not exclude any observation statements]" (p. 47).

This conclusion calls, I think, for at least two comments.

First of all, it seems useful to bear in mind the specific reasons for which the criticized maxim was advanced: it was advanced to point out that many admirers of the theories of Freud, Adler et al. mistook vice for virtue when they emphasized the complete compatibility of those theories with all known (and possible) facts, and also their power to 'explain' any facts whatsoever; while in a testable, precisely formulated theory both these qualities, i.e. compatibility with all known facts and explanatory power, are highly desirable, in an irrefutable, vague one they are simply indications of lack of any contact with observable facts or at best of imprecise, undetermined relations with such facts and not at all of its truth or rich content. It was in this spirit that I proposed in my article mentioned by Bartley [1] to regard the refutability requirement as a restriction to be imposed on the 'compatibility-with-all-known-facts rule of acceptance of hypotheses'. The maxim 'Irrefutability is not a virtue but a vice' was clearly an exhortation directed to those who mistook lack of precise empirical content for a virtue, that is, for an indication of the truth of their theories.

Secondly, has the argument presented in Bartley's paper (or in those quoted by him) indeed established that 'the maxim . . . is simply untrue'? I do not see that it has. If we disregard the metaphorical formulation of the maxim, agree – for the sake of the argument – to apply 'true' and 'untrue' to an apparently evaluative statement, and interpret 'not' as 'never', then Bartley's contention that the maxim is false is equivalent to the following statement: 'Irrefutability is sometimes a virtue and not a vice'. Surely by 'virtue' we usually mean in such contexts a property of an object *owing to* which that object is valuable to us or praiseworthy. But all that has been shown in Bartley's paper (or in those quoted by him) is that sometimes we regard certain irrefutable theories as valuable, but not *because* they are irrefutable but rather *in spite* of this fact. Similarly, for certain purposes we use theories that are not only false but known to us to be false, for example, if they are simpler or more intuitive or easier to remember or to use in calculations: but this does not tempt us to say that falsity is sometimes a virtue. Irrefutable statements are evils which have to be tolerated because one hopes to develop those statements into empirical ones by inventing tests for them and because better alternatives are for the time being not available. I think therefore

---

[1]   'A generalization of the refutability postulate', *Studia Logica* **10** (1960).

that Bartley's own position, so far as it is indeed supported by
the examples quoted by him, should not be the denial of the maxim
'Irrefutability is never a virtue but a vice' but rather the claim
that 'Sometimes irrefutable statements are of interest to scientists
and play an important role in the development of science'. The
argument presented in the paper would, therefore, be pertinent
against the contention that 'Irrefutable statements are never of
any interest to scientists and never play any role in the development of empirical science'. Has Popper ever made such a contention?

The answer to the above question given in the paper under
discussion is, I think, the following: Popper wrote (in *Conjectures
and Refutations*) that 'nontestable statements are of no interest
to empirical scientists', called such statements 'unscientific' and
'non-empirical', said that science is concerned with empirical
statements; also he regards refutability or the degree of testability
as the only or at least the main *criterion of acceptance* (choice) of
hypotheses, so that irrefutable statements are thereby disqualified
and have no chance against any refutable statement. If, however,
some irrefutable statements *are* of great interest to scientists and
play an important role in the development of science, then it is
not true that a refutable theory is always more *acceptable* than
or is preferable to an irrefutable one and that refutability (or degree
of refutability) always plays an essential role in the *evaluation* of
statements.

This line of argument requires a closer analysis of the concept
or concepts of 'acceptance' of hypotheses, which will be the substance of my second comment.

2. *Are non-empirical statements ever acceptable? The three concepts
of acceptance.* It is, of course, well-known that the concept of acceptance is ambiguous, vague and far from clear. It was originally
introduced into the language of the methodology of empirical
science when the method of logical reconstruction of science became
a standard method used by many philosophers of science, and it
was analagous to, and a pragmatical and non-deductive counter-
part of, 'theorem'. Unfortunately, unlike 'theorem' which can be

defined in terms of rules of derivation, 'accepted' or 'acceptable' cannot be similarly defined because there are no agreed-upon rules of acceptance of hypotheses. Nevertheless both concepts are usually regarded as having certain properties in common, e.g. just as the set of all theorems of a deductive theory is subject to the requirement of consistency, so also is the set of all statements accepted at a given time: no pair of mutually inconsistent statements may be accepted at one and the same time. Some authors [1] even say that acceptance in this sense is based on some non-deductive rule of detachment and that this is a peculiarity of Popper's methodology of testing hypotheses as opposed to Carnap's recent approach. Of course, the 'detached' statements, or the statements accepted in this sense, remain hypotheses, may and should be further tested, and are confirmable by positive results of tests. It is clear, therefore, that only empirical statements, and in Popper's terminology this means refutable statements, qualify for acceptance in this sense.

Now, when Bartley speaks about non-empirical, alternative theories as acceptable or preferable, it is not acceptance in the above sense that is involved, since alternatives are usually incompatible with the established theory and with one another and so cannot be simultaneously accepted in the above sense; they do not replace the established theory altogether – no example of a non-empirical theory replacing an empirical one is known – and being non-empirical they are not confirmable by the results of observations or experiments. They may, of course, be acceptable or accepted in a quite different sense, namely, in the sense of being contemplated as *potential* alternatives to empirical theories, of being regarded as worthy of study and further development and as a basis of criticism of the established theory [2]. I suggest therefore,

---

[1] Cf. H. Kyburg's contribution to the present Colloquium, in II, *The Problem of Inductive Logic*.

[2] Incidentally, does the solution presented in Bartley's paper of Goodman's choice problem between the 'ordinary' 'All' hypothesis and the 'All ... until t ...' take into account the need for having alternatives to the 'natural' 'All' hypothesis? It would seem that the suggestion implied by the 'All ... until t ...' hypothesis that our universe is not 'steady' but changing, is

that there are at least three quite distinct senses in which 'acceptance' is used by Bartley – and by Popper for that matter – namely: (a) acceptance of a statement in the sense of its inclusion into the presumably consistent set of, for the time being, well-tested empirical hypotheses; this is the closest idea to the concept of 'theorem'; (b) acceptance of a statement in the sense of its inclusion into the set of alternative, mutually incompatible empirical but as yet not well-tested hypotheses, that are worthy of testing and can supply empirical criticism of the established theory, which may some day be replaced by one of them; (c) acceptance of a statement in the sense of its inclusion into the set of non-empirical statements which are regarded as *potential* alternatives to the empirical theories, if suitable tests are invented for them or correspondence rules are given to some of their terms, and which are in any case believed to throw interesting light on, or suggest a criticism of, the established theory.

Besides these three classificatory concepts of acceptance ('accepted', 'not-accepted'), there are of course relative or comparative and quantitative ones used by Popper and by Bartley.

Testability (the degree of testability and the degree of confirmation) may and indeed do serve as criteria of choice (or of ordering or of evaluation) of statements so far as the first two concepts of acceptance, and correspondingly the first two types of statements, are concerned. This is Popper's position, as I understand it [1]. Of course, even here one may wish to dispute whether all actually used criteria of acceptance or of ordering (preference) may be reduced to testability and confirmation – in their classificatory, comparative or quantitative meanings; and I personally doubt that they can. However, the main point here is that it is only in the case of statements involved in acceptance (or preference, or evalu-

---

interesting enough to justify its consideration, if only to criticize the 'All' hypothesis, even if mineralogists at present are not interested in it. After all, it took astronomers quite a long time to get interested in the heliocentric hypothesis.

[1] It must be admitted, however, that the tendency to disclaim any justificational character of the testing procedure may have the effect of blurring the distinction between e.g. (a) and (b).

ation) in sense (c) that no criterion of empirical character of statement or measure of empirical content plays any role. Besides, consideration of acceptance in sense (c), although it undoubtedly enriches philosophical analysis, seems to go beyond the reconstruction of the customary testing procedure of science into the reconstruction of some, admittedly interesting, historical details in the development of theories and into heuristic processes from which empirical theories emerge [1]. As we know, in the opinion of some contemporary philosophers of science such extension of the field of interest is desirable even in non-historical investigations of the development of science, but this view is not universally accepted even to-day and it certainly was not in the past. Since, moreover, *a theory which has no clear connections with experimental procedures is at best regarded by scientists as an unfinished product from which a full-fledged empirical theory may or may not emerge, I do not think that Bartley succeeded in showing that the problem of demarcating statements under (a) and (b) from those under (c) becomes 'relatively unimportant' or of little interest once the role of unempirical alternatives in the development of science is taken into account.* It seems that empirical criticism remains for an empiricist *the main* method of criticism (whether 'empirical' is defined in a Popperian or in any other way) and statements which are nonempirical cannot for him form the main body of science, although they may be very influential and useful in the historical changes of science [2]. But according to Popper, statements involved in (a)

---

[1] Is it not significant that on the same page (257) of *Conjectures and Refutations* (1965 edition) from which Bartley quotes the sentence 'Those which are non-testable are of no interest to empirical scientists' the following passage also occurs: '. . . we must not try to draw the line [of demarcation] too sharply. This becomes clear if we remember that most of our scientific theories originate in myths. The Copernican system, for example, was inspired by a Neo-Platonic worship of the light of the Sun who had to occupy the 'centre' because of his nobility. This indicates how myths may develop testable components. They may, in the course of discussion, become fruitful and important for science. In my *Logic of Scientific Discovery* I gave several examples of myths which have become most important for science, among them atomism and the corpuscular theory of light . . .'

[2] The recently growing interest in studying the development of science

and (b) differ from those involved in (c) exactly in that the former have to be refutable while the latter are not, and Bartley does not dispute Popper's explication of 'empirical' in terms of 'refutable' but claims that the demarcation between (a) and (b) on the one hand and (c) on the other is unimportant and of little interest. Now, judgements of the importance and interest of problems, distinctions etc. may be hunches based only on intuition and as such are not easy to evaluate. So far, however, as the arguments presented in the paper under discussion are concerned, they do not seem to me to give sufficient support to the claim that the problem of demarcating empirical hypotheses from other statements, however influential, is at present of no interest or philosophical importance.

3. *Were there two distinct but confused problems (and criteria) of demarcation in 'Logik der Forschung'? The importance of being rational.* Let us finally consider the claim that there were two distinct but confused problems and criteria of demarcation in *Logik der Forschung* (for the sake of convenience I shall refer to those problems and concepts as syntactical and pragmatical, respectively), that the concept of refutability involved in the first is irrelevant to the evaluation or acceptance of hypotheses, and that *the* problem is not to find criteria of distinguishing between scientific-empirical and non-scientific statements but between rational and irrational procedures.

The first of the above mentioned problems is clearly historical. To discuss it properly one ought, it seems to me, to study the relation between *purely logical* and the *pragmatical* approaches to philosophy of science in the period between the two wars. As we know, there was a very strong anti-psychological reaction among logically-minded philosophers who in this case were in a unique and somewhat strange alliance with the disciples of E. Husserl, the arch-antipsychologist. Originally it was a reaction against the mentalistic-psychological interpretation of the 'laws' of logic. How-

----

makes some philosophers of science treat almost with contempt any structural, 'static' approach, an extremism perhaps understandable but hardly justified.

ever, psychologism was so strongly resented that even in the field of the methodology of science any considerations going beyond the relations between sentences were discouraged and regarded as somehow inferior to purely logical considerations; pragmatical problems and concepts were converted into logical, namely syntactical ones, though this was not always easy or satisfactory. It seems to me that many passages of *Logik der Forschung*, and of some other contemporary works, bear witness to this conflict between extreme antipsychologism and the wish to consider certain pragmatical components of science such as attitudes, decisions etc. In the case of basic statements, for example, this may be seen in Popper's refusal to consider experiences of observers as justifications for accepting basic statements, and the insistence that statements may only be justified by other statements, though they may be – and according to Popper are – accepted on the basis of decisions [1]. In the case of refutability as the criterion of demarcation, Popper was originally faced – as we know from his 'Personal Report' – with a pragmatical contrast between, on the one hand, the attitudes, behaviour, decisions of Freudians, Adlerians etc., who on the whole tended to be apologetic, evasive, vague in formulating and defending their theories, and on the other hand those of modern physicists, who were more critical, precise and not so evasive. The syntactical definition of a refutable statement was proposed in the course of *logical* or *rational reconstruction* of the analyzed examples of theories and of attitudes towards them and this definition was qualified by the proviso that on the basis of the definition in actual practice it was impossible to decide of a system of statements whether or not it was empirical, since attitudes and conventionalist stratagems had to be taken into account.

---

[1]   Nothing would seem easier than to assume e.g. that observation statements (formulated in non-psychological terms) are accepted on the basis of experiences of reliable or independent observers and that, of course, this involves a theory of reliability or of independence of observers (or of measuring instruments), thus impregnating observation statements or terms with theoretical content. However, this would not have solved the problem of avoiding infinite regress in justification with which empiricists were concerned, again by analogy to a similar problem in appraising the foundations of deductive theories.

What is the relation between syntactical and pragmatical refutability? The syntactical concept of refutability is applicable only
to systems of statements in a logical reconstruction of science in
which pragmatical, behavioural factors are disregarded. The pragmatical concept of refutability is applicable to procedures, behaviour, decisions etc. A syntactically refutable statement may be
rendered pragmatically irrefutable (or rather – would be irrefutable
if considered from the pragmatical point of view) and a syntactically
irrefutable statement may be pragmatically refutable, if special
rules are adopted. The latter applies particularly to probability
statements but also to any 'metaphysical' statement which one
chooses to make rejectable. So the syntactical and the pragmatical
concepts of refutability are distinct both in their meanings and
extensions, and so far Bartley is right. However there are also
distinct syntactical and pragmatical concepts of proof, of deductive
inference, of deductive theory, of definition etc. but they are
usually regarded as representing different 'aspects' of the studied
phenomena – the syntactical concepts represent the purely formal
or structural properties, the pragmatical ones – the behavioural,
historical and psychological properties. In a logical reconstruction
of science, whether in the thirties or now, one would concentrate
on the syntactical or semantic analysis, disregarding any pragmatical considerations; since Bartley seems to be more interested
in historical-pragmatical research it is no wonder that he should
find the pragmatical concept of refutability more interesting and
important. It seems to me, however, that many misunderstandings
in the discussion of the mutual relation between refutability and
rationality will be avoided, if one bears in mind that *the original
problem of empiricism*, whether in its older versions or in the more
recent logical-positivist version, was the pragmatical problem of
finding *criteria of empirical rationality* which might be used to
criticize extravagant claims to knowledge based on mystical experiences, intuition, divine inspiration etc. [1] This originally prag-

---

[1] Cf. in this respect the significant title of a pre-war article by K. Ajdukiewicz, 'Der logistische Anti-Irrationalismus in Polen', *Erkenntnis* 5 (1935),
pp. 151–161.

matical problem was 'translated' by the logically minded empiricists into the language of syntax (and later also of semantics) because the methods of syntactical analysis were better developed than the methods of pragmatical analysis. The syntactical solutions, such as the syntactical definition of refutability, were however regarded from the beginning as at least partial and idealized solutions of the pragmatical problem of rationality, so it would be belated to suggest, to Popper or to any other empiricist, that *the* problem is not to demarcate scientific-empirical from non-scientific statements but the rational from irrational procedures. Of course the concept or concepts of rationality were later more fully analyzed and studied, of this there is no doubt.

As mentioned before, syntactically non-falsifiable statements may be rendered rejectable, if special rules of rejection are adopted. In *Logik der Forschung* there is an analysis of probability statements from this point of view, in which it is shown that probability statements although non-empirical are useful in science and in fact used by scientists, who however make them rejectable relative to certain rules. This was, I think, the earliest extension of the concept of refutability to rejectability or revisability or criticisability. By the stipulation of the rules of rejection probability statements are not rendered falsifiable or empirical in the narrower sense of the term, but their acceptance or rejection is made to depend on the results of experiments and on certain conventions. In this way empirical criticism and choice criteria for hypotheses are extended. Coupled with logical criticism of consistency, which in its non-formal applications outside mathematics has always been known under the name of 'internal criticism', the critical method of science thus goes beyond the empirical method in the narrower sense of refutation-or-confirmation by the results of observation, incompatible or compatible, with the given hypothesis. One further point relevant in this context and which will not be elaborated here, deserves at least a mention: the method of empirical science has been regarded by Popper and by other empiricists [1] as simply a

---

[1] See *The Open Society and Its Enemies, The Poverty of Historicism.* Cf. also the pre-war controversy between F. Hayek and O. Lange on the possibility of rational economic planning in a socialist society.

refinement of the trial and error method with the help of which humans acquire their common sense knowledge and all animals try to solve their problems. Although successful problem-solving certainly depends on the state of the world and on our expectations of it, rationality acquires new dimensions in the practical affairs of social life and then such expressions as 'adaptability' or 'elasticity' or 'rigidity' or such phrases as 'it works' are used to assess it.

To sum up, I think that the paper under discussion, in its present form at least, does not provide sufficiently strong arguments to support its claims that (1) irrefutability is sometimes not a 'vice' but a 'virtue', (2) empirical character and content, for example as defined syntactically in *Logik der Forschung*, is inessential in the evaluation or acceptance of hypotheses, (3) the recently growing emphasis on the role of non-empirical theories in the development of science makes it necessary to revise the doctrine of empiricism so that the distinction between empirical and non-empirical statements becomes 'unimportant' or 'uninteresting', (4) there were two distinct but confused problems of demarcation in *Logik der Forschung*, and (5) empiricists proposing various criteria of demarcation between scientific-empirical and non-scientific statements have overlooked a more important problem – that of demarcating rational from irrational procedures or decisions.

A. E. MUSGRAVE: *On a demarcation dispute.*

Back in 1964 Dr. Bartley claimed to have solved the second and third of the 'three principal problems of philosophy', aided by 'the epoch-making contributions Karl Popper has made to the first problem' [1]. Bartley now claims that one of Popper's problems (the problem of demarcating science from non-science) is unimportant, and that Popper's solution to it is not only unimportant but incoherent. In fact, Bartley's new presentation of Popper's theory *renders* it incoherent and misses its importance. Bartley goes on to 'suggest to Popper' that what *is* important is 'the demarcation of the rational from the irrational, the critical from the uncritical'

---

[1] See his 'Rationality versus the theory of rationality' in *The Critical Approach to Science and Philosophy*, edited by Mario Bunge, 1964, p. 3.

(p. 64). In fact, Popper suggested this to himself long ago, and has successfully followed up his suggestion by solving, with its help, an impressive list of philosophical problems.

1. Bartley claims that Popper's theory of demarcation is 'not quite coherent' because it 'deals with several problems which should be sharply separated. The *first problem of demarcation* is that of demarcating those theoretical statements which are not – *even when regarded with the most critical scrutiny* – subject to *empirical* argument or refutation' (p. 45); the 'second problem of demarcation' is 'to exclude from science theories . . . which have built-in devices for avoiding or deflecting critical arguments – empirical or otherwise' (p. 45).

Bartley says that the first kind of demarcation does separate science from non-science but is unimportant, whereas the second kind of demarcation is 'quite valuable' (p. 46) but does not separate science from non-science.

In *The Logic of Scientific Discovery* Popper emphasized that for a theory to be falsifiable it is *not* enough for it to stand in certain logical relations with 'basic statements'; it is also necessary that a certain critical *method* or *policy* be adopted towards the theory. If this is correct, then Bartley's attempt to separate 'sharply' the considerations of method or policy in Popper's theory of the demarcation between science and non-science from the considerations of logical relations, and to discount the former as not especially relevant and the latter as unimportant, will indeed transform that theory into an incoherent and unsatisfactory one.

Popper suggested that 'empirical science seems to be characterized not only by its logical form but, in addition, by its distinctive *method*' [1]. Considerations of method, or policy, are indispensable in solving the problem of demarcation because a theory which might be falsifiable can be rendered unfalsifiable by being

---

[1] *Logic of Scientific Discovery*, p. 39; see also pp. 49–50. (For a further discussion of this aspect of the problem of demarcation, see I. Lakatos' comment on T. S. Kuhn's paper 'Logic of discovery or psychology of research?', in Lakatos–Musgrave (*eds.*) *Criticism and the Growth of Knowledge*, 1968.)

treated in a systematically defensive way. Hence a purely logical criterion of demarcation, which ignored this fact, would fail to exclude from empirical science systems against which no adverse empirical argument will be admitted. Because of this, Popper, before proceeding to what he calls the 'Logical Investigation of Falsifiability' (section 21), discussed various 'conventionalist stratagems' such as: the introduction of auxiliary hypotheses, surreptitious changes of meaning, interpretation of a theoretical system as a system of implicit definitions, appeal to hoped-for future results to discount present refutations, imputing refutation to the unreliability or dishonesty of the experimenter, or using another part of the system under investigation to discount or explain away a refutation [1].

In connection with this last stratagem, Bartley remarks (p. 46) that the existence within a theory of a component which *might* be used to deflect criticism is not necessarily bad. Quite so – it was always the stratagems themselves which were under attack, not the theoretical components which might be exploited in this way.

Popper's antidote to all such stratagems was to propose methodological rules which tell us to maximize empirical testability – these rules are an important part of his 'empirical method'. Methodological considerations are thus an indispensable part of his theory of demarcation [2]. Popper's 'Logical Investigation of Falsifiability'

---

[1] I have added (from Popper's later writings) the last stratagem (the only one mentioned by Bartley) to the list given in *The Logic of Scientific Discovery* (pp. 81–83), which 'makes no claim to completeness' (op. cit., p. 82.)

[2] This is clear from the opening of the chapter on 'Falsifiability', which will:

'examine how far my criterion of demarcation is applicable to theoretical systems – if it is applicable at all. A critical discussion of a position usually called 'conventionalism' will raise first some problems of method, to be met by taking certain *methodological decisions*. Next I shall try to characterize the logical properties of those systems of theories which are falsifiable – *falsifiable, that is, if our methodological decisions are adopted*'

Logic of Scientific Discovery, p. 78; the second set of italics are mine. Incidentally, to emphasize the rational discussability of such matters, Popper would now speak of 'proposals' for methodological rules rather than of 'decisions'; see *The Open Society and Its Enemies*, I, note 5, ★(3), to ch. 5.

(sec. 21) was prefaced with the proviso: 'Let us assume we have successfully banned these conventionalist stratagems by our rules: we may *now* ask for a *logical* characterization of... falsifiable systems' [1].

To make matters quite plain, Popper pointed out that '... it is possible to interpret any given scientific system as a system of implicit definitions' [2], and that this 'must inevitably destroy the empirical character of the system' [3]. It follows that:

> '... it is impossible to decide, by analysing its logical form, whether a system of statements is a conventional system of irrefutable implicit definitions, or whether it is a system which is empirical in my sense; that is, a refutable system. This however only goes to show that my criterion of demarcation cannot be applied immediately to a *system of statements*... The question whether a given *system* should be regarded as a conventionalist or an empirical one is therefore misconceived. *Only with reference to the method applied* to a theoretical system is it at all possible to ask whether we are dealing with a conventionalist or an empirical theory' [4].

It seems clear from all this that the application of the 'empirical method' to a theory is indispensable in rendering that theory criticizable by empirical tests, and hence scientific. So the 'requirement of falsifiability', which is to be satisfied before a theory

---

[1] *Logic of Scientific Discovery*, p. 84 (I have italicized 'now'). Earlier, in sec. 9, entitled 'Why methodological decisions are indispensable', Popper had criticized those who 'see empirical science as a system of statements which satisfy certain *logical criteria*, such as meaningfulness or verifiability' on these grounds: 'If... we characterize empirical science merely by the formal or logical structure of its statements we shall not be able to exclude from it that prevalent form of metaphysics which results from elevating [by the use of conventionalist methods] an obsolete scientific theory into an incontrovertible truth' (ibid., pp. 49–50; see also the first two paragraphs on p. 42, and *The Open Society and Its Enemies*, 1945, II, ch. 23, pp. 218–220 in the 5th ed., 1966).

[2] *Logic of Scientific Discovery*, p. 80.

[3] Ibid., p. 74 (see also p. 145).

[4] Ibid., p. 82 (his italics).

is admitted as scientific, has two parts, a methodological part and a logical part [1]. If we misinterpret this requirement as a purely logical one, we may be puzzled, for example, by Popper's assertion that Marxism was once refutable (and refuted), but has now become (through the use of conventionalist stratagems) irrefutable [2]. We may also be puzzled by Popper's treatment of probabilistic hypotheses, which he declared to be formally irrefutable, but which he then proceeded to 'make refutable' by proposing special methodological rules [3].

Bartley bases his contention that considerations of method should here be 'sharply separated' from logical considerations on the (hardly original) observation that 'stratagems for weakening criticism can arise in or out of science – in ethics, metaphysics, politics, theology, and elsewhere' (pp. 47–48) [4]. Quite so – but they can *also* be used to deflect *empirical* criticism, which is what Popper was concerned to avoid in *The Logic of Scientific Discovery*. Bartley would have been correct had he written that 'there is no point . . . in calling a method which [simply] avoids these stratagems "the empirical method" ' (p. 47). But avoiding such stratagems was only a *part* of Popper's empirical method, which also included an appeal to experience.

2. Having lopped off ('sharply separated') the methodological component of Popper's theory of demarcation, on the curious

---

[1]   As Popper puts it on p. 88; elsewhere (p. 54) he says that the rules of the empirical method are 'closely connected' with the criterion of demarcation, or 'depend upon' it, since they 'are constructed with the aim of ensuring the applicability of our criterion' (he also speaks of a 'methodological supplement' to the criterion).

[2]   See *Conjectures and Refutations*, pp. 37 (and the reference in note 2), 333.

[3]   See *Logic of Scientific Discovery*, esp. pp. 146, 189–191, 198–205 (the point is also discussed by Giedymin in his note, *this volume*, p. 76).

[4]   Bartley would agree that his remark is hardly original, and that the existence of criticism-reducing stratagems outside science has been pointed out, and criticized, for example by Popper (see, e.g., the references in note 3, p. 85) and by Lakatos, in a detailed and penetrating analysis of their use in mathematics, an analysis which could easily be applied in other domains (cf. his 'Proofs and refutations I–IV', *The British Journal for the Philosophy of Science*, 14, 1963–64).

ground that by itself it fails to demarcate science from non-science, Bartley asserts that the truncated remains, viz. the logical criterion of refutability, 'has little evaluatory importance' (p. 47). Now the evaluatory role of refutability was not confined to a contrast between testable and untestable theories [1]; it was extended to a comparison of *degrees of refutability* of competing theories within science, and thence to a measure of the content, explanatory power, simplicity, and degree of corroboration, of scientific theories.

Presumably Bartley regards these latter concepts as having as little evaluatory importance as the idea of refutability on which they depend.

Incidentally, one reason why Popper regarded the problem of demarcation as important [2] is that his solution of it provides the key to his analysis of these crucial evaluatory concepts within science (see *Logic of Scientific Discovery*, pp. 55, 191).

A second reason was the widespread belief that 'only the inductive method could provide a satisfactory *criterion of demarcation*'; this belief makes it essential for a non-inductive philosophy of science to give an alternative solution to the problem of demarcation (see, for example, *Conjectures and Refutations*, p. 53). Popper expresses the close connection between the problems of induction and demarcation by saying that the 'problem of induction is only an instance or facet of the problem of demarcation' (op. cit., p. 54) – Bartley accepts the word 'facet', but dislikes the word 'instance' (p. 64).

3.   Although I do not agree with Bartley that a criterion (in this case, refutability) becomes unimportant as soon as the hope of generalizing it to a broader criterion (criticizability) is mooted, I

---

[1]   On the evaluatory importance of this contrast, see J. Giedymin, *this volume*, pp. 68–70.

[2]   Incidentally, Popper does not (on p. 254 of *Conjectures and Refutations*) *describe* the problem of demarcation as 'one of the two fundamental problems of *philosophy*' as Bartley asserts (p. 41, my italics). He merely *mentions* his first (unpublished) book, whose title properly translated, as Popper does translate it on that page, was 'The Two Fundamental Problems of *Epistemology*' (my italics).

do agree that the generalized criterion is important [1]. It was proposed by Popper long ago. In listing the contributions to this generalization by Popper, I shall contest Bartley's assertions that Popper was 'more positivistically inclined and anti-metaphysical in the 1930's than he is today' (p. 50) and that Popper has 'failed to state explicitly how and why his ideas have changed' (pp. 49–50).

An explicit statement about how Popper's ideas on metaphysics have changed is to be found in the English edition of *The Logic of Scientific Discovery*:

> 'Although when writing this book I was aware of holding metaphysical beliefs, and although I even pointed out the suggestive value of metaphysical ideas for science, I was not alive to the fact that some metaphysical doctrines were rationally arguable and, in spite of being irrefutable, criticizable'[2].

This footnote explains both Popper's disinclination in *The Logic of Scientific Discovery* [3] to argue metaphysical theses *and* his opposition to the positivists' attempt to dismiss all metaphysics as meaningless. The 'suggestive value of metaphysics for science' was always one of the planks of Popper's anti-positivism: in his very first publication on the problem of demarcation (1933) he pointed out that 'metaphysics . . . from a historical point of view can be seen to be the source from which the theories of empirical science spring' [4].

Thus Popper has made clear the (limited) extent to which he

---

[1] That Popper intended empirical refutability to be considered as a special case of criticizability is clear from *The Logic of Scientific Discovery*, was stressed in 1940 (see *Conjectures and Refutations*, p. 313, paragraph 2), and was stated explicitly in two notes added to the English edition of *The Logic Scientific Discovery* in 1958 (see p. 44, note ★1, and p. 98, note ★1).

[2] Op. cit., p. 206, footnote ★2 (added 1958). In this note, and for example in note ★4, p. 212, or in note ★2, p. 247, Popper explains that he now upholds metaphysical views which he once dismissed.

[3] See, for example, pp. 61, 198, 203, 216, 247–248, and esp. pp. 252–253.

[4] See Popper's letter to *Erkenntnis* now translated in appendix ★1 of *The Logic of Scientific Discovery*, p. 314. The same point was elaborated with examples, in sec. 85 (1934), and in many later passages of Popper's writings.

was once 'anti-metaphysical' and the extent to which his ideas on metaphysics have changed. He always disagreed with the positivist condemnation of all metaphysics:

'I do not think there is much justification for fighting metaphysics *in general*, or that anything worthwhile will result from such a fight. It is necessary to solve the problem of the demarcation of science from metaphysics. But we should recognise that many metaphysical systems have led to important scientific results . . . I believe, at the same time, that we should fight those metaphysical systems which tend to bewitch and confuse us. But clearly, we should do the same even with un-metaphysical and anti-metaphysical systems if they exhibit this dangerous tendency' [1].

It turns out, however, that in calling Popper 'positivistically inclined' Bartley means only that he took positivism seriously! Quite so – Popper could hardly have given his criticisms of positivism *without* taking it seriously.

Popper first attempted to argue rationally about a metaphysical system (incidentally, one of the 'bad' ones, which 'tend to bewitch and confuse us'), and thus contributed further to 'Bartley's problem' of demarcating 'the rational from the irrational, the critical from the uncritical', soon after *The Logic of Scientific Discovery*, in his 'What is dialectic?' (1940). (He showed there that dialectic contains within it a doctrine which might be used as an *optimum* criticism-reducing stratagem, the doctrine of the fruitfulness of contradictions [2].)

In his *The Open Society and Its Enemies* (1945), Popper rationally argued for and against various extra-scientific doctrines, described how some of these can become 'reinforced dogmatisms' through the use of conventionalist stratagems [3], and generalized the 'em-

---

[1] *The Open Society and Its Enemies*, II, (1945), footnote 52 to ch. 11 (in the latest edition the passage is on p. 299). The last sentence quoted is an allusion to positivism itself, and especially to Wittgenstein's *Tractatus* which Popper had just criticized there.

[2] This paper now forms ch. 15 of *Conjectures and Refutations*; see esp. pp. 316 ff.

[3] See, for example, II, pp. 40, 215, 297 (in the 5th ed., 1966).

pirical method' of testing in science to the method of critical rationalism. And he applied this general method to the rational evaluation of non-scientific doctrines (e.g. to utilitarianism, which he reformulated in a 'negativist' way) [1]. Further examples of this are to be found in his 'Towards a Rational Theory of Tradition' (1948), 'The Nature of Philosophical Problems and Their Roots in Science' (1952), and 'Back to the Presocratics' (1958) [2]. In all of these Popper also points out the origins of scientific theories in metaphysical speculation.

In 'The Problem of the Irrefutability of Philosophical Theories' (1958) [3] Popper addressed himself specifically to the problem of how we can rationally evaluate empirically irrefutable theories, and gave various criteria for such evaluations, all of which depend on seeing the theory as a solution to a certain *problem*: '... every *rational* theory, no matter whether scientific or philosophical, is rational in so far as it tries to *solve certain problems*. A theory is comprehensible and reasonable only in relation to a given *problem-situation*, and it can be rationally discussed only by discussing this relation.'

These are some of the contributions made by Popper to the problem which Bartley now suggests is important [4]. They show

---

[1]   See II, chs. 24 and 25.

[2]   These papers now form, respectively, chs. 2, 4, and 5 of *Conjectures and Refutations*.

[3]   A broadcast in 1957, first published in January 1958; it is now re-published in *Conjectures and Refutations*, pp. 193–200 (the passage quoted is on p. 199). Popper's criteria for evaluation are also discussed in Bartley, *The Retreat to Commitment*, 1962, pp. 156–161. Popper first stressed the importance of problems in 1944: see *The Poverty of Historicism*, esp. pp. 98, 121 of the book edition, 1957. See also his 'Science: problems, aims, responsibilities', *Proceedings of the Federation of American Societies for Experimental Biology*, 22, No. 4, July–August, 1963, esp. pp. 966–969.

[4]   He was once well aware of Popper's contributions to the problem (and of those made by others); discussing various methods of criticism, he once wrote:

'Popper has already focused attention brilliantly on one of the means [of criticism] – the check of empirical experience ... The problem of how to criticise, to reduce error in those of our theories, such as the metaphysical ones, which are *not* subject to empirical check has been that we have, in Popper's writings, a continuous attempt to 'demarcate the rational from the irrational, the critical from the uncritical', *beginning* with his demarcation between science and non-science, which distinguishes those theories which are criticizable by empirical evidence from the rest.

4. To conclude, a persistent pattern of 'criticism' in Bartley's paper is as follows: use some of Popper's views (without mentioning that they are Popper's) to try to 'criticize' some other view, or more often, alleged view, of Popper's.

One example, as we have seen, is Bartley's 'suggestion' to Popper about the importance of the general problem of demarcating 'the rational from the irrational, the critical from the uncritical'. A second example is Bartley's use, against Popper, of the suggestive value of metaphysics for science, a persistent theme of Popper's writings. A third, minor, example occurs in Bartley's discussion of the problem posed by Goodman's 'grue hypothesis'. Bartley first 'imagines' how a Popperian would solve it; he then drops this and proposes his own solution, by implication a non-Popperian one – but this is nothing more than Popper's idea that theories should be evaluated *qua* solutions to problems.

Finally, an even less important though intriguing example: Bartley instructs us 'do not consult the partial translation of [a letter of Bellarmino] in K. R. Popper ... which omits a crucial passage' (p. 60, footnote 1) – implying that Popper is not to be trusted. But why does Bartley refer us *only* to the original version of this paper, now out of print, and not also to the revised, more accessible, version in *Conjectures and Refutations*, as he does in *all* similar cases? The answer seems to be that in the latter Popper himself had pointed out [1] that his quotation was selective: 'Bellar-

---

discussed ... by Popper himself and by such philosophers as J. W. N. Watkins (political philosophy, ethics, and metaphysics), Joseph Agassi (non-empirical principles of interpretation in physics), and Imre Lakatos (mathematical conjecture).'
Cf. his *The Retreat to Commitment*, 1962, p. 157 (references are given there).
[1] Op. cit., p. 98, footnote 2, my italics.

mino . . . was by no means a convinced instrumentalist, *as other passages in this letter show'*!

Dr. Bartley's present paper, it seems to me, exemplifies only too well its own opening sentence.

K. R. Popper: *Remarks on the problems of demarcation and of rationality.*

All criticisms are valuable, though some are more valuable than others.

The most valuable kind of criticism is one that takes a theory, formulates it as clearly and sharply as possible, putting it in its best possible shape, as it were, and which then proceeds to show that, nevertheless, there is something wrong with it.

The least valuable kind of criticism is one that misunderstands or misinterprets a theory, and shows that there is something wrong with the theory when thus misunderstood or misinterpreted. It is my firm belief that usually even this kind of criticism has *some* intellectual value: it may teach us where our approach is open to misunderstandings and misinterpretation; where we might have chosen a better formulation; and perhaps more important, where the general approach of our critic differs from ours in such a way that, to resolve the misunderstandings or misinterpretations, we have to discuss our problems on a deeper level.

I hate to be too abstract. So let me take an example. Tarski's theory of truth – that is, his rehabilitation of the view that we may meaningfully talk of the correspondence of a statement to a fact – has been for years combatted by some philosophers with the argument that Tarski speaks of true or false *sentences*, while only assertions, or statements, or propositions can be true or false, but *not sentences*. Sentences, these philosophers say, are strings of words conforming to certain rules of syntax. They can be used to express assertions or statements or propositions but are not themselves assertions, or statements, or propositions. Thus they cannot be true or false; and Tarski's theory must be mistaken.

This I think is an example of perhaps the least valuable kind of criticism, for it misinterprets (or even misrepresents) Tarski who speaks, quite explicitly, of *'meaningful* sentences', and thus, clearly, of a syntactically correct string of words *plus* the meaning which it expresses in the language in question; and this is hardly different from saying that he speaks of *propositions*, expressed or formulated in some language.

Looked upon in this way, the criticism lacks any value. It is a purely verbal misunderstanding, hardly excusable by the fact that Tarski, after explaining that he speaks of *meaningful* sentences, frequently omits, obviously for the sake of brevity, the adjective 'meaningful', so that the critic can, if he so wishes, quote many passages in which Tarski simply speaks of true or false sentences.

From the critic's point of view the many important problems solved by Tarski with his theory of truth can then be simply ignored, since it has been established, to the critic's satisfaction, that Tarski's theory cannot possibly be a theory of truth, in any sense which is considered relevant or interesting by the critic.

I suggest, however, that even this kind of criticism, although it does not really touch Tarski's theory, is not entirely without its intellectual value. It is, first of all, of considerable interest for anybody who wishes to *present* Tarski's ideas. But it is also of interest because it shows how great is the gap which has to be bridged between the school of language analysts in the tradition of G. E. Moore, and a mathematician like Tarski; in this respect it is quite analogous to G. E. Moore's very careful but nevertheless completely irrelevant criticism of Bertrand Russell's 'Theory of Descriptions' [1]. A gap like this *can* be bridged; but only if all those involved in the discussion have the will to search together for the truth and for what is of intellectual value in the theory in question, and only if they can trust each other that the search for truth (rather than, say, the scoring of points) is their overriding motive.

I now come to Professor Bartley's criticism of myself.

For various reasons this criticism came as a shock to me. Bartley came to me as a graduate student in the autumn of 1958, that is,

---

[1] In *The Philosophy of Bertrand Russell*, The Library of Living Philosophers, ed. P. A. Schilpp, 1944, pp. 177–225.

seven years before he delivered his present lecture. I found him a brilliant student, one of the very best I ever had, and a thinker of considerable originality. We worked very closely together. For years, until a few months before he gave this lecture, we discussed in great detail all the problems he mentions in his lecture, and many others besides. I had, and still have, the greatest respect for his outstanding gifts as a philosopher.

You will understand why I was entirely unprepared for his lecture, and for the kind of criticism it contains. For I can only describe it as that least valuable kind of criticism – one that misunderstands, misinterprets, and even misrepresents the theory it criticizes, as can be seen if his claims are compared with my published work – to say nothing about my unpublished work to which Bartley had free access.

How could this happen with a brilliant former student who had any amount of opportunity of discussing these matters with me, and who always freely took advantage of these opportunities? I do not know, and I cannot understand it. The nearest approach to an understanding – but it is still very far from any real understanding – seems to be this.

According to Bartley's present lecture, Bartley and I still hold very similar views on many fundamental problems of philosophy: his lecture confirms this very clearly, since I am in agreement with almost [1] all of the positive philosophical positions he adopts, explicitly and implicitly, in his paper – a fact of which, incidentally, he should be well aware. Thus I disagree in the main not with the philosophical views he presents, but only with his interpretation, presentation, and misrepresentation, of my own views. But he and I arrived at this philosophy – a rationalist philosophy which equates the rational attitude with the attitude of criticism, and of readiness to accept criticism; which stresses the *significance of problems* for the understanding of theories; and the *significance of criticizability* for the demarcation between more valuable theories and those

---

[1] One point of disagreement, as I often told him, is his preoccupation with psychological ideas such as the problem of a man's 'identity and integrity'. Another is, it seems to me, that my attitude towards knowledge, and its theory, is more optimistic than Bartley's.

which are not so valuable – by different ways and at different times from two very different sides.

Bartley comes to philosophy from the philosophy of religion – from an analysis of the epistemological crisis in Protestantism. I come to philosophy mainly through an interest in science, an interest in the growth of our knowledge of our world: my main aim is to improve my extremely limited understanding of the world – including ourselves, and our knowledge, which are part of this world.

It seems to me that, on the one hand, there may be *some* parallelism between my own youthful intellectual experiences and those of Bartley: I learned early in life to fight against dogmatism, epistemological relativism, and woolly verbal pretentiousness which I experienced in the fields in which I was interested. He seems to have had similar experiences in his first field of interest: in theology and the philosophy of religion. This may explain why he took so eagerly to the views which are indeed the basis of my teaching: that the theory of knowledge is at the very heart of philosophy, and that the awareness of our fallibility, and the attitude and practice of criticism, is at the very heart of the theory of knowledge.

On the other hand, it seems to me not impossible that some (but only some) at least of Bartley's misunderstandings in connection with the 'problem of demarcation' may be explicable by our different starting points.

Elsewhere [1] I have told the story of how I arrived, in 1919, at the 'problem of demarcation'; and there I formulated the problem as follows:

'The problem which troubled me at the time was neither, "When is a theory true?" nor, "When is a theory acceptable?" My problem was different. *I wished to distinguish between science and pseudo-science*; knowing very well that science often errs, and that pseudo-science may happen to stumble on the truth.' [2]

---

[1]   In a lecture first given in Cambridge in 1953 and first published in 1957; now ch. 1 of my *Conjectures and Refutations*, p. 33.

[2]   Bartley quotes this passage up to the words *'science and pseudo-science'* (but without my italics, and with a full stop instead of a semicolon) in his footnote 4, p. 44, introducing it with the words: 'But it

This was the original form in which the problem of demarcation presented itself to me. My first solution was that, in order to be scientific, a theory must be able to clash with the facts: it must be *'falsifiable'* or *'refutable'*.

At the time, I did not take either my 'problem of demarcation' or its solution very seriously. I did not even give it a name. As I said in the lecture just quoted (p. 39): 'At that time, in 1920, it seemed to me almost trivial, although it solved for me an intellectual problem which had worried me deeply . . .'

Later I became interested in the problem of induction, and I found that we never 'induce' a theory from repetitions which form a 'habit' (as Hume thought), but jump to unwarranted conclusions to which we are inclined to cling dogmatically, but which – if we are scientists – we test by trying to refute them. (This method was, obviously, a perfectly 'rational' one, so that Hume's despair in reason turned out to be due to an avoidable mistake.)

It was later still that I saw the connection between my solutions of the two problems: demarcation is solved by *refutability*; the method of science is one of *attempted refutations*. This led me to see that induction, conversely, was believed in by scientists (and philosophers) because they thought that it was the method of induction which functioned as the criterion of demarcation between science and non-science: if we give up induction, they thought, we give up the claim that science, by its method, is superior to non-science (for example, 'metaphysics').

---

should be mentioned that there is one curious passage where Popper . . . appears to give a different impression.' Different from what? From a concern of mine with the question of *'justification or validity'*. But being *concerned with questions* of justification or validity does not (as Bartley suggests) entail that my aim is, or ever was, to show that we can justify, or assert, the validity of a theory: my aim was always the precise opposite, as everybody can ascertain from my writings. See my *Logic of Scientific Discovery*, p. 315: 'Scientific theories can never be "justified", or verified.' This passage dates from the Prague Congress of 1934 and was first published in 1935. The passage quoted in the text which Bartley calls 'curious' appears so to him only because it clashes with his interpretation of my views, an interpretation of which he himself says that it is newly acquired, and that it conflicts with his earlier interpretation.

It was only then, when I found that the problem of demarcation was behind the belief in induction (and when I found that my criterion of demarcation was not so obvious as I had thought but apparently quite unrecognized) that I began to take the problem of demarcation seriously. This led me, encouraged by Herbert Feigl, to write my (unpublished) book, *Die beiden Grundprobleme der Erkenntnistheorie* ('The Two Fundamental Problems of the Theory of Knowledge': the title was an allusion to Schopenhauer's *Die beiden Grundprobleme der Ethik*). The two problems were the problem of induction and the problem of demarcation.

Although this shows that I started with problems of the philosophy of science, it does not show that I was an enemy of metaphysics. As early as 1933 I wrote a letter [1] to the Editors of the positivistic journal *Erkenntnis* in which I said of metaphysics that 'from a historical point of view [metaphysics] can be seen to be the source from which the theories of the empirical sciences spring'. I always adhered to this view, and I developed it first at some length in my *Logic of Scientific Discovery* (first edition 1934), sec. 85, and later in many lectures, for example in 'Towards a Rational Theory of Tradition' (1948) [2]. I also made it clear in my *Logic of Scientific Discovery* (explicitly on p. 252) that *I myself was, metaphysically, a realist*. I still am a metaphysical realist, and an epistemological optimist in the sense that I hold that the truthlikeness ('verisimilitude') of our scientific theories can increase: this is how our knowledge grows.

In my *Logic of Scientific Discovery* (1934) I discussed my solution of the problem of demarcation in a manner which, I think, can be described as highly self-critical [3]: I first presented it briefly, and

---

[1] The letter is republished in the English and American editions of my *Logic of Scientific Discovery*, pp. 312 ff. The quotation is on p. 314.

[2] First published in January 1949, and later republished in *Conjectures and Refutations*.

[3] I may perhaps here correct a slip of memory in Dr. Wisdom's contribution to this discussion. I did *not*, as he suggests, hold in *The Logic of Scientific Discovery* that theories are falsifiable, or falsified, by 'observations'. If he looks up for example my sec. 22, 'Falsifiability and Falsification', he will find that I said that to falsify a hypothesis we need a (corroborated) *falsifying hypothesis*,

then proceeded to elaborate and discuss all sorts of possible objections to it; and I showed that these objections could only be met if we modify the solution, and especially if we assume that what characterizes the scientific approach is a highly *critical attitude* towards our theories rather than a formal criterion of refutability: only in the light of such a critical attitude and the corresponding critical methodological approach do 'refutable' theories retain their refutability.

My *Logic of Scientific Discovery* is a book on the philosophy of science. (It had in its first 1934 edition the subtitle '*Zur Erkenntnistheorie der modernen Naturwissenschaft*', that is, 'On the Epistemology of Modern Natural Science'.) I believed, and tried to show, that the problems of the epistemology of *science* lie at the root of most if not of all epistemological questions, and are thus important for *philosophy in general* [1]. *If I understand Bartley at all, this belief of mine is now the central target of his criticism.*

Now I am most ready to admit that this belief of mine may be mistaken. It is a kind of historical hypothesis about the evolution of philosophy and it is difficult to test: it is the kind of thing which I have sometimes called a 'historical interpretation'. One can show (but only by *selected* historical evidence) that there is something in it; but this does not mean that a better case could not be made for some other historical interpretation.

In fact, when Bartley told me some years ago that, in his opinion, it is not the problems of demarcation (which he now misinterprets) and of induction, but the *problem of rationality* which is 'fundamental' for the history of philosophy, I was quite impressed; and I repeatedly encouraged him to write a historical account to support this thesis.

---

[1] I have never said that these problems are *the* fundamental problems of philosophy, as Bartley suggests. Bartley also seems to forget that in my *Logic of Scientific Discovery*, p. 84 (to which he refers in his note 1, p. 48) the term 'system' (or 'systems'), as in all other places (except when I use a term like 'metaphysical system') means as a matter of course '*scientific* system'. His remark in this note 'Thus Popper is wrong . . .' is therefore wrong. Moreover, his remarks on ethics in his text, before and after this note of his, repeat a thesis which was one of the main topics of a lecture course of mine on Ethics, in 1959, which he attended.

I still believe that such an account may be intensely interesting, and that a very good case may be made for this claim that the problems of rationality are the 'deeper' problems of the two groups. In fact, by showing that the demarcation between science and metaphysics is a special case of the wider problem of demarcating criticizable from non-criticizable theories, I have myself shown that the latter problem is at any rate the *more general* one.

Yet I wish to stress that it does not seem to me very probable that the question of the depth (or, to use Bartley's term, of the 'priority') of these two groups of problems will, in its turn, become a very important philosophical problem; if for no other reason, because the two groups of problems are historically extremely closely interrelated. At any rate, Bartley's suggestion that I have dogmatically stuck to the view that the problem of demarcation is *the* fundamental problem of philosophy is quite fantastic in view of my repeatedly expressed hopes (still held) that he would be able to support by historical studies his thesis that the problems of rationality are the deeper ones of the two groups.

Quite a different matter is Bartley's suggestion that I have been so much concerned with the *problem of demarcation* that I have not seen the more general *problem of criticism*, or the solution of what (I believe) he calls the problem of rationality; that is, *the thesis that the attitude of rationality, or of reasonableness, is identical with the critical attitude.*

In contesting this suggestion of Bartley's I must point out the following. Already in *The Logic of Scientific Discovery* of 1934, the thesis that empirical refutability and empirical refutation are part of a more general idea of criticizability and refutation by criticism is at least implicit [1]. At any rate, this thesis was made quite explicit in a lecture 'What is dialectic?' which I gave in 1937 and which was first published in *Mind* in 1940 (and later in a revised and expanded version in *Conjectures and Refutations*). I will quote one passage from this lecture at length as it first appeared in *Mind*.

---

[1]   See for example *Logic of Scientific Discovery*, p. 50, where I speak of 'that critical attitude which is in my view the proper one for the scientist'.

'If the method of trial and error is developed more and more
consciously, then it begins to take on the characteristic features
of *scientific method*. This method can briefly be described thus:
Faced with a certain problem, the scientist offers tentatively
some sort of solution – a theory. But this theory is at first
only tentatively accepted by science; and it is the most characteristic feature of scientific method that scientists will do
everything they can in order to criticize and to test the theory
in question. Criticizing and testing go hand in hand: the theory
is criticized from very many different standpoints in order
to bring out those points which may be vulnerable. And the
testing of the theory proceeds by [exposing] its vulnerable
sides to as severe an examination as possible. This again is
the trial and error method. Theories are put forward tentatively
and tried out. If the outcome of a test shows that the theory
is erroneous, then it is eliminated: the trial and error method
is essentially a *method of elimination*. Its success depends
mainly on three conditions, namely, that sufficiently many
and sufficiently different theories are offered, and that sufficiently severe tests are made. In this way we may secure,
if we are lucky, the survival of the fittest theory by a process
of elimination' [1].

In this passage, you have in a nutshell many of those views
which I have later developed more fully and which are now turned
against me; especially (1) the emphasis on *problems*; (2) the emphasis on the *general method of criticism and critical discussion* of which
empirical testing forms merely a part; (3) the emphasis on *multiple
hypotheses* competing with one another. Yet this passage is just

---

[1]   Quoted from 'What is dialectic?', *Mind* N.S., **49** (1940), p. 404. Where
I have added a word in square brackets ('[exposing]'; perhaps it was
'subjecting') a word has been omitted, obviously by mistake. In an improved
form the passage can be found in *Conjectures and Refutations*, p. 313. The
quotes there round 'scientific method' and 'method', and the footnote '2',
are new additions: it was only in my London lectures from 1946 or 1947
onwards that I used to begin my course on scientific method with the remark
that a 'scientific method' (in the sense of a method which, if properly
practised, *must* yield results) does not exist.

a brief characterization of science; and it is later made clear, in the same paper, that the question of criticism (and escape from criticism) applies also to philosophical theories; for example, to Hegelian dialectics [1].

The thesis that the attitude of rationality, or of reasonableness, is the critical attitude, and that it is most important for us to be rationalists in this sense, and to combat irrationalism, especially also in ethics and politics, is the central topic of ch. 24, 'The Revolt against Reason', of my book *The Open Society and Its Enemies* (1st ed. 1945, 5th ed. 1966).

I discussed this chapter very often and very extensively with Bartley, from 1959 on [2] and since he criticized some of my formulations, I made some significant alterations to one of its pages (II, p. 231) in the fourth English edition of 1962. These alterations were suggested by him, and I acknowledged them in a new *addendum* to that edition (see II, p. 369) with the words: 'I am deeply indebted to Dr. William W. Bartley's incisive criticism which not only helped me to improve chapter 24 of this book (especially p. 231) but also induced me to make important changes in the present *addendum*'.

These words meant, of course, exactly what they said: I am always grateful for any criticism, and ready to adopt it in the hope of clarifying my point of view. I *do* think that the altered passages on that page (II, p. 231) were clarified. That the matter is one of *clarification* rather than of any real *change* of my views may be seen by anybody who reads ch. 24 carefully and who compares the pages 231 of vol. II in the fourth English edition and in the preceding (third and second) editions, of 1957 and 1952, which is

---

[1] Cp. also my note 3 to sec. 11 of *The Logic of Scientific Discovery* (p. 55), of 1934, on 'the critical – or, if you will, "dialectical" – method of resolving contradictions' in philosophy, which, as I say in the text to this note 'is applied also within science itself, but . . . is of particular importance in the theory of knowledge'. (Incidentally, most of this goes back to a still older paper of mine, published in Vienna in *Die Quelle* 81 (1931), pp. 607–619.)

[2] Bartley writes in the Acknowledgments to his *The Retreat to Commitment*, 1962 and 1964, after acknowledging especially the influence of some of my papers of 1949, 1958, and 1960: 'I am also deeply indebted to Professor Popper for many exciting conversations on these and related matters.'

textually (apart from one merely stylistic change) the same as pp. 416f. of the first American edition (1950).

In these editions (the first American edition of 1950 and the second English edition of 1952) I did introduce an improvement of some significance in connection with the problem of rationality: in note 5 to ch. 5, I introduced a new paragraph 3 (starred, which characterized it as a new addition) in which I paid tribute to Professor L. J. Russell for his suggestion to use the term *'proposal'* in order to stress that a *decision* may be reached by way of a *critical discussion of proposals*. (Incidentally, I now find that I had previously, in 1944, used the term 'proposal' myself in this sense [1].) I accordingly often replaced in these later editions the term 'decision' (which is open to misinterpretation) by the term 'proposal', and sometimes by 'proposal, or decision'; for example on that p. 231 in vol. II of *The Open Society* whose text I improved considerably 12 years later with the help of Bartley's valuable criticism. This shows, certainly, that I developed my views – especially in regard to emphasis and to clarity of formulation. But it also shows that I did my best to draw attention to the changes.

The idea that *empirical refutation is just part of the general critical work of improving theories (including metaphysical theories) by searching for errors* was developed by me in great detail, in a long series of lectures starting even before *The Open Society*. I may mention *The Poverty of Historicism* (first published in 1944–45; latest edition 1966; see the Index under 'criticism, critical method'); the lecture 'Towards a rational theory of tradition' of 1948; and many others. This series is still continuing. Some of these lectures are published in *Conjectures and Refutations*. (The point was already clearly stated in my lecture 'What is dialectic?' which I gave in 1937; see my above quotation from this lecture, and *Conjectures and Refutations*, p. 313.)

Thus when Bartley sums up his lecture with the admonition: 'I suggest to Popper that the problem lies not in the demarcation

---

[1] See 'The Poverty of Historicism', *Economica*, N.S. 11, No. 43, August 1944, p. 120: 'The social sciences have developed very largely through the criticism of proposals for social improvements . . .' In the book editions (1957, and later editions) the passage is printed on p. 58.

of the scientific from the nonscientific but in the demarcation of the rational from the irrational, the critical from the uncritical', I can only say that I have constantly suggested this (ever since 1937) to my readers and to my students (and especially also to Bartley); I formulated it as the main theme of 'critical rationalism' in ch. 24 of *The Open Society*, and I did stress the point in countless lectures, only partly published, which Bartley attended, and to some of which he refers, either in his present lecture or in some of his previous publications. I suggested to my students on countless occasions that it is greatly clarifying to identify 'the rational' (I prefer the term 'the attitude of rationality') with the critical attitude, with the critical approach to science *and* philosophy.

I should perhaps also mention that in a broadcast given in 1957 [1] entitled 'The problem of the irrefutability of philosophical theories' (*'Das Problem der Nichtwiderlegbarkeit von Philosophien'*) I discussed in detail how to criticize metaphysical theories. I took in this broadcast as my main examples (1) metaphysical determinism (also discussed at some length by me in 1950 [2]); (2) idealism; (3) irrationalism; (4) voluntarism; (5) nihilism (in Heidegger's version); and I tried to show how to criticize these metaphysical theories, and why I supported the metaphysics of (1') indeterminism; (2') realism; (3') rationalism; and in addition to these, also metaphysical views opposed to (4) and (5) [3].

In view of all this, you will, I hope, understand that I was puzzled and, indeed, shocked by Bartley's comments on my philosophy. (I was also surprised by his remarks on my alleged philosophical development and the influences on it, about which he

---

[1] First published – without my permission – in the *Deutsche Universitätszeitung* in January 1958 and a little later in *Ratio* **1**; it is also in *Conjectures and Refutations*, pp. 193–200.

[2] Cp. *The British Journal for the Philosophy of Science* **1** (1950), pp. 117–133 and 173–195, see esp. pp. 120–126.

[3] Incidentally, Bartley's examples for nonscientific theories, in the middle paragraph of his p. 45, are taken from this broadcast of mine (see *Conjectures and Refutations*, p. 196) in which I gave *critical arguments* to show why those nonscientific and non-falsifiable statements may be rejected as false.

says in his lecture things that are completely imaginary, though
he could easily have tried to check his hunches critically, simply
by asking me about them.)

I was, more especially, shocked by the remark that I 'failed to
state explicitly how and why [my] ideas have changed', giving as
evidence the final passage from my lecture 'What is dialectic?'
(that very lecture of 1937 in which I show that empirical refutation
is part of criticism) in its version as published in *Mind* in 1940,
and as republished in *Conjectures and Refutations* in 1963. (See
Bartley's quotations on p. 50, and remember that the italics are
his.) I *did* alter the words 'For their task' to 'One task'. This is
certainly a correction: the first version implied that *'the'* task of
philosophy 'is the critical study of science', and apparently I found
that it is silly to say this, especially at the end of an article which
is not a critical study of science but a critical study of certain
metaphysical theories [1].

Incidentally, I said in my Preface to *Conjectures and Refutations*
that 'I have revised, augmented, and re-written' most of the
lectures and essays of the book.

Bartley's accusation that I 'failed to state explicitly how and
why [my] ideas have changed' is, I think, most undeserved. In
fact, I have done more in this respect than anybody I know of.
I have actually spoiled the later editions of my *Logic of Scientific
Discovery* by a host of starred footnotes which state, as precisely
as possible, which of my ideas have changed, [2] leaving at the same

---

[1]   I found, by accident, that the correction in question is contained in
a copy in which I thoroughly revised the article (first published in 1940)
in July 1941.

[2]   See for example the starred footnote 1 on p. 44 of *The Logic of Scientific
Discovery*:

'I have since generalized this formulation; for inter-subjective *testing* is
merely a very important aspect of the more general idea of inter-subjective
criticism, or in other words, of the idea of mutual rational control by critical
discussion. This more general idea, discussed at some length in my *Open
Society and Its Enemies*, chs. 23 and 24, and in my *Poverty of Historicism*,
sec. 32, is also discussed in my *Postscript*, esp. chs. ★1, ★2, and ★6.'

(It will be seen that in this starred footnote I failed to refer to my lecture
of 1937 'What is dialectic?', *Mind* 1940, which I have quoted here at some
length; see p. 96 above.)

time the text together with the old footnotes of 1934 untouched, so that anybody can compare my old views with my later views. I have tried to do something similar in the starred footnotes of *The Open Society*. I hope that my views will continue to change, and to develop, for the rest of my days. So far I have found that my old views (including my metaphysical realism) of 1934–37 and 1944–45 on demarcation and the method of rational criticism, and on the impossibility of induction by repetition, on *empirical content*, on the significance of *problems* for understanding theories, on the theoretical component in all observations, on the identification of rationality with critical discussion (and many more) were surprisingly effective in guiding me in my later development.

I have also always gladly and fully acknowledged, whenever there was any occasion of doing so, any contribution made by others and any help or influence received from others – and especially any original contribution made by any of my pupils.

Let me sum up. Although I find Bartley's change of mind which took place between April 1965 and July 1965 in the main inexplicable, I conjecture that the clash between Bartley's original interests in the philosophy of religion and my original interest in the philosophy of science may explain, to some extent, at least two of Bartley's criticisms. (By eliciting this conjecture, these criticisms may be regarded as having some intellectual value.)

The first of these two criticisms of Bartley's, often and variously repeated, is that the problem of demarcation and my views on it (which he misinterprets) are unimportant. 'Importance' is one of those questions that are difficult to discuss. At any rate, some great scientists and historians find the problem, and my views on it, important for their practical research work. (Bartley mentions by name one of them, Sir Peter Medawar, in a passage criticizing me. Yet Bartley knows that Medawar is one of those scientists who found my *Logic of Scientific Discovery* and my views on demarcation 'important'.) I am aware of the fact that among *philosophers* comparatively few think that the problem is important. (Their number seems to be decreasing: Bartley used to be one of them.)

The second of these criticisms of Bartley's seems to be that the problem of rationality – rationality in the sense of criticism – is more important than demarcation; more important, that is (if I understand him well), *for the clarification of the history of philosophy.* (That it is more general than demarcation since demarcation is *part* of the critical approach I have long held myself.) I do not deny this historical thesis; on the contrary, the idea seems to me very interesting and very promising. But it is obviously wrong to accuse me of dogmatism because I have not pursued this historical idea myself; although I have long asserted that, since the days of Thales, the method of rationality is the critical method, the idea that the problems of rationality are *the* basic problems of the history of philosophy is *Bartley's own.* All I can do is to encourage him (as I did repeatedly and for years) to substantiate his thesis by a historical investigation. I wish again to express my hope that Bartley will carry out this programme, and I look forward to his contributions in this field: knowing his great gifts, to which I have often testified, they cannot fail to be of outstanding interest.

W. W. BARTLEY, III: *Reply.*

I. *Reply to Jerzy Giedymin.*

Had my talk on demarcation done no more than rouse Dr. Giedymin to elaborate his brief comments at the Colloquium into his most interesting paper, 'Empiricism, refutability, rationality', I should be satisfied that my talk was worth giving. Although his paper is primarily a criticism directed to what he interprets to be my ideas, in the course of this he injects some interesting, positive points of his own. I shall first comment on his criticisms of my paper, and then try to contribute briefly to his constructive remarks.

    Giedymin attributes five theses to me, and criticizes these in turn. It is to be noted that his criticism is a qualified one in so far as it is intended to establish not that the conclusions he takes me to be advocating are wrong, but that my arguments are not sufficient to support these conclusions. In replying, I shall follow his order of presentation.

1. *That it is untrue that irrefutability is always a vice and never a virtue.* 1.1. I would accept Giedymin's suggestion that there may have been uncritical thinkers who regarded the (often built-in) irrefutability of their theories as the very hallmark of scientific virtue; and that one should remember that Popper's maxim, 'Irrefutability is not a virtue but a vice', was often directed towards this kind of thinking. That does not, however, change the situation: (a) Popper's use of this slogan was not restricted to such contexts; (b) the slogan remains, strictly speaking, incorrect. It would have been better for Popper to have said: 'Irrefutability is not *necessarily* a virtue; it *may* be a vice.' Or perhaps Popper means little more than *'caveat emptor'*? I suppose, however, that one cannot expect precision in slogans – even when they are the slogans of the philosophy of science.

1.2. I cannot agree with Giedymin's remark that compatability with all known facts and 'explanatory power' [1], when found in an irrefutable, vague theory, are 'simply' indications of lack of any contact with observable facts. The matter is almost always more complicated than that. Fortunately, Giedymin himself qualifies this remark by speaking of how these features function 'at best' in irrefutable theories.

1.3. I cannot agree that we regard some irrefutable theories as valuable not because they are irrefutable but rather *in spite of* this fact; or that such theories are 'evils which have to be tolerated'. This is just the attitude which I wanted to combat. If it is true that genuinely original theories – such as Kepler's or Faraday's for example – are initially often very vague, couched in what may well be regarded as metaphor or even *arcana*, empirically irrefutable; if we do indeed wish to *encourage* the development of such theories as *indispensable* aids to maximizing criticism of our current well-tested theories; then it hardly behooves us grudgingly to tolerate these theories with the invidious proviso: *'in spite of* their irrefutability.'

1.4. Giedymin remarks that 'a theory which has no clear connections with experimental procedures is at best regarded by

---

[1] I imagine that Giedymin meant to write 'interpretive power' here.

scientists as an unfinished product.' I believe that Popper would agree with me that theories which *do* have clear connections with experimental procedures also ought to be regarded as 'unfinished products'.

2. *That empirical character and content – in the sense of refutability and degree of refutability defined in 'Logik der Forschung'* [1] *– is inessential in the evaluation or acceptance of hypotheses.* 2.1. I presume that Giedymin is thinking of scientific hypotheses; but if so, I have never maintained this thesis, and am puzzled that Giedymin should attribute it to me. I did not write that empirical character and content is 'inessential'; what I did say is that Popper's falsifiability criterion is 'relatively unimportant'. If I may quote myself, I wrote: 'It is not being suggested that empirical tests are irrelevant in evaluation; what I am saying is, that the question whether any particular theory is testable (or 'refutable') in Popper's first sense is not very important in evaluating it.'

2.2. I do indeed believe that empirical character and content are inessential in the evaluation and acceptance of some non-empirical theories, including some ethical theories. But I do not believe that Giedymin has said anything that would counter this view; nor do I think he would want to do so.

3. *That the distinction between empirical-scientific and other statements becomes uninteresting once the role of non-empirical statements in the development of science is taken into account.* 3.1. Not only does Giedymin incorrectly ascribe this thesis to my paper; he strengthens it to report me as claiming that 'the problem of demarcating empirical hypotheses from other statements, however influential, is at present of *no* interest or philosophical importance' (my italics). This claim, which, like Giedymin, I would regard as indefensible, is worlds away from the thesis that in fact appears in my paper. My paper was addressed to Popper's discussion of

---

[1] Popper's pioneering work is now fortunately available again in German, as vol. 4 of the series: 'Die Einheit der Gesellschaftswissenschaften: Studien in den Grenzbereichen der Wirtschafts- und Sozialwissenschaften', J. C. B. Mohr, Tübingen, 1966, DM63.

demarcation; and Popper describes the problem of demarcation as one of the two fundamental problems of the theory of knowledge. By contrast, I described Popper's falsifiability theory of demarcation as 'relatively unimportant'. There was no suggestion that these issues are of no philosophical interest. Quite the contrary.

3.2. As for the philosophical importance of the problem, I agree with Giedymin that such matters are not easy to assess. But my thesis was, I thought, clear: that there are confused in Popper two different problems of demarcation; that the first problem is relatively unimportant for purposes of evaluation; that the second problem, although highly important for purposes of evaluation, ought not to be described as a problem of demarcation between science and non-science. My thesis may be right or wrong; but it is different from the thesis which Giedymin attributes to me.

4. *That there were two distinct but confused problems and criteria of demarcation in Popper's work.* 4.1. Giedymin has several interesting things to say in this section of his paper, some of which I shall comment on below. Meanwhile, I fail to see why he concludes that we differ over this point, for he writes: 'the syntactical and the pragmatical concepts of refutability are distinct both in their meanings and extentions, and so far Bartley is right.'

4.2. I believe that Giedymin and I are also by and large in agreement in our historical view of the situation. Giedymin writes of the main problem of empiricism [1] 'whether in its older versions or in the more recent logical-positivist version' as a pragmatical problem; and also observes, correctly, that I am more interested in pragmatical problems.

4.3. Giedymin and I begin to disagree when he describes the logical positivists as having simply 'translated' the original pragmatical problem into the language of syntax and, later, of semantics. This appears to me to be at best a misleading account; for the view of many of the early positivists was that the pragmatical

---

[1] Giedymin speaks of this as the 'original' problem of empiricism, and may well be right in doing so. But I have, I hope without his disagreement, changed this description to 'main' in order to avoid historical exegesis here.

problem could be *solved* once and for all by use of a syntactical approach. Since this view is incorrect, it is not surprising that it could lead to a confusion between syntactical and pragmatical considerations – even where, as in Popper, there is no suggestion that syntactical considerations can provide sufficient criteria of rationality.

5. *That empiricists proposing various criteria of demarcation between empirical-scientific and non-empirical or non-scientific statements have overlooked a more important problem – that of demarcating rational from irrational procedures.* 5.1. Once again, Giedymin ascribes to me a thesis stronger than and different from the one I did in fact propound. Indeed, I argue explicitly in sec. 11 of my paper that the positivists were concerned with the problem of the demarcation of the rational from the irrational in the broadest sense. But there has been a tendency on the part of empiricists rather over-optimistically to regard their tentative solutions to the problem of rationality as definitive, and thereby to produce unsatisfactory conceptions of rationality – theories of rationality – which have often been turned against empiricists and other rationalists by their irrationalist opponents. This explains the title of my contribution to Popper's *Festschrift* 'Rationality versus the Theory of Rationality'. The positivists, in grappling with the problem of rationality, got carried away with the demarcation between meaningful and meaningless propositions; similarly, Popper, in grappling with the positivists, got carried away with the demarcation between scientific and non-scientific (in his several senses). What I am suggesting is that the problem of the rational evaluation of hypotheses is far broader and more difficult than either of these evaluational programmes would indicate.

In sum, on the first point there seems to be a straightforward disagreement between Giedymin and me, which I hope we can explore in future discussions. On the fourth point, I believe that Giedymin and I are in substantial agreement, despite his indications to the contrary. As far as points two, three, and five are concerned, Giedymin attributes to me theses which differ in important ways from those I propounded, and consequently his arguments against these theses – arguments with which I often agree – do not affect my related comments.

I should now like to comment on several of Giedymin's interesting positive points.

(1) *The anticipation of Popper's ideas by Jan Łukasiewicz.* I found Giedymin's report of the contents of Łukasiewicz's article 'On the creative nature of science' very exciting – but also very frustrating, since Polish is not one of those languages which I can read. I should, therefore, like to take this occasion to make an historical comment – doubtless an obvious comment, but one that ought to be made repeatedly now. I imagine that Giedymin would agree that it is becoming more and more possible to study the outlines of the historical background of contemporary philosophy of science in some perspective, and that most of the major documents of the period since 1900 are readily available in English, German, and, to a much less important extent, in French. But as more and more Polish work has been translated, it has become apparent that no accurate account of the development of philosophy of science in this century can be written if the contributions of the Polish philosophers and logicians are not taken into account. And, as we know, most of these thinkers were in contact with similarly minded men in Berlin, Prague, Vienna and Cambridge. It would, therefore, be most useful and – to my mind at least – most important if some way could be found to speed the translation of these works into English or German. This would be a most constructive and comparatively uncontroversial way of contributing to the recently increasing dialogue between the eastern and western European countries.

(2) *Giedymin's remarks about psychologism.* What Giedymin has to say about the curious anti-psychological alliance formed between the two wars between 'logically-minded philosophers' and the disciples of Edmund Husserl is also very thought-provoking and deserves independent development and exploration, to which I hope Giedymin will contribute. Giedymin restricts himself to commenting on the effects of this attitude in logic and the phi-

losophy of science. It is worth remarking that similar attitudes were to be found far from what is ordinarily thought to be the province of the philosophy of science. F. W. Bateson has recently reminded us of the animus against what was once called the 'biographical fallacy' in literature in the heyday of the New Criticism [1]. And of course the various movements of literary criticism during the twenties and thirties were in some contact with the philosophy of science – through the work of Ogden and Richards, for example. I alluded to this interaction briefly in the second section of my paper.

II. Reply to J. O. Wisdom.

Professor Wisdom's anecdote about what I shall call the 'Unidentified excited near-Popperian' is amusing – and revealing. I assume that the 'very little paper' to which Wisdom modestly refers is his 'The refutability of "irrefutable laws" ', published in 1963 in the *British Journal for the Philosophy of Science*, in which he gives examples from physiology (All bodily changes are due to physical causes), from psychology (All mental changes are due to physiological causes), and from physics (Energy occurs in all possible quantities – or is continuous). Both Wisdom and the unidentified excited near-Popperian who thought such statements 'refuted Popper' may be interested to learn that this type of scientific statement was discussed at some length, in the course of a criticism of Popper, as early as 1936 – by Rudolf Carnap, in 'Testability and meaning' (*Philosophy of Science*, October 1936 and January 1937). Whether such statements are in fact incompatible with Popper's theory of demarcation may be discussed; but it is in any case a pity that more Popperians do not know 'Testability and meaning'. I for one do not subscribe to many of Carnap's conclusions; but it is clearly impossible to understand the course and development of logical positivism following the publication

---

[1] F. W. Bateson, 'An ugly-faced man', *The New York Review of Books*, December 29, 1966, pp. 13f.

of *Logik der Forschung* without reading Carnap's important paper carefully.

To turn to Wisdom's other point, I would agree with him that it would be wrong to suggest that the theories of Freud and Marx are necessarily irrefutable, but I would remind him that I spoke of an 'uncritical Freudian'. Moreover, if I may defend Popper for a moment, I do not believe that he would want to argue that the theories of either Marx or Freud are necessarily irrefutable.

The remainder of Wisdom's final two paragraphs I was unable to follow. He remarks that one cannot usually tell *a priori* whether a theory is irrefutable but that sometimes, by taking a little trouble, one can force an irrefutable theory to a test. Moreover, on his account, an untestable theory is 'entirely useless.' I am not sure whether these remarks belong to the same family. Would Wisdom, for instance, really want to suggest that Freudian theory was entirely useless (except for its possible value as a stimulus) until someone had forced it to the sort of test a Popperian would accept as satisfactory?

III. *Reply to A. E. Musgrave.*

It is especially fortunate that Mr. Musgrave's editorial labours did not prevent him from writing his brief, dignified essay 'On a Demarcation Dispute' for this volume, particularly since there was insufficient time for him to speak at the original Colloquium session. But it is to be regretted that Musgrave's references to Popper's discussion of the 'distinctive method' (to use Musgrave's words) applied by scientists, as well as the form of scientific theories, are not sufficient to rescue Popper's theory from its difficulties, or to refute my suggestion that there are two separate problems of demarcation.

If Musgrave will read again sec. 4 of my paper, he will find that I described the first problem of demarcation as (italics in the original) 'that of demarcating those theoretical statements which are not – *even when regarded with the most critical scrutiny* – subject to empirical argument or refutation.' The italicized passage in my paper, which, incidentally, Musgrave himself quotes, was of course a direct allusion to Popper's discussion, in *The Logic of Scientific Discovery*, of what Dr. Giedymin would call pragmatical considerations. So no attempt was made in my paper to separate sharply, as Musgrave would suggest, 'considerations of method or policy . . . from the consideration of logical relations'. That is an incorrect construction that Musgrave puts upon my paper, a construction that Giedymin, quite rightly, does not make [1]. Musgrave's long digressions and footnote references reporting Popper's heuristic – Popper's interesting discussion of 'conventionalist stratagems' and of 'the rules of the game of science' – are, therefore, completely beside the point. And the same may be said of the criticisms of my paper to which his misreading of it gave rise.

Perhaps I may insert a personal anecdote that might persuade Musgrave, not to accept, but at least to entertain, the idea that I have indeed read chs. 2 and 4 of *The Logic of Scientific Discovery*, where these issues are discussed. I remember very vividly one of my first conversations with Popper, which took place after his lecture at the London School of Economics on October 21, 1958. We had just crossed Houghton Street, to enter the foyer of the London School of Economics, and Popper was waiting for the staff elevator to take him to his office. I told him that I had read his *Logik der Forschung* in 1955 as an undergraduate, and that his discussion there of the rules of the game of science (*die Regeln des Wissenschaftsspiels*) had reminded me of Wittgenstein's discussion of language games. In my naivety, I had meant the remark as a compliment, but Popper was not amused. For a moment I thought he would explode. But then a broad smile spread over his face; he pushed me into the staff lift, and conducted me to his office – where he gave me a brilliant off-the-cuff lecture on his differences with that other famous Viennese. Yes, I have had good reason to study Popper's remarks on scientific method or policy, and I hope to show Musgrave and Popper later on in these remarks that I know how to use them.

---

[1] Another incorrect construction which Musgrave makes is to be found in his report that I think that the first kind of demarcation I discuss *does* successfully separate science from non-science. I made no such claim.

If Musgrave's reading of one of the main points of my paper is, then, incorrect, he is nevertheless quite right to call attention to the fact that my observation that 'stratagems for weakening criticism can arise in or out of science – in ethics, metaphysics, politics, theology, and elsewhere' – is hardly original. I would certainly not want to claim originality for this point; and I am sure Musgrave is right in reporting that Dr. Imre Lakatos, as well as Popper, has said many interesting things about these matters. Actually, I learnt heuristics as an undergraduate or earlier from reading William James and C. S. Peirce, and from studying with Professor Morton White, whose book, *Toward Reunion in Philosophy*, had influenced me very much before I came to study with Popper. Or does Musgrave wish to suggest that Lakatos originated mathematical heuristic and Popper the study of criticism-reducing stratagems in other domains?

Musgrave is also right to insist that my emphasis on problems, in my solution of Goodman's paradox, is compatible with a Popperian approach. It is, therefore, all the more to be regretted that Popper did not himself bother to solve Goodman's paradox in his own discussion of Goodman's predicates (which Popper wrongly insists on calling 'Agassi-predicates') in *Conjectures and Refutations* [1].

Musgrave takes issue with my suggestion – hardly intended as a personal criticism of Popper! – that Popper was 'more positivistically inclined and anti-metaphysical in the 1930's than he is today'. To prove his point, Musgrave quotes or cites passages from Popper's works, most of them starred footnotes added to the *Logic of Scientific Discovery* when it was translated into English in the middle fifties. I should have thought that most of these quotations supported my interpretation, not Musgrave's. I would remind Musgrave that I wrote, in sec. 6 of my paper, as follows: 'It might be argued that Popper has in his later works begun to emphasize metaphysics more. *This is so*; but his remarks are confusing just because he has retained the old slogans along with the new emphases, and failed to state explicitly how and why his ideas have changed'

---

[1] P. 284, note 72a and text.

(italics added here). Musgrave might also be reminded of one of Popper's own methodological rules, which Musgrave himself lists: namely, one ought not to use 'another part of the system under investigation to discount or explain away a refutation'.

Musgrave even comes up with an explicit statement from one of Popper's own footnotes (written in the middle fifties) in which Popper admits that when he wrote *Logik der Forschung* he was 'not alive to the fact that some metaphysical doctrines were rationally arguable and, in spite of being irrefutable, criticizable'. Curiously, Musgrave fails to notice that Popper's remark here refutes one of Musgrave's main points: namely, that it is not true that Popper was more positivistically inclined in the 1930's than he is today. Musgrave's quotation from Popper fails even to support his contention that Popper has been explicit about the changes his thought has undergone in this area. For I had requested an explicit statement of *how* and *why* his ideas on this subject have changed. We do not get this in the footnotes. More important, we do not get it from Popper's 'Personal Report', which also dates from the middle fifties, and which is precisely where one would expect to find such an important change announced.

Musgrave does catch me out on one point, where, further commenting on my description of Popper as more positivistically inclined in the 1930's than he is today, he dwells on my statement that I mean by this that Popper took the positivists seriously. I expressed myself badly and would like to explain what I meant and should have written. One could give earlier references than Musgrave does to show that Popper was not a positivist. Already in his doctoral dissertation, *Zur Methodenfrage der Denkpsychologie* (Vienna, 1928), Popper was combatting 'physicalism', in the form given it by Schlick, in order to defend some of the ideas of Karl Bühler [1]. Despite Bühler's own indications that he thought physicalism then more or less a dead horse, Popper insisted in his thesis that it was essential to dispute the epistemological foundations of

---

[1] Popper's thesis examiners were, as it turned out, Bühler and Schlick. One might add that Popper's dissertation is an interesting work: there are some passages, in the introduction for example, where Popper appears to be anticipating the *later* Wittgenstein!

physicalism, as expounded for example by Schlick. So, if I were able to rewrite my paper now, I would say, in further defence of what I think is my *correct* historical statement – that Popper *was* more positivistically inclined in the 1930's than he is today – that Popper was at this time so *preoccupied* with battling positivism that he occasionally saw his task in a badly distorted perspective. In effect, his preoccupation with positivism blinkered him; and in the course of his debates a little positivism, not surprisingly, rubbed off on Popper's own ideas. I repeat that I fail to see how this can be regarded as a personal criticism of Popper: this is the way one learns and develops. Were someone to tell me that five years ago I was preoccupied with Karl Popper's ideas to such an extent that I was blinkered by them, I would have to agree; but one could hardly regard this as a personal criticism. After all, as Popper himself says, one cannot predict today what one will learn tomorrow; and I might have turned out even worse, even less to Popper's liking, had I followed another route.

As for Musgrave's final section, I should like only to suggest that he study yet another of Popper's rules for scientific procedure, again one which Musgrave himself lists: 'Do not impute refutation to the unreliability or dishonesty of the experimenter'. I would point out that Popper altered the passage referring to Bellarmino in 1959 at my suggestion and that the book in which the quotation appears is a very influential and well-known one, often consulted by students, and available in most philosophical libraries. I did not know that it was out of print, and assume that this will be only temporary.

IV. Reply to Karl R. Popper.

In his novel, *Cards of Identity*, Nigel Dennis has the President open the annual conference as follows: 'Ladies and Gentlemen. This is our fortieth annual session, which means that for forty years, at great expense of time *and money*, we have gathered annually to hear speeches from those of us who believe they have something to say. . . . I am sure it has been worth it, though I must say that when I look back over the thirty sessions I have attended, all I can remember of them is the funny bits. I cannot recall a single word spoken in gravity and mimeographed in solemnity. Nonetheless, the mere fact of having endured these agonies assures me that for thirty years I have enjoyed a continuing identity. Surely this is the purpose of an intellectual session – not to exchange views but to reaffirm our self-conceptions?' [1].

Since I have a horrible suspicion that I shall remember Sir Karl Popper's dispute with me, it must have been a funny one. And Nigel Dennis's President was in any event surely right to relate the "funny bits" to our reaffirmations of "our self-conceptions". So at the no doubt considerable risk of further disturbing Sir Karl by what he describes as my 'preoccupation with psychological ideas such as the problem of a man's "identity and integrity"', I shall note that the problem of identity has been linked to that of territoriality in biology. To give only one example, Ward H. Goodenough, Professor of Anthropology at the University of Pennsylvania, has written as follows: 'Identity is not simply territory in a physical sense, but a neuropsychic phenomenon in which physical territory forms but one of many potentially significant dimensions. More generally, we might say that an organism's "territory", where it actively fights intrusion, is comprised of those aspects of its physical, social, and psychological environment by which it discriminates its own identity. . . . the ego-space in man is not so specifically coded genetically as it is among birds and other animals. If my land is an important aspect of my identity, I may resent trespass upon it. Also, if my professed ideas are important to me, I resent anyone's tampering with them. Whether it is my occupation, my children, my home, my favorite chair, my social prerogatives, my pet hero, or, if I am a small child, my fetish blanket, a liberty taken with something with which I identify myself (or which I identify with myself) is a liberty taken with me. The humiliation and the murderous impulses aroused by invasion of ego-space may represent the homologue in man of mammalian territoriality' [2].

[1] Nigel Dennis, *Cards of Identity*, Penguin Books, 1966, p. 116.
[2] See *Zygon*, University of Chicago Press, Chicago, 1966, p. 226.

To judge by Popper's reply, as well as by that of his distinguished colleague Musgrave, I suppose that some sort of latent territorial dispute must be involved here – the territory being the theory of rationality. Popper appears to have shifted the problem from that of demarcating science from nonscience to the problem of demarcating Popper's theory of rationality from mine. I gladly concede this particular problem of demarcation to Popper; it bores me – as do most similar priority claims.

However subtle and distinctive Popper's and my *theories* of rationality no doubt are – subtle and distinctive; both; no doubt – it is no tribute to the rationality of either of us or of our colleagues, however striking a witness it might be to our mammalian heritage, to turn what I intended as a modest criticism of Popper's views on demarcation into a squabble over priority. *No man owns the theory of rationality*; and it is absurd for Popper to attribute originality to me – apparently as a concession? – for the familiar idea that what I have called the problem of rationality is central to philosophy.

In *The Retreat to Commitment* I wrote that I would be proud to think that the impact on me of Sir Karl's thought had influenced every page. I have not revised that opinion, and would be proud to think that the impact of Popper's thought influenced every page of my paper on demarcation as well. In particular, I was influenced by his paper, 'Back to the Pre-Socratics', the first formal lecture I heard him deliver, in which he enjoins students to follow the example of the ancient Ionians, and to criticize, and to attempt to improve upon, the work of their teachers.

Whether my short paper on demarcation, printed in this volume, is in any way an improvement on Popper's work in this area is hardly for me to judge. But one can only express regret that Popper should have been 'shocked', to use his word, to see one of his students attempting to criticize his ideas – even if it is true, as Popper seems to hold, that I botched the job.

It is also to be regretted that Popper, instead of discussing the substantive issues raised in my paper (which in any case he does not report correctly) chose instead to dismiss them as the 'least valuable kind of criticism' and to devote his long reply primarily to his footnotes and references to his unpublished manuscripts, and to comments which the general reader would probably find obscure about our personal relationship and discussions during the period (from 1958–63) when I was privileged to be first his student and then his colleague at the London School of Economics.

Although one gathers the impression that Popper takes a verificationalist, rather than falsificationalist, approach to the examination of his own intellectual development, it would hardly be becoming for me to attempt, in a haggling or quibbling way, to correct the details of Popper's statements about our relationship from my own memories and unpublished manuscripts, or by quoting our mutual correspondence. Nor do I imagine that it would be of general interest to do so. Therefore I shall remain as silent as possible, apart from noting that Popper's conception of our relationship differs radically from my own. Since Popper has seen fit to raise such matters, however, I am forced to comment on several points, for a few questions of integrity are involved.

(1) *Popper's unpublished manuscripts*. Popper refers several times to unpublished manuscripts which he alleges me to have seen which ought to have prevented me from making the remarks I did in my paper. I have never read his unpublished early book, 'Die beiden Grundprobleme der Erkenntnistheorie': Popper has always politely but firmly refused my requests to be allowed to read it. From 1959–61 I read and helped edit at least a half-dozen manuscripts by Popper which have now been published – several of them in *Conjectures and Refutations*. I have also read the galley-proofs of his unpublished *Postscript*, the first chapter of which I have studied carefully. These date, I believe, from 1955 and 1956. I have also read those manuscript and other corrections to the *Postscript* which were made up until the late summer of 1961. Popper has doubtless made further changes in the *Postscript* since then, but I do not know their content. Since I have been forbidden to quote from Popper's unpublished work [1], I am unable to challenge his reports about the contents of his manuscripts.

---

[1]   Dr. Bartley was informed that he must obtain the author's permission for any quotations he wished to make from unpublished works [*Eds.*].

(2) *My philosophical background.* Although I should have thought my personal background to be of little interest to anyone but myself, I think Popper does himself an injustice in suggesting that one may need a background in combatting obscurantism to be receptive to his ideas. In any case, Popper's statement that I came to his philosophy from the 'philosophy of religion' is not quite correct. My undergraduate training was largely in history (including, to be sure, religious history). At the beginning of my senior year at Harvard, I transferred to the philosophy department, where I wrote my undergraduate honours thesis in defence of 'The Popper–Hempel model of scientific explanation'. Most of my graduate training at Harvard was in the philosophy of science, the philosophy of history, and the philosophy of law. Although I have always had a deep interest in religion, it was not until 1959, after coming to Popper's department, that I began the really serious study of the philosophy of religion which is, I hope, reflected in such things as *The Retreat to Commitment.* Moreover, *The Retreat to Commitment* was originally conceived as a book on the philosophy and practice of American education. This idea, which I never carried through, did originate with two early articles I published as a student in *The Harvard Crimson*, the undergraduate daily newspaper which I edited, articles which might indeed be construed as skirmishes with obscurantism. The first, 'Communism at Harvard', was written at the height of the McCarthy episode; the second, 'Religion at Harvard', was in part a discussion of the role of ideology and commitment in education [1].

(3) *Popper's 'Lectures on ethics'.* Simply because, as Popper knows, I am at present engaged in writing a book on ethics, I am compelled to comment on his suggestion (note 1, p. 94) that the brief remarks which appear in sec. 5 of my paper 'repeat a thesis which was one of the main topics of a lecture course' of Popper's on

---

[1] W. W. Bartley, III, 'Communism at Harvard', (written in November 1954) published in *The Harvard Crimson* in April 1955, and later serialized in a revised version in *The Boston Globe*, June 10–15, 1956; and 'Religion at Harvard: To what values, if any, should a free university give allegiance?', *The Harvard Crimson*, March 28, 1958; reprinted in *The New Republic*, April 21, 1958.

Ethics, given in 1959, which I am said to have attended. This is simply false. I do not believe that Popper gave a course on Ethics in 1959, and no such course is listed in the L. S. E. Calendar for 1958–59. Popper may have meant to refer to a course he gave in the Summer Term of 1960 (27 April–5 July 1960), listed in the L. S. E. Calendar for 1959–60, where a detailed syllabus is given, as 'Philosophy of the social sciences'. I did attend that series of lectures and have shorthand notes of it. Much of the first part of the course was devoted to Hume and Rousseau, after which there was a transition to problems and standards of explanation in the natural sciences and in history, economics and the social sciences; and to the problems of rationality raised in my book and my paper, 'Rationality versus the theory of rationality'. The latter subject was introduced into the course as a result of the discussions following my letter to Popper of Monday, 18 April 1960, where I first presented to him my ideas about rationality, and my idea of nonjustificational criticism, as a criticism of some of his own views. Popper replied to my letter on 23 April 1960; and our correspondence continued during the following summer, two months of which I spent in Holland, and was the subject of considerable discussion in Popper's graduate seminar in the autumn of 1960.

(4) *Popper's notion that my views on demarcation represent a sudden change that took place between April and July 1965.* I refer him to page 105 of *The Retreat to Commitment*, (1962), footnote 8 and text, where I distinguish the problems of the demarcation of science from non-science, the demarcation of rational beliefs from irrational beliefs, and the demarcation of true beliefs from false beliefs. I note there that these problems 'have often been identified, thus causing considerable confusion'. The manuscript of *The Retreat to Commitment* was in circulation amongst the members of the staff of the Department of Philosophy, Logic and Scientific Method at the London School of Economics beginning in August 1960.

(5) *Popper's alterations in ch. 24 of the fourth edition of 'The Open Society'.* Since this issue is not raised in my paper on demarcation, I do not know why Popper now raises questions concerning

the alterations he made, in the light of our discussions about rationality, in ch. 24 of *The Open Society* (4th ed., 1962). That sleeping dog might better have been left lying. Since Popper has chosen to awaken it, I record my disagreement with his statement that 'the matter is one of *clarification* rather than of any real *change* of my [Popper's] views'. My own view that a profound change took place can be corroborated – for example – by Popper's paper: 'Utopia and violence', *The Hibbert Journal*, 1948. I shall discuss this matter on some other occasion.

I wish to express my embarrassment at having to put these personal remarks on paper, and my profound disappointment that Popper did not choose to discuss the substantive issues raised in my talk. Eddington once wrote something that may well be relevant to this controversy: "I say 'my philosophy', not as claiming authorship of ideas which are widely diffused in modern thought, but because the ultimate selection and synthesis must be a personal responsibility" [1].

---

[1] Sir Arthur Eddington: *The Philosophy of Physical Science*, Cambridge University Press, Cambridge, 1949, p. viii.

THE MATURATION OF SCIENCE

MARIO BUNGE

McGill University, Montreal

1. *Growth: Newtonian and Baconian.* Scientific knowledge can grow at the surface or in depth, i.e. it can expand by accumulating, generalizing and systematizing information, or by introducing radically new ideas overreaching the available information and explaining it. The first kind of growth, characteristic of both early and routine research, may be called Baconian because it was championed by the two Bacons, whereas growth in depth may be termed Newtonian because Newton invented the first large scale and deep scientific system. Growth in volume requires both surface and depth growth: growth in surface alone is blind and bound to stop for lack of ideas, whereas exclusive growth in depth risks ending in uncontrolled speculation.

Yet certain periods in the history of every discipline are characterized by the predominance of one of the two kinds of growth: breakthroughs are usually preceded and followed by stages of vegetative growth. The most frequent development is, of course, growth in surface, achieved when attention is focused on description, systematization, and prediction at the expense of bold theorizing. This is still the case of most nonphysical sciences and of large areas of physics, e.g. elementary particle physics. Even though there is theoretical activity in these fields, it is mostly of the fact-systematizing or phenomenological type, either because too little is still known to conjecture detailed mechanisms or because the very hypothesizing of mechanisms is discouraged by a superficial philosophy.

Surface growth is necessary but insufficient to attain maturity, and mature science is what we should strive for even if complete maturity is (hopefully) unattainable. Science can be expected to mature when breadth, depth and cogency are sought, i.e. when research not only widens a field but also makes it more profound and better organized. Everyone knows what is meant by 'logical organization', but what does 'profundity' mean? Depth is easier to recognize than to elucidate, yet it is not unanalyzable. It can be enhanced essentially in two ways: (1) by introducing hypotheses involving unobservables, in contrast with assumptions concerning surface or observable characteristics, and (2) by inventing mechanisms conjectured to be responsible for the facts under consideration. In either case epistemological depth is hoped to mirror ontological depth: the deeper ideas are intended to refer to deeper-lying levels of reality – but the hope may of course be unfulfilled.

Depth is best exploited when accompanied by logical organization. Why an improvement in logical organization should contribute to maturity is clear: upon formalizing or just axiomatizing a body of ideas we recognize its essential (indispensable and source-like) components. And these are the deeper ideas in the system: only logically strong ideas can explain, and phenomena (perceptible events) can be explained only by hypothesizing imperceptibles, as illustrated by atomic theories.

The ideal maturation process is one involving all three moves toward fundamentals referred to above, i.e. the invention of theories that (1) employ unobservables which (2) they tie up in the form of mechanism hypotheses which are in turn (3) organized axiomatically. Let us take a look at these moves.

2. *Concepts: empirical and transempirical.* A concept can be called theoretical if it belongs to some scientific theory; theoretical factual if it occurs in a factual scientific theory. Examples of theoretical factual concepts: 'energy' (physics) and 'subjective utility' (utility theory). Theoretical factual concepts can be generic or specific: the former occur in a number of scientific disciplines whereas the latter are typical of individual theories. The generic concepts, such as 'law' and 'theorem', are not of our present concern: they may occur in any body of scientific ideas, whether shallow or deep. The typical traits of a theory, in particular its depth, are determined by its specific concepts.

Specific theoretical concepts in factual science can be observational or nonobservational according as they refer to observable objects or fail to refer to them. The nonobservational ones can be called constructs; they are typical of science as opposed to ordinary knowledge. Examples of observational theoretical concepts: 'body', 'moving', and 'number of reinforcements'; examples of constructs (nonobservational theoretical concepts): 'momentum', 'mutation', and 'learning'. Notice that the dichotomy observational/nonobservational is not strict but makes room for transition species, and that it does not coincide with the ordinary/scientific partition. Moreover, in advanced science observation reports contain constructs.

Every theory contains constructs even if its referents are intended to be at least partially observable, as is the case of liquid and solid bodies, the referents of continuum mechanics. In fact the concepts of mass, stress, and viscosity, which occur in this set of theories, are all nonobservational: they represent properties that cannot be pointed to with the finger. This does not make those theories empirically untestable: it makes empirical tests far more than touching and smelling.

Some theories have no observational concepts at all; e.g., all pure field theories and theories of atomic and subatomic entities. True, the variables representing, say, the position of an electron and the strength of an electromagnetic field, are sometimes called *observables*; but this is a joke, and not even a good one. Indeed none of the referents of such variables can be observed in the epistemological sense of the word: the measurement of such variables requires not only complex laboratory paraphernalia but also additional theories (macrophysical ones) to design the pieces of apparatus and interpret their readings. The variables occurring in these theories may or may not be all of them objectively meaningful: if the theories are altogether false such variables may fail to have an objective referent although they were intended to be factually meaningful. But in any case, whether they refer to real entities or to imaginary objects, they have no empirical content: they refer to no experience proper such as a perception or an action and they do not even refer to scientific experience (measurement or experiment), if only because experiential events are many-sided and must therefore be accounted for by a whole bunch of theories.

Take for instance the sentence 'The value of the energy of the electron a at the place b at the instant c is E'. This phrase is (factually) meaningful all the time, whether it expresses a true statement or not and whether or not an attempt is made to ascertain by empirical means what its truth value is. It is fashionable to declare, though, that a sentence like that is meaningless as long as no such empirical operation is made; but of course some non-technical concept of meaning must be involved in the damnation. And in any case even when a sequence of empirical operations (enlightened by a set of theories) is performed which lends support to the phrase, this is still empirically meaningless though factually meaningful. A measurement of the energy of the electron will allow us to assign it a numerical value, or rather a number interval: it is not designed to endow the expression with a meaning. And such a measurement, let us repeat, is far from direct: it requires the collaboration of further theories, some of which (like classical mechanics) are logically incompatible with the theory in which the given statement makes sense.

That the 'observables' of the quantum theories do not represent directly observable traits is further seen from their usual definition. This reads: 'A dynamical variable is an observable iff its eigen-values are real and its eigenfunctions form a complete set'. Certain mathematical properties, not observability, constitute the specific difference that marks the quantum-mechanical 'observables' off from other dynamical variables. Similarly, in general relativity the 'observables' are not defined in terms of empirical operations but as the magnitudes that remain invariant under arbitrary coordinate transformations. In either case the notion of 'observable' is Pick-wickian and the name a misnomer the effect of which is to create the illusion that the quantum theories and general relativity have a direct empirical content. What the 'observables' of these theories are actually supposed to represent in a symbolic way are objective (operator independent) properties of physical systems; they are not observational concepts but high level constructs, some of which represent indirectly measurable traits. An observable proper – a concept taking part, say, in the description of a flash in a scintillation counter – is a more or less complicated function (or rather functional) of two sets of variables: 'observables' referring to microsystems and macrovariables referring to pieces of apparatus.

In any case the deeper theories are characterized by nonobservational concepts or constructs, be they microvariables or macrovariables. Observational concepts will appear in the applications of basic theories to empirical situations – though not to the exclusion of constructs.

Two kinds of constructs are usually distinguished in the philosophy of the behavioral sciences: intervening variables and hypothetical constructs. The former mediate or intervene between observational concepts whereas the latter are hypothesized to refer to unobservable entities and properties, such as the energy levels of atoms. 'Center of mass' in macrophysics and 'habit strength' in behaviorist psychology would be intervening variables, whereas 'gravitational field strength' and 'production cost' would be hypothetical constructs.

The chief difference between intervening variables and hypothetical constructs seems to reside in the referent assigned to them and is therefore determined by the interpretation postulates of the theory in which they occur – postulates that up to a point can be changed without modifying the formalism. Thus one and the same construct, such as 'field strength', or 'drive', will be regarded as a hypothetical construct in one interpretation of a theory and as an intervening variable in another. The distinction can therefore be made in semantical terms independently of methodological considerations: intervening variables refer to the system as a whole whereas hypothetical constructs refer to parts or traits of supposedly real individual objects. In other words, intervening predicates are wholistic whereas hypothetical constructs are atomistic. Thus in electromagnetic field theory the potentials and the total energy may be regarded as intervening variables whereas the field strengths and the various densities are hypothetical constructs. And seen in this light behaviorism is semantically, though not methodologically, in the same category with gestaltism.

Clearly, hypothetical or atomistic constructs are deeper than intervening or wholistic variables. We shall presently see that the former allow us to build the deeper hypotheses.

3. *From information packages to hypotheses.* A formula will be called a factual hypothesis iff (1) it refers to facts that are as yet unexperienced or in principle unexperientiable and (2) it is corrigible in view of fresh knowledge. From the point of view of their ostensiveness or empirical immediacy hypotheses may be classed into observational and nonobservational, according as they contain observational concepts alone or at least one nonobservational concept. 'Children take to their parents' is an observational hypothesis because it refers in observational terms to a class that overflows the set accessible to individual experience. On the other hand 'The angular momentum of a point mass in a central field is conserved' is clearly a nonobservational hypothesis. Whereas the former is extensionally hypothetical, the latter is both extensionally and intensionally hypothetical.

As with concepts so with hypotheses: the deeper a body of knowledge the more nonobservational ideas it will contain. An omniscient being would presumably have no use for nonobservational concepts and hypotheses; but to man most of reality is hidden and must therefore be conjectured. No wonder therefore that the initial assumptions (axioms) of scientific theories are all nonobservational hypotheses and, in particular, operationally meaningless (though testable). Even if they refer ultimately to empirically accessible objects, such as man-sized bodies, they deal immediately with ideal schematizations of such objects and they pay little if any attention to phenomenal properties. Thus in solid body mechanics mass distributions and possible motions rather than appearances are studied. Appearances, such as those presented to the observational astronomer, are complex objects not accountable by physics alone but by physiological optics and physiological psychology, all of which are based on nonobservational hypotheses.

Now, nonobservational hypotheses can be modest or ambitious: they can restrict themselves to describing a system from the outside, as a whole, or they can burrow into details of the composition and inner workings of the system they refer to. The former may be called phenomenological or black box hypotheses, the latter mechanism hypotheses though not in the strict sense of invoking a play of mechanical parts. Phenomenological hypotheses can contain intervening variables but no hypothetical constructs, whereas mechanism hypotheses contain hypothetical constructs (and eventually intervening predicates as well); and both may be stochastic or nonstochastic.

Phenomenological hypotheses are far deeper than information-packaging statements but not as deep as mechanism hypotheses. Take for instance population ecology. Three kinds of hypotheses can be discerned here: (1) the functional relations (or curves) that summarize and generalize the data relating the observable parameters, (2) the differential equations expressing the rate of change of the population size, and (3) more complex statements accounting for the population size in genetical and ecological terms. If we are interested in compressing, extrapolating, and interpolating empirical data, we shall remain content with curve fitting. It is only when we harbor the ambition of explaining rather than summarizing and generalizing, that we seek to set up higher level hypotheses, e.g. differential equations whose integration should yield the empirical curves or observational hypotheses.

Thus the growth of a one-species population can be represented by any of an infinite set of curves as long as they keep reasonably close to the empirical data. But one prefers the so-called logistic model, i.e. $dN/dt = rN(K-N)$, even though it cannot possibly contain every bit of relevant information, because it says something about the growth process – namely that the population change is proportional to the size N of the population itself and to the difference between the saturation value K and the instantaneous value N. But even this hypothesis, though logically stronger and semantically deeper than any of the empirical curves, is insufficient: we know that population growth is controlled by additional variables, internal ones such as mutation frequency and external ones such as the strength of the competition with interacting species. The ecologist will accordingly try to invent deeper hypotheses encompassing these factors and eventually analyzing the phenomenological (or intervening) variable r (the growth rate): they will be mechanism hypotheses.

A similar trend can be discerned in every other factual science: from data packages to phenomenological hypotheses to mechanism hypotheses. As a science matures it becomes deeper, i.e. it introduces more and more mechanism hypotheses – with the sole condition that they be neither wild nor altogether untestable. The reasons for that are multiple: (1) the deeper hypotheses may reach deeper levels of reality (ontological import); (2) the deeper hypotheses are the logically stronger since they entail (eventually in conjunction with further hypotheses) the information-packaging hypotheses (logical import); (3) the mechanism hypotheses are better testable than the black box ones – although they are less directly testable – because they are sensitive to more minute detail and to more varied evidence: being stronger they say more and therefore they commit and expose themselves much more than the safer and simpler phenomenological hypotheses (methodological import). No wonder that every theoretical breakthrough is a gain in depth and is followed by an unprecedented growth in surface.

4. *From the black box to the mechanism.* Let us recall that a theory proper is an infinite set of formulas closed under deduction. If these formulas have an intended real referent, the theory may be called factual. In this case some of the initial formulas will be purely formal (e.g., determining the mathematical structure of a concept), others will be semantical – they will map symbols into their intended referents – others will be factual hypotheses proper, and finally others will be subsidiary assumptions such as approximations or even data.

For example, in the classical theory of gravitation, the assumption that the potential is a real scalar field is formal; the assumption that this mathematical field represents or refers to an extended medium, the physical field, is semantical; the field equation and the equations of motion are hypotheses proper and indeed the leading assumptions of the theory; and the expression of the numerical value of the gravitational constant, as well as any special assumption such that the field concerned is coupled to a material sphere, are subsidiary assumptions. Other parts of the theory are either definitions (e.g., the definition of density) or theorems (e.g., a formula representing the trajectory of a test particle in the field). Needless to say, the theory contains no operational 'definition' yet it is physically meaningful and also testable.

Factual theories are supposed to map real systems: fields, bodies, organisms, societies. The mapping can be global or detailed: it can model the system and its environment as blocks or it can analyze them to various degrees. In either case the system of interest (the referent) may be regarded as a box, only in the external or global approach it will not be decomposed into smaller units whereas in the internal or atomistic approach it will be analyzed as regards its components and inner working. The first approach can be called phenomenological or global, the second mechanistic or atomistic.

In either case the environment of the system may be schematized, to a first approximation, in a global way by a set of input variables and another set of output variables, which may but need not all of them be empirically accessible. Any theory whose leading hypothesis is a fixed relation (law) between inputs and outputs is a phenomenological theory; and any theory that takes the risk of hypothesizing something mediating between inputs and outputs, i.e. a mechanism triggered by the inputs and which has the required outputs, is a mechanistic theory. In either case the central hypothesis may be symbolized thus: $O = MI$, where M can be thought of as an operator that converts inputs into outputs. If M is an intervening variable then the theory is phenomenological or a black box; but if M is assumed to represent an unseen mechanism responsible for the transformation of inputs into outputs, then the theory is mechanistic or representational. Thus whereas classical thermoelasticity relates global parameters such as conductivity and elastic moduli, the quantum theory of solids analyzes such parameters in atomic terms. Clearly, though both theories are necessary, the quantum theory is the deeper: it goes deeper into the structure of matter and, at least in principle, it explains the phenomenological theory.

We see now what makes theories deep: (1) the occurrence of high level constructs, (2) the assumption of mechanisms, and (3) a high explanatory power. The relation among these three properties of a deep theory is clear: transempirical concepts (constructs) are necessary to describe hypothetical mechanisms, which are in turn necessary to explain the behavior of the system, and eventually the appearance it presents to an observer.

We can take a further step and introduce the following definition of the relational concept of theory depth: If T and T' are factual theories, then T is deeper than T' iff (1) T includes more or higher level constructs (unobservables) than T' does (epistemological aspect); (2) these constructs occur in the description of hypothetical mechanisms underlying the facts referred to by T' (ontological or semantical aspect); and (3) T entails a large part of T' but not conversely (logical aspect). In particular, if T entails the whole of T', then T' can be said to be reduced to T. Solid state physics provides various examples of theory reduction. But even if, as in the case of the relation of statistical mechanics to thermodynamics, the reduction is still incomplete (i.e. the intersection of the two theories is nonempty), the deeper theory is the finer, the less deep the coarser one.

The advantages of the deeper or translucid box theories over the more superficial or black box theories should be obvious. The realization of such advantages should have important consequences in both science and philosophy: it should stimulate scientists to invent more theories of the deep and daring type even if they are more likely to fail, and it should persuade philosophers that a dogmatic adherence to the coarser or black box theories – favored by empiricism and conventionalism – is sheer obscurantism. For example, the available theories of unstable particles, which can compute the decay probability without explaining in detail why the process should occur, might be included in a deeper theory hypothesizing some decay mechanism even if the latter theory continued to be stochastic and therefore incapable of predicting the exact time of decay of an individual particle. But such mechanism or translucid box theories will not even be tried unless the philosophies which disapprove of them are abandoned: scientific research does not grow in depth if it must pay heed to a superficialist philosophy.

5. *From subsumption to interpretative explanation.* Explanation, too, can be superficial or deep. Logically speaking every explanation is a subsumption under a set of premises; in the case of theoretical science some of these premises are theoretical formulas (in particular law statements), others are special assumptions that permit the application of the theory to the given state of affairs. If, in addition to being an entailment of this kind, an explanation shows how something comes about, i.e. if at least one of the premises is a mechanism hypothesis, then we have what is sometimes called an interpretation of the fact concerned and which will be called an interpretive explanation. We recognize, then, two kinds of scientific explanation: the subsumptive and the interpretive ones.

When the deviation of a light ray is accounted for in terms of Snell's law and the particular value of the refractive index of the medium, we are faced with a subsumptive explanation. When the process is explained with the help of light waves that satisfy the Huygens principle we gain in depth. And when light is assumed to be a group of electromagnetic waves, and a structure of the medium is hypothesized, we have a still deeper explanation of the same fact: both the medium and the light ray are assigned a structure describable only in terms of constructs.

As with facts so with laws. If a law statement is subsumed under higher-level hypotheses we say that we have explained the law. But we might wish to go further and inquire how the real pattern referred to by the law statement came to be. That is, we may wish to find out the emergence mechanism of a given law out of other laws. These other laws will belong to levels other (usually lower) than the one to which the given law belongs. These other levels may be coexisting or temporally successive. Thus a task of quantum chemistry is to explain the laws of chemistry in terms of the quantum laws of systems of electrically charged particles; insofar as it succeeds in performing this task quantum chemistry supplies an interpretative explanation of a system of laws in terms of laws characterizing a coexisting lower level of organization. And a task for psychology would be to disclose how the learning patterns emerged in the course of evolution from biological laws – an interpretive explanation in terms of laws characterizing a prior evolutionary level.

The deeper theories supply the deeper explanations, i.e. explanations of the interpretative kind or explanations in depth, although both are subsumptive or covering in the sense that they argue from general laws. The reason interpretative explanations are deeper than the subsumptive ones is clear: some of their premises perform a deeper analysis in an ontological sense: they attain deeper layers of reality. Explanation depth, then, parallels theory depth.

The explanatory power of a theory must then depend not only on the extension and accuracy of the theory but also on its depth. The first two factors make up the coverage of a theory. The concept of theory coverage can be elucidated in a quantitative way in terms of the concept of partial truth. But whatever formula one adopts for the coverage $C(T)$ of a theory T, one is tempted to write: $E(T) = C(T) \cdot D(T)$ for the explanatory power of T, where $D(T)$ is the depth of the theory. Unfortunately one does not know how to assign a measure proper to the concept of theory depth. An obvious suggestion is to assign $D(T)$ an ordinal measure according to the number n of levels (or of sublevels) crossed by the theory – a number which is rather arbitrary. Thus a learning theory that analyzes the organism in terms of physical, chemical, biological, psychological, and ecological variables could be assigned a depth $D(T) = 5$. But owing to the somewhat arbitrary nature of this measure of theory depth, this index n must be regarded as comparative rather than as quantitative. Yet there is no known reason why theory depth could not be quantified in a strict sense. In any case the index $E(T)$ can be taken as a quasi-measure of the explanatory power or volume of theories: at least it summarizes the idea that the size of a theory is determined not only by its extension and accuracy but also by its depth.

If it were possible to set up a fully quantitative measure of theory volume or explanatory power, we could measure the growth of knowledge in a much more exact way than by counting the number of papers published in a given field. We might in fact follow the variation of $E(T)$ in time, as new theorems are derived and put to the test, and we might even compute the average growth rate of T over a time interval Δt, defined as $r = \Delta E / \Delta t$. We might moreover determine the growth of theoretical knowledge in a whole field, namely thus: (1) take all the nonrival theories T_i in the given field and form their logical union $T = \bigcup T_i$; (2) compute the explanatory power of T at two different instants; (3) compute the growth rate r of T. In this way we might follow the vicissitudes of theories and of whole areas of theoretical science, becoming better aware of periods of stagnation, sometimes disguised under heaps of printed matter. But this is *Zukunftmusik*. And anyway it would be a purely black box account of the growth of knowledge: we need, in addition, an explanation in depth involving the problem situation, the available conceptual and empirical tools, and the extrascientific – mainly the social and philosophical – factors that codetermine the evolution of knowledge. We need, in short, an interpretive explanation of the growth – and the stagnation – of knowledge.

6.   *From the draft to the axiom system.* A theory, whether discrete or nosy, can be in any of a number of development stages: it can be embryonic and unorganized – as is always the case in the beginning – or reasonably worked out but still unorganized (like most theories in use), or unexpanded but well organized (as some new mathematical theories), or both well worked out and well organized (as some logical and mathematical theories). If a theory is poor either in the number of actually proved theorems (in contrast with the potential infinity of unknown theorems) or in logical organization, then it is immature no matter how deep it may be.

The latter is the case of Einstein's theory of gravitation. One of the troubles with this most admirable and deep theory is that it has not yet been organized in a satisfactory way. As a consequence, heuristic or theory construction principles such as general covariance are often taken for constitutive principles or axioms proper; sometimes the theory is even credited with statements it cannot possibly contain, such as the equality of the inertial and the gravitational mass – an equality it cannot state because the distinction between the two masses does not occur in the theory. Therefore too many discussions on the physical meaning and the value of the theory as compared with rival theories are muddled and distorted by crude philosophical tenets such as operationalism. Fortunately the main ideas of the theory are there and they are deep, so that its maturation is a matter of hard work and critical discussion.

Few factual theories are both reasonably expanded and logically organized. Classical particle mechanics and continuum mechanics are among the few exceptions but even in this case the best available axiomatizations – the ones due to McKinsey and Suppes and to Noll – can be improved on particularly on the semantical side. All other theories are in a worse shape in this connection. As regards logical organization, then, factual science is on the whole still immature. The scientist's intuition usually makes up for this defect: he can usually recognize the leading or essential assumptions of the theory even though he may fail to state explicitly all the assumptions that surround those fundamental hypotheses.

On the other hand intuition is much less effective to detect the essential or undefined concepts of a factual theory. For one Levi Civita who, without axiomatizing Newtonian mechanics, realized that mass and force are mutually independent primitive concepts of the theory, there are thousands upon thousands of physicists who claim to define those concepts in one way or another (not excluding by means of Newton's second law) just because they confuse definitions with equations and even with measurements. The essential or primitive concepts of a theory cannot be discerned with clarity and certainty unless the theory is axiomatized, as this kind of (incomplete) formalization consists precisely in taking a bunch of specific primitives and tying them up with the help of concepts borrowed from logic, mathematics, and eventually other factual theories as well, to constitute the basic assumptions (axioms) of the theory. And as long as there is no clarity concerning the building stones (primitive concepts and axioms) of a theory, discussions on fundamental problems are likely to be confused, hence immature.

An example of this kind of immaturity is afforded by quantum mechanics. The anthropocentric or subjectivist interpretation of it might have been rendered impossible if the theory had been properly axiomatized, for in this way it would have been apparent that neither experimental set-ups nor observers play a role in the theory, for the corresponding concepts cannot occur in it either as primitives or defined if only because both measuring instruments and operators are macrosystems to be eventually analyzed with the help of quantum mechanics.

It is sometimes felt that the axiomatization of a theory is bound to stiffen it to death, deterring criticism and therefore blocking progress. From a purely logical point of view this is false: the evaluation of a piece of scientific research is the easier the better organized that piece is: conceptual analysis, criticism, and evaluation are facilitated by a clear indication of what are the main assumptions and the chief consequences of a theory. In short, axiomatization can promote the growth of knowledge although it hardly constitutes a breakthrough in itself. But it is psychologically true that axiom systems occasionally produce a feeling of awe which leads to dogmatism. This seems to have been the case with Carathéodory's axiomatization of thermostatics and with von Neumann's axiomatization of first quantization. This undesirable side effect of logical reconstruction derives from a misunderstanding of the nature of axiomatics and can be prevented by becoming more familiar with it. In this way one can see that the axiomatization of a body of factual ideas comes *post faestum* and is not unique, and that its main virtue is that, by laying the foundations bare, it facilitates fundamental criticism and repairs. By focusing on essentials, foundations research contributes to the maturation of science.

7. *The philosopher and the maturation of science.* Scientific research can pass through several phases of maturation, the degree of maturity attained depending on the depth and the logical organization of the ideas involved. Computation and empirical operations, however indispensable and no matter how plentiful and accurate, are independent of profundity and overall cogency and therefore are not indices of maturity. Consequently in most pieces of scientific research questions of depth and logical organization do not come up. Hence the very traits of maturity tend to be overlooked. Even research in deep fields, like solid state physics, evolutionary biology, or learning theory, can be shallow if routinized, i.e. if it attempts to answer isolated and routine questions rather than fundamental and interconnected problems. And logical and semantical clarity concerning fundamentals are not acquired by hopping from one problem to the next but by first analyzing, then criticizing and eventually reconstructing a whole body of ideas grown in a spontaneous and usually wild fashion. In any case scientific maturity is a question of quality, not of number: it is possessed by sophisticated and well-knit hypotheses concerning the roots of things rather than by huge heaps of isolated and superficial items, and is therefore to be expected from artisanal work rather than from mass production. In short, the difference between immature science and mature science is like the difference between a sponge and a brain.

Supposing we choose the brain rather than the sponge, what are we to expect from the philosopher as regards the maturation of science? Barring the widespread indifference to science, the philosopher can either oppose the maturation process or promote it, according to the maturity of his own philosophy. Hitherto the philosophers who have thought of science have played no significant role in its maturation. In the best of cases they have been sympathetic toward the improvement in logical organization, but in recent times most of them have been diffident toward depth. Yet the philosopher can do more than applaud the increase in cogency and semantical clarity: he can contribute himself to this aspect of maturation provided he masters both the subject matter and the tools for logical reconstruction. Since most scientific theories are so far in a natural rather than in an axiomatic form, the philosopher has here a wide field that should prove more rewarding than barking at colleagues.

Things do not look so bright on the other side of maturity, namely depth. Philosophers of the empiricist trend have always been suspicious of depth partly because obscurity and wild speculation had only too often been taken for profundity. They reacted against obscurantism by recommending maximal conceptual shallowness and simplicity and, on occasion, no theorizing at all. They failed to realize that genuine depth was at hand for the first time, namely in modern scientific theory. Thereby they placed themselves on the side of the enemies of science – paradoxically enough, in a naive effort to dodge antiscience. And, when faced with successful and deep theories, they tried to explain them away as mere bridges among allegedly theory-free observations or as nonrepresentational tools for the calculation of possible observations.

A typical attempt of this kind uses the so-called Craig theorem, which is actually an impossible technique for theory demolition. Roughly, the technique prescribes deriving and collecting all the lower level theorems of a factual theory T, theorems alleged to contain only observational concepts, and finally taking their conjunction as the axiom basis of a philosophically expurgated theory T^*. This amorphous set, which is supposed to contain no theoretical or 'auxiliary' terms, is regarded as superior to T precisely on this count. But the technique does not work. Firstly, a theory proper must be there before it can be demolished. Secondly, it is impossible to derive all the theorems, which are infinitely many: one can talk about them before deriving them, but one cannot manipulate them effectively. Thirdly and most important, the technique rests on the presupposition that, by carrying deduction far enough, one can get rid of non-observational concepts, i.e. constructs. But this would be sheer magic: deduction cannot eliminate essential concepts; and observational concepts cannot validly be introduced in the theory except via definitions in terms of the primitive concepts. In short, the expurgated 'theory' T^* does not exist, so the genuine theory T cannot be reduced to it. Thus by integrating the equations of motion of a dynamical theory one does not eliminate the very referents of such statements, namely an ideal model such as the point particle. There are no recipes for detheorizing a hypothetico-deductive system save to ignore it altogether and remain on this side of the growth of knowledge.

Theoretical science has paid little attention to the antidepth war waged by radical empiricists and conventionalists, even though some of the best theoreticians have been inconsistent enough to espouse an antitheoretical philosophy. The philosopher must therefore make his choice: either he imitates the schoolmen who derided

Galilei, by sticking to his tenets and refusing to see growth in depth; or he learns from modern theoretical science and modifies accordingly his philosophy and eventually helps the scientist get rid of a philosophical deadwood extant from a period prior to the birth of modern theoretical science.

If the maturation of science is adopted as the ultimate desideratum of research, philosophical casualties should not matter, especially since the depth charges employed by philosophers were manufactured to fight an enemy which no longer exists – medieval scholasticism. If the nondogmatic way is chosen and a constructive rather than a destructive attitude is adopted, new philosophies will have to be built in place of the new scholasticism devoted to the cult of data (dataism) and the cult of simplicity (dadaism). Which presents a second challenge to the philosopher: the construction of mature philosophical theories to match the maturation of science. Such theories should not only keep pace with the maturation process of science but should also stimulate it: in this way philosophy would help understand scientific growth as well as cope with the information explosion. In both fields, science and philosophy, the slogan is still: *Down to fundamentals* [1].

---

[1] For a more detailed discussion of the black box vs. representational approaches see the author's 'A general black box theory', *Philosophy of Science* **30** (1963), p. 343 and 'Phenomenological theories', in *The Critical Approach to Science and Philosophy*, ed. M. Bunge in Honor of K. R. Popper, The Free Press, New York, Macmillan, London, 1964. For a discussion of the concepts of level and simplicity, see *The Myth of Simplicity*, Prentice-Hall, Englewood Cliffs, N.J., 1963. For a discussion of the semantics of physical theories, see *Metascientific Queries* Charles C. Thomas, Springfield, Ill., 1959 and 'Physics and reality', *Dialectica* **19** (1965), p. 195. For several examples of physical axiomatics, see *Foundations of Physics*, Springer Verlag, New York, 1967. The concepts of theory coverage, predictive power, and its relatives are discussed in detail in *Scientific Research*, Springer Verlag, New York, 1967, vol. I, chs. 9 and 10.

L. L. WHYTE: *Science and philosophy of science.*

1. Professor Bunge's remarks on the Philosopher and the Maturation of Science touch a most interesting and timely issue. Some theoretical physicists consider that the solution of certain outstanding problems may involve a new conception of the real world i.e. a transformed idea of existence. I believe that this is correct, and that what is needed now is a new unifying outlook transcending the adjustments of the classical, nineteenth century, view, which were produced by relativity theory and by quantum theory. If so there is now an exceptional opportunity for any philosophically oriented minds deeply interested in physics since 1900 to make a contribution to the advance of scientific knowledge. A philosophical re-adjustment of attitude, or perhaps many attempts in this direction, may be necessary as preliminaries to the next authentic advance in basic theory.

2. If I have understood him correctly, Bunge considers that major advances in the scope of fundamental theory necessarily involve a higher degree of abstraction in the basic concepts, principles, or mathematical methods. Einstein took this view, and it is certainly supported by the history of physics since, say, 1800. But it may not always be so. Indeed I would suggest that what is needed now is not further abstraction, i.e. still more abstract fundamentals than those of general relativity theory and quantum mechanics, but the re-interpretation of the immediately given spatial and temporal relations of three-dimensional patterns changing in course of time. This involves the re-tracing of recent steps of abstraction, the return to simple quasi-classical ideas of space and time, and their re-interpretation in terms of some new model of changing spatial relations. This, as I see it, is well possible, though of course at this stage only a conjecture. But if it is possible in principle, one sees how risky it is to build a philosophy of science on the experience of a particular historical period. The 'philosophy of science', if it is to be worthy of its pretentious name, must be as cautious, subtle, and imaginative as science proper.

K. R. POPPER: *Non-apparent depth, depth, and pseudo-depth.*

I am, of course, very much in favour of depth and maturity in science, and so far as I have understood what Bunge says of it, I am basically in agreement with him. There is just one place where I do not entirely agree. Bunge like myself, is worried about the publication explosion. Here depth seems to be sacrificed to volume: an insistence on depth would eliminate most publications, so that insistence on depth could be used as a kind of contraceptive against unwanted publications. But if we were to insist on depth as a kind of controlling criterion, then we would kill the growth of science. For deep theories sometimes have an embryonic stage in which their depth is far from apparent. The emergence of a theory as a deep one is a result of much Socratic midwifery, that is, critical discussion, among scientists. To insist upon depth from the start would be fatal to the growth of science.

Bunge criticises positivism because in ruling out metaphysics it rules out the deepest theories of science in favour of less deep phenomenological theories. It is interesting that positivism itself is based upon an out-of-date attempt, made by Mach, to introduce real depth into the theory of matter. Positivists, for example Philipp Frank, often said that metaphysics was nothing else but out-of-date science; but positivism is out-of-date science also. Mach lived in a time when the theory of matter was involved in what Professor Yourgrau might call 'paradoxes'. There were really serious difficulties in the theory of matter because of the clash between continuum theory and atomic theory. Mach made a most interesting proposal to introduce new depth into the physical theory of matter by doing without matter. This was a serious and extremely bold proposal. Just as we have learned to do without the substance heat in the theory of heat so also, said Mach, we should do without matter in the theory of matter. And this very interesting proposal was then, about a generation later, incorporated into a philosophical theory, positivism. So positivism is really nothing but an outdated physical theory.

In conclusion I would just like to say one other word. I first heard of Mario Bunge years ago, when I was on the editorial board of the *British Journal for the Philosophy of Science* and received a manuscript of his called 'Strife about Complementarity'. When I read this manuscript I heaved a sigh of relief, for here at last was one person who dared to say something really strong and straightforward against the break-in of the subject into physics, and against complementarity. Although this is considered by very many people to be one of the deepest ideas in modern physics, Bunge and I might perhaps agree that it is a paradigm of pseudo-depth.

E. H. HUTTEN: *Maturity, depth and objectivity in science.*

In some ways it is obvious that one has to agree with Professor Bunge: a mature theory is indeed better than any other theory. But it depends very much on what you mean by 'mature'. A purely logical definition of 'maturity' at which he wants to arrive, if I understand him correctly, seems to me to be quite impossible and even nonsensical.

Maturity is a term which comes originally from the discourse of psychology. There is a very important point to be made here. It is that the purely logical analysis of a theory is interesting but of limited value for our understanding of it. We have always to bring in the most various psychological and historical reasoning if we want to judge our theories correctly. The Correspondence Principle in physics demonstrates that the new and the old theory must relate to each other through the asymptotic agreement of a basic formula. The Correspondence Principle regulates the historical growth of science (*ex post facto*, of course) in two ways. Of the many theories that can be (and often have been) imagined, the Principle selects the one that is related to the old, and established, theories in the proper manner. Moreover, the new theory corrects the old one by restricting its range of applicability. Quantum mechanics and relativity mechanics are so related to Newtonian mechanics, as everyone knows. The Correspondence Principle rules the development of a science and it demonstrates the self-correcting method and openness that characterizes scientific reasoning.

Science is a human activity, and as everything human beings do it must be explained scientifically, by means of an appropriate theory. Science, or knowledge, is a natural phenomenon and so subject to the process of evolution as everything else that occurs in human life. Science is the product of the mental-emotional-social evolution of mankind which is part and parcel of the bio-genetic process of evolution. Thus we must investigate how the basic concepts of science evolved if we want to understand them. This brings me to the concept of 'depth' which is indeed very important as Bunge pointed out.

However, what do we mean when we say that the atomic theory, for example, is deeper than mechanics? The naive analogy that springs to one's mind, namely, that we dig deeper below the surface and then find atoms is not quite enough; for that matter, we might say, too, that the conceptions of general relativity and of cosmology are deeper though we go there far above the surface, into the sky. Psychology alone can help us here in understanding of what we mean by 'depth'. We must remember that all knowledge begins with simple, bodily experiences – this is amply demonstrated by the development of both the individual and of mankind as a whole. Science began with the Ionian speculations about simple substances. Gradually, knowledge expands and covers a wider range of phenomena; and, correspondingly, our concepts have to become more 'abstract', that is, removed from ordinary, simple conceptions that can be used in everyday life. Quantum mechanics and relativity theory are more 'abstract', in this sense. Abstraction is the criterion for the depth of a theory; and though accompanied by increasing logical power of the concepts that are being used in a more 'abstract' theory, psychological explanations come in, by necessity. I would want, however, to express here my agreement with Bunge in this point that deeper theories are characterized by the occurrence of concepts or variables that are not directly observable.

This does not mean that objectivity in science consists in banishing the human being from his participation in the process of measurement. This seems to me to be a completely false standard of objectivity which has come about only through the idealizations accepted in classical physics. I can hardly believe that Bunge wants this kind of objectivity though he seems to argue in its favour, if I do not misinterpret him. The observer does play an essential role in quantum mechanics – the more advanced and 'abstract' theory than Newtonian mechanics – although this does not make quantum mechanics 'subjectivist'. On the contrary, it is more 'objective' than Newtonian mechanics because it includes all the variables needed for a complete description. It is true that the biographical details of the observer are irrelevant: what is relevant is the experimenter as the creator of information. This brings in the Uncertainty Principle which, in fact, provides a more realistic and, therefore, more objective basis for our information.

Let me end, however, with remarking how much I do agree with Bunge when he condemns the new scholasticism – the cult of data and of simplicity. I would include the exaggerated import ascribed by philosophers to the logical analysis of science, or logicism, in the condemnation. This scholasticism is the main reason why the life sciences – psychology – are so misjudged and undervalued – even by some of their practitioners.

M. BUNGE: *Reply.*

I. Reply to Whyte.

I could not agree more with Dr. Whyte's suggestions that basic theoretical physics is presently in an impasse and that the next genuine advance in this field will require a deep change of philosophical attitude. I also think that it is the philosopher's duty to remind the scientist that most of his achievements are bound to be provisional, and that it is the philosopher's privilege to speculate on possible solutions to problems that are not solved in a satisfactory manner or that have not even been noticed by scientists – as long as the speculator proceeds knowledgeably and imaginatively, and that he is willing to listen to scientific criticism.

On the other hand we seem to disagree about how to remedy our present ailments. I do not think that a single medicine will cure them because they are many and varied – and precisely for this reason, I am in favour of free and bold speculation at the moment. In particular, I do not believe that salvation will come by returning to immediately given spatial and temporal relations and by trying to interpret them in semiclassical ways, as Dr. Whyte suggests. The main reasons for my disbelief are the following.

Firstly, every breakthrough in physics has involved some change in our ideas of space and time, and every such change seems to have taken man farther away from his original intuitions. Moreover, all attempts to base our refined ideas of spatio-temporal relations on 'the given' – e.g., Whitehead's method of abstraction – have failed precisely because they stick to appearances and reject the traditional way of science, which involves daring leaps beyond intuition. Secondly, there are some indications that what may be most at fault in our present picture of nature is the classical view of space-time as a continuum describable by non-random variables such as the coordinates occurring in relativity and wave mechanics. On a relational (non-absolute) view, space-time does not exist by itself but is a net of relations among events (changes of state of physical entities). And if there are no continuous sequences of events everywhere, then space-time will not be continuous. In any case the spatio-temporal continuity assumed hitherto may have to be surrendered. Daring conjectures concerning the nature of space-time should be welcomed, as long as they yield, as a limiting case, the view now dominant.

II. Reply to Popper.

I agree with Popper that depth should not be used to control the growth of science. I only claim that depth is desirable and should therefore be encouraged. I do not even claim that the actual growth of knowledge is always accompanied by an increase in depth. Indeed, after a deep but false or fruitless theory a shallow but truer one is very often needed – as exemplified by the present vogue of dispersion relations and group-theoretical considerations in the domain of high energies. (I do hope that some deeper theory – presumably a field theory – will eventually be produced, but meanwhile physicists must use a phenomenological approach, not because it is the best, but because there is nothing better at the moment.) I only claim (a) that the maturation of science involves both increasing depth and increasing logical tightness, and (b) that depth is a desideratum as long as it is consistent with testability.

I agree that Mach's attempt to dispense with the concept of matter was bold, but I do not think it was deep. To try to account for reality in terms of sensations is as old as animism and it is superficial because it leaves sensation, a highly complex process, as an unanalyzed building block of the universe. If Mach had proposed that we explain matter by fields or by some other physical entities, he would have been a revolutionary. But Mach hardly mentioned field physics and – as Popper himself has shown – his views were very much a return to Berkeley. Yet this is only a detail: I agree with Popper's central thesis that positivism is obsolete science – something made obsolete by the 'discovery' (corroborated conjectures) of unobservable entities such as fields and atoms. And I think Popper would agree that it is an urgent task to find out how it has been possible for an antipositivist science to be permeated by a positivist philosophy.

Finally, I fully subscribe to Popper's remarks on the pseudo-depth of the complementarity 'principle' – not to be mistaken for Heisenberg's scatter relations, said to be just an illustration of the 'principle'. It is amazing that scientists should have taken the attitude of the foggiest of philosophers, by regarding as deep what is merely obscure. For complementarity, like dialectics, is an excuse for lack of clarity. So much so that, when asked what is complementary to truth, Bohr is reported to have replied: 'Clarity'. (From which it follows that complementarity itself is either true but unclear, or clear but false, and in either case useless.) There is no master key to all problems: there are only heuristic clues and unifying principles – but complementarity is neither. Indeed, it has no heuristic value: it has suggested nothing new except tactics to disguise inconsistencies and hush up criticism. And it is not a unifying principle, for it just enthrones and generalizes the so-called particle-field duality, which can be shown to be a hangover of classical physics.

III. Reply to Hutten.

I agree with Dr. Hutten that a full understanding of science is not only a matter of logic but also of history, sociology and psychology – as long as the latter is not mixed with the pseudo-science of psychoanalysis. Yet it seems undeniable that the sciences of science are unnecessary to grasp a piece of scientific knowledge. Luckily enough, individual learning is not a synopsis of the history of knowledge; thus, in order to learn molecular biology one need not start with Thales. Since most of the trials that have led to present knowledge have been failures, it would take a very lengthy psychohistorical research to understand the psychogenesis and sociogenesis of any major event in science. Moreover the psychology of science is practically nonexistent as a science, and the history of science has only too often been distorted by philosophical prejudice – as exemplified by the account of relativity and the quanta as children of positivism. The history and the psychology of science are valuable both by themselves and as a means for evaluating present achievements, shortcomings, and trends, but they do not replace the understanding of a body of scientific knowledge.

I do not agree with Hutten's claim that 'maturity' and 'depth' are terms borrowed from psychology and that it is nonsensical to extrapolate them from it: after all, there were mature fruits before psychology and deep waters before Freud's muddy ones. There is nothing psychological in the contention that the synthetic theory of evolution is deeper than Darwin's, and that a dynamical (or rather field-theoretical) account of the vicissitudes of the 'elementary particles' would be deeper than the present purely structural, taxonomic and kinematical account. These examples certainly fall under the characterization of theory depth proposed in my paper. I claim the right to propose elucidations of the metascientific, not the psychological, senses of the terms 'depth' and 'maturity'.

Concerning the participation of the observer in quantum mechanics, I disagree with Hutten's view, which is essentially the traditional one known as the Copenhagen doctrine. Some of the reasons for disagreeing with this interpretation and thinking that an alternative interpretation of the same mathematical formalism is called for, are the following.

Firstly, a physical theory is by definition concerned with physical systems and events not with people. Therefore any presentation of quantum mechanics containing nonphysical predicates, such as 'observer', 'observable', 'taking cognizance of the position of a meter', and the like, is unphysical. To be sure, these terms are all right in experimental physics, but quantum mechanics happens to be a branch of theoretical physics, and the aim of theoretical physics is to build subject-free, observer-independent models of reality.

Secondly, the interpretation of the quantum theories in psychological terms is *ad hoc*, as shown by an analysis of its basic concepts. Thus most 'observables' are supposed to be imperceptible properties of physical entities, and the operators representing them are automorphisms of an infinitely dimensional function space. Both the operators and the state function are 'defined' on the set of physical systems (or rather on the set of pairs microsystem-environment), not on the set of cognitive subjects. Nowhere in quantum mechanical formulas do the observer coordinates occur, and no postulate of the theory characterizes the observer, who is just a philosophical trespasser on the objectivity of science.

Thirdly, the quantum theory of measurement should not be used in expounding the basic hypotheses of quantum theories (a) because so far there exists no quantum theory of measurement capable of yielding definite predictions concerning actual measuring processes: the existing theory is too sketchy and generic for this; (b) because a reasonable quantum theory of measurement should be an application of basic quantum mechanics and not the other way around – if only because experimental arrangements are constituted by systems satisfying quantum mechanics. The role of the observer is to observe – and to plan and interpret observations – not to become the subject of physical theory.

None of this is intended to dismiss Hutten's plea for the psychology of science. But physics must be kept strictly physical whereas psychology, dealing as it does with highly complex systems that are basically physical, cannot afford to ignore physics. Moreover, one hopes that quantum chemistry will eventually help to explain and even read some brain functions, whereas psychology is incapable of explaining the behavior of atoms, for the simple reason that brains are made up of atoms, not the other way around. Physicalism is certainly exaggerated, but not so much as psychologism; and in any case physicalism has been fertile, whereas psychologism leads us back to anthropomorphism. Reversing Hutten's recommendation, I would say that physics has had enough of psyche whereas psychology can never have enough of physis [1].

---

[1] For a strictly physical (in particular, nonpsychological) formulation of the basic physical theories, including quantum mechanics, see M. Bunge, *Foundations of Physics*, Springer Verlag, New York, 1967.

SCIENTIFIC METHODOLOGY AND THE CAUSAL THEORY OF PERCEPTION [1]

GROVER MAXWELL

Minnesota Center for Philosophy of Science,
University of Minnesota

A couple of years ago, B. F. Skinner published an essay in celebration of the fiftieth birthday of behaviorism titled, 'Behaviorism at fifty' [2]. I mention this as an opening wedge for the only half-facetious remark that a subtitle for this paper might well be, 'Behaviorism, senile at fifty-two?' One of its main theses is that all the members of a family of current methodological, epistemological, and metaphysical positions – a family that might be characterized by dubbing it 'excessive empiricism' and which, of course, includes behaviorism as a member – should be rejected in favor of the view that I shall try to explicate and defend here. I believe that the strongest considerations against an excessive empiricism come from the empirical sciences themselves. The arguments for this contention that I want to advance in this essay [3] begin with (one version of) the causal theory of perception. I shall next summarize briefly and, thus, in an oversimplified and inaccurate manner what I take this version to assert.

Our perceptions (or perceivings) i.e. our seeing, hearing, etc. are

[1] The author is grateful to the National Science Foundation of the U.S. and to the Minnesota Center for Philosophy of Science of the University of Minnesota for support of research.

Several paragraphs that appeared in my 'Philosophy and the causal theory of perception', *The Graduate Review of Philosophy*, **5**, No. 3, (1964), pp. 9–21 are reproduced in this essay with modifications and with the kind permission of the editors of that journal.

[2] *Science* **140** (No. 3570) May 31, (1963), pp. 951–958.

[3] The arguments here presuppose a realistic interpretation of science. This, in turn, is argued for in my 'The ontological status of theoretical entities', in *Minnesota Studies in the Philosophy of Science*, H. Feigl and G. Maxwell, eds., Minneapolis, University of Minnesota Press, 1962, and in some of the literature cited in that essay.

caused by entities (objects, events, etc.) some of which are external to our bodies and all of which are external to our minds. Moreover, these entities are pretty much as current science says they are. If there is conflict between the account of the nature of such entities given by science and the account given by common sense (including 'direct observation'), it is the latter which, in most cases, must back down [1].

It is commonly charged that the 'causal theory of perception' is merely a scientific theory and is (thus) without philosophical credentials. What *would* count as a 'philosophical theory' of perception? As a fairly typical answer we may take, I suppose, the one given by Ayer in *The Problem of Knowledge*. A satisfactory theory, according to him, would furnish an analysis of our perceptual judgments: it would tell us what they mean and how we are justified in accepting them. He contends that the causal theory fails to meet these requirements. This brings us near the heart of the matter almost too soon: I shall argue that no satisfactory theory of perception will merely tell us what our perceptual judgments mean and how we are justified in accepting them – simply because, taken as we ordinarily mean them, such judgments are generally false.

The considerations that have been and could be given supporting

---

[1]   Many philosophers strongly disagree, of course. See for example Gilbert Ryle's *Dilemmas*, chs. 1, 5, 6, and 7. For detailed and cogent arguments against Ryle see M. Mandelbaum, *Philosophy, Science, and Sense Perception*, The John Hopkins Press, Baltimore, 1964. The latter book and also a work by John Beloff, *The Existence of Mind*, The Citadel Press, New York, 1964, chs. 2 and 3, first came to my attention after this essay was in press. Both contain excellent arguments for the relevance of science, in general, and the causal theory of perception, in particular, for philosophical problems as well as arguments against naive realism and for a radical *critical realism*. However, I am sure that both of these authors would agree that the results of science are, themselves, always to be taken with a healthy grain of salt. Since science grows out of and is an extension of common sense, it is only a little less prone to error and no more immune to critical scrutiny than is common sense. I believe that the failure to recognize this is, paradoxically enough, in large part responsible for the hostility of many philosophers toward science and for their zeal in protecting common sense and/or philosophy from 'scientistic' encroachment.

this contention are so numerous that not all of them can even be mentioned here. Many of them are well known. There are, for example, the traditional arguments against naive realism (and against any direct realism), the distinction between primary and secondary qualities and, later, the attack on such a distinction. Recall the arguments of Democritus and the Skeptics, of Galileo, Descartes, Locke and Berkeley, of Poincaré, Schlick, Bertrand Russell and the latter day 'critical realists'. Remember the arguments from the relativity of perception, from illusion, from hallucinations and dreams – from psychophysiology, neurophysiology, and physics.

Some of these arguments are indeed weak, and, historically speaking, they have often been stated badly and misused. Furthermore, they are not conclusive either severally or jointly. However, jointly they *do* seem to me to make the world view I am advocating the most justified among its competitors. As examples, I shall cite just two of the most cogent of these plausibility arguments. We may call them the *argument from neurophysiology and psychophysics* and the *argument from physics and neurophysiology*. They are directed against naive realism and against any kind of direct realism. Or, in other words, they argue that the properties (such as colors) that we ordinarily ascribe to external objects on the basis of *direct perception,* so-called, actually do not belong to the object at all but are, as a matter of fact, wholly in the mind. The first is introduced in a very clear manner by Eccles [1], '. . . the only necessary condition for an observer to see colours, hear sounds, or experience the existence of his own body is that appropriate patterns of neuronal activity shall occur in appropriate regions of his brain as was first clearly seen by Descartes. It is immaterial whether these events are caused by local stimulation of the cerebral cortex or some part of the afferent nervous pathway, or whether they are, as is usual, generated by afferent impulses discharged by receptor organs.' Now it seems to me that this makes it extremely implausible that colors as seen and other such properties are anywhere except

---

[1]   O. O. Eccles, *The Neurophysiological Basis of Mind,* Clarendon Press, Oxford.

in the mind. For, if a true and complete explanation and causal account, for example, of our seeing a certain color expanse is given in terms none of which, prior to mentioning the conscious experience itself, refer to color (i.e. terms referring to retinal stimulation, afferent nerve impulses, neuronal activity patterns in the brain, etc.), then it seems excessively anthropocentric if not completely gratuitous to postulate the existence of a color expanse *external* to our seeing of it – an expanse which is supposed to be causally prior not only to our seeing it but to the retinal stimulation, the neural current, etc. The very least that can be said for the argument is that it shows that it is *possible* – not only logically possible but physically and psychically possible – that colors are nowhere but in the mind.

The argument from physics and neurophysiology simply fills in the details alluded to above. It points out, for example, that the stimulation of the retina is accomplished solely by photons emitted from the atoms comprising the surface of the material object in question. The material object just *is* this collection of submicroscopic particles and the relations that subsist among them; there is no plausibly describable manner in which a color (as seen) *could* inhere in its surface; and even if *per impossible* there were, the color-in-the-surface would play no role in the emission of the photons, which are both sufficient and necessary for the retinal stimulation which causes us to see colors.

These, then, are just a couple of examples of the many considerations which make naive realism or any kind of direct realism untenable. This holds for the 'primary qualities' as well as the 'secondary' ones; the arguments of Berkeley and other familiar ones, though not without flaws, seem quite cogent on this point to me. Thus, everything that we usually consider to be perceived properties of external objects must be recognized as existing *wholly* and *only* in the mind. The phrase, 'in the mind' is admittedly a difficult one; I shall ask your indulgence in permitting me to use it in a common sensical, broad, and vague manner. It is not my purpose here to advocate any specific theory of mind or to introduce technical terms such as 'sense data'. I *can* adumbrate what I intend by giving examples: we *are* inclined to say that the properties we 'observe' in dreams and hallucinations *are* wholly in the mind. My central contention here is that the properties we ordinarily would say that we observe in external objects are just as much in the mind as those we experience in dreams or hallucinations. I know, of course, that some philosophers deny that they *have* experiences or that anything is going on in their minds when they observe or perceive, but I should like to avoid this issue here. I can only reply to such objections by saying that *I* certainly have experiences and find it incredible that others do not [1].

In a real and important sense, then, all of the external world, including even our own bodies is unobserved and unobservable. Obviously, however, if we are to retain our starting position, the causal theory of perception, we must maintain a realist position regarding the sphere of the nonmental, and just how this can be accomplished is by no means clear at this point. As a preliminary, let us consider a couple of objections often advanced against representative realism, which is not the position I shall defend but is similar to it in some respects. The first asks how we can *know* anything about the nature of the external world or, even, that it exists. This is a weak objection and easily answered. In some senses of 'know,' we cannot have such knowledge – for example the sense in which 'know' connotes *known directly by experience, or entailed by such knowledge, or inferable by simple enumerative induction from such knowledge.* But it seems evident that such conceptions of knowledge are much too restrictive – that most of our common sense knowledge, even, is something like *hypothetico-deductive* in character, in short that our beliefs about the external world are *theoretical* beliefs, albeit we *do* and *ought to* believe very strongly that this 'theory' – in broad outline – is close enough to the truth for many purposes.

The second objection, no doubt, sounds even more cogent to contemporary ears, to say nothing of those who have felt the full poignancy of Berkeley's powerful arguments. How, it asks, can we *conceive of* or *meaningfully* ascribe any properties to the entities

---

[1] For *arguments* against such philosophers, see the works of Beloff and Mandelbaum mentioned in an earlier footnote.

of an external world – entities whose only links with our perceptions are mere causal ones? Inherent in this question is what may be termed the objection from *concept empiricism* or, better, *concept idealism*. The lines along which an adequate answer is to be given have been suggested by various writers, among them Poincaré, Schlick [1], perhaps Wittgenstein – certainly he exerted a profound influence on Schlick in these matters – and, especially, Bertrand Russell (see, e.g., the first four sections of *Human Knowledge, Its Scope and Limits*). In brief, the answer is that the only aspects of the nonmental world of which we can have any knowledge or any conception are purely structural (or, in other words, purely formal). The *details* of the answer consist of an explication of 'structural' or 'formal' adequate to the task at hand. To my knowledge, this has not yet been completed in a satisfactory manner, although a considerable amount of valuable work has been done by those mentioned above and by others, and I do not believe the task is as formidable as it appears at first blush. Here, there is space for only a crude synopsis.

The notion of *form* or *structure* needed here may accurately be said to be logical (and/or mathematical) and, in a sense, abstract; *characterizations* of instances of it will be in terms of logic alone, i.e. the logical connectives, quantifiers and variables – they will contain no descriptive terms. However, to put the matter this way may be misleading. For we are inclined to think of the *logical* and the *mathematical* as being opposed to the *factual* and the *contingent* and of the *abstract* as being opposed to the *concrete*; but *structure*, in the sense we require, *must be factual and contingent and*, at least in its exemplifications, *concrete*. Furthermore, it cannot be emphasized too strongly – what should already be obvious – that structure is *not* linguistic nor, even, conceptual in character; it is an objective feature of the real world. A crude, and in some ways illegitimate, example may be of value. The system consisting of the set of

---

[1]   Schlick's account is suggestive but, it seems to me, seriously confused and mistaken in many respects. For example, he maintains that we cannot talk about experiential *content* at all but only about *form* or *structure*. His reasons are the usual Wittgensteinian and Malcolmian ones. (See M. Schlick, *Gesammelte Aufsätze*, Gerold and Co., Vienna, 1938, ch. 8 [in English].)

physical objects and the relation *outweighs* (as measured on a spring balance) has a certain *structural similarity* to the system consisting of the set of minerals and the relation *scratches*. Or, to put it in another way, the two systems share a certain *formal* property – *namely* the property such that any system having the property consists of some set of entities and some relation which is asymmetric and transitive within the set. In other words: A system, U, has the formal property, $\mathbf{F} = df, (\exists S)(\exists R)\{(U = \langle S, R \rangle)$ and for any x, y, and z in S $\{[(Rxy \supset \sim Ryx)$ and $(Rxy \cdot Ryz \supset Rxz)]\}$. Both systems mentioned above have the formal property $\mathbf{F}$, for both the relations of outweighing and of scratching are asymmetric and transitive in the respective sets. Note *both* that $\mathbf{F}$ is defined in logical terms alone *and* that it is nevertheless a purely contingent matter that the two systems mentioned exemplify it. The system consisting of say, the set of humans and the relation of *loving* would not exemplify $\mathbf{F}$. Thus it may be, and often *is*, the case that whether a system has a certain *formal* property (structure in our required sense) is a purely contingent matter. There is not space here for the details that would be involved in legitimizing this example or in developing a satisfactory general framework with any degree of rigor. I have made a beginning of this elsewhere [1] and feel that the results are encouraging.

Let me state the position I am advancing again, this time using Kantian language. On the one hand there is the realm of phenomena. These are wholly *in the mind* (in our sense). Of the phenomena and only of the phenomena do we have *direct knowledge*. On the other hand, there are the things in themselves, and here our divergence from the views of Kant is great; although we have no *direct* knowledge of the latter, the bulk of our common sense knowledge and our scientific knowledge *is* of them. Among them are not only electrons, protons, forces, and fields but also tables, chairs, and human bodies. All of our knowledge of these is, of

---

[1] In 'Theories, perception, and structural realism,' in *Pittsburgh Series in Philosophy of Science* IV, R. Colodny ed., University of Pittsburgh Press, Pittsburgh, forthcoming. Actually the account in the present essay is not only incomplete but contains a serious error: structure should not be identified with form; rather it is form plus causal connections with experience.

course, indirect and may be generally characterized as hypothetico-deductive (or, better, hypothetico-inferential). It is confirmed according to the usual hypothetico-deductive standards, e.g. success in explanation and prediction. Also, let us remember, all of this knowledge is purely structural – purely formal – in the sense I have tried to adumbrate. The implications of this are manifold and profound. In fact, it requires considerable time and thought – for most of us at least – to realize what a drastic revision of our usual conceptions, including our scientific conceptions is required. After this is accomplished still more time and effort are required to see that the outrage to common sense and scientific practice is not nearly as extreme as it seems. For example, it follows that we can *name* neither individuals nor properties of the external (non-mental) world. Strictly speaking, expressions referring to the things in themselves will contain only logical signs – including, let it be emphasized, existentially quantified variables – they will contain neither proper names nor predicate constants. Strictly speaking, we cannot name chairs, tables or dogs or any properties they may have. However, let us recall that many of the terms we ordinarily think of as names are better characterized as abbreviations for definite descriptions. In analogous fashion, constants can be introduced into expressions referring to nonmental entities. (For more detailed considerations concerning this see the reference in the preceding footnote.)

Hopefully, the *structural realism* just outlined overcomes the alleged difficulties of *representative realism* by showing how we can talk meaningfully about the external world and how we can confirm and disconfirm our theories and of singular hypotheses about it, even though we can never observe any portion of it directly. It is *not* essential to the position that the sense impressions or perceptual experiences, or whatever we decide to call them 'resemble' the physical objects which may be among their causal antecedents. However, as an accidental bonus, it turns out that not only can good sense be given to such a notion but also that, in many cases though by no means all, the best hypothesis seems to be that such resemblance holds. It is merely necessary to note that sense impressions themselves have structure in our sense of 'structure'

To postulate a similarity between a sense impression and the physical object hypothesized to be its causal antecedent would be to postulate a *structural* similarity, i.e., to postulate that at least a certain subset of the features of the impression are isomorphic with a subset of the features of the physical object. (Incidentally, this provides a viable distinction, or rather a slippery slope, between primary and secondary properties, the stronger the structural similarity of a (physical) property with the sensory qualities produced by its instances, the further towards the 'primary' end of the spectrum it belongs.)

Concerning the problem of other minds, it is my contention, contra Schlick et al., that, regarding the thoughts, feelings, sense impressions, etc. of others, our knowledge is *not* limited to the purely structural; in this area we properly form and test hypotheses concerning, for example, sensory *content* as well as structure. The contention is that since the most reasonable guess is that others have experiences which are qualitatively identical with, or at least very similar to, our own, the objection from concept idealism does not apply and we are not limited to structure here but can hypothesize about the sensory content of others' experience as well. This 'guess' about the experience of others is confirmed by the usual canons of common sense and scientific investigation (same cause, same effect; hypothetico-deductive success, etc.). It is an oversimplification to the point of distortion to refer to such confirmation as an argument from analogy. The 'no criteria' objections of Malcolm and others may be dismissed as either implausible dogma or as based on a crude positivism – a narrow and time and again discredited verificationism [1]. If 'criteria' means logically necessary or sufficient conditions, or, even conclusive evidence, then we never have criteria for tables, chairs, past events – hardly anything at all! On the other hand, if 'criteria' means (nonconclusive) evidence, then we *do* have abundant criteria concerning the qualitative, intrinsic nature of experiences of others.

We may now summarize a reply to Ayer. The theory which

---

[1] See, e.g., G. Maxwell and H. Feigl, 'Why ordinary language needs reforming', *Journal of Philosophy* 58 (1961), pp. 488–498.

meets his first requirement, i.e. which tells us what our perceptual judgments mean (as we usually make them) is naive realism. It seems undeniable to me that naive realism or some form of direct realism is built into or presupposed by our usual ways of thinking and talking, whether in the street or in the laboratory. For most purposes, including most scientific ones, this is no handicap. This is fortunate, for I think that J. J. C. Smart (private conversation) is correct in contending that the tendency to conceive of the world in a naively realistic manner is 'programmed into us' from birth; it is with considerable difficulty that we are able to think of it otherwise. But for *some* philosophical and scientific purposes it is necessary. Thus Ayer's first requirement is inadequate. His *second* requirement cannot be met at all, for, strictly speaking, we are never justified in accepting our perceptual judgments as ordinarily made, simply because naive realism and, thus, the judgments themselves, are literally false. As the theory which survives critical scrutiny and which still, for the most part, 'saves the appearances,' the causal theory is the only satisfactory theory of perception of which I am aware.

I began this paper with a polemic against what I called excessive empiricism. What is the relevance to this of all these considerations about the causal theory of perception, structural realism, etc.? Well, one distinguishing feature of many brands of excessive empiricism is their exhortation to restrict our discourse to the directly observable. One thing that I have tried to show is that this would restrict us to the realm of the mental. Not only would talk of electrons, protons, super-egos and ids be excluded, but talk of tables, chairs, bodies and, thus even *behavior* would be prohibited as well. It is true that I have not given arguments against *subjective idealism* in this paper, but I assume that it is not a view held by any of us and that it would almost certainly be explicitly rejected by most excessive empiricists.

Now most excessive empiricists, particularly when they make pronouncements on scientific methodology, advocate further restriction – restriction to the publicly observable. Supposedly, publicly observable things are a subclass of directly observable ones. And indeed this is true, but only because the null class is a subclass of every class. Before I pursue this matter further, permit me to make a couple of points which I think are important but which, strictly speaking, are digressions. I think that many of the motives of most excessive empiricists are quite admirable, and I wish to disclaim any desire to give aid and comfort to obscurantisms. (I suspect there *would* be disagreement in some cases, however, about what it is to be obscurantist.) And, although I do believe that the role of observation in the scientific enterprise has been greatly over-emphasized, nevertheless, it, or something similar to it, remains essential, indeed, crucial; it is a truism that the evidence (to be sharply distinguished from the meaning or referents) for or against a statement or a theory is always observational. Even here, however, 'evidence' must not be interpreted broadly enough to include all reasons for tentatively accepting or rejecting a theory or statement.

In the second digression, I want to consider a view which neither entails nor is entailed by excessive empiricism but which, historically, has been associated with many instances of it. I shall label this straw man 'traditional materialism' although I believe that a considerable number of contemporary philosophers hold views almost indistinguishable from it. When the materialist contends that everything consists of matter, he is usually referring to matter in the customary sense, i.e. the naive realist sense. Matter for him is something with color, hardness, and solidity (i.e. it feels a certain way to the touch). It is something which is extended (in space) and which moves (in space) – again with 'space' having its customary sense. But we have seen that these properties are all wholly in the mind; this is true even of *space* insofar as we *observe* things extended in it and moving in it. Thus the matter of the materialist, like all naive realistic entities, is a confused and illegitimate hybrid of the mental and the nonmental. Ironically, however, the mental predominates. Whether or not materialism can be coherently reformulated within the framework I have been advocating, I do not know. But I strongly suspect that if this *were* accomplished, the position would have lost much of whatever plausibility it had in its old incoherent form as well as much of the appeal it had for those who find it attractive. For example, there would no longer be the good old solid, publicly observable matter – not even the particles of matter called atoms, protons, etc. as customarily conceived; there would be only the things in themselves – of which our only knowledge is purely structural. Just what kind of attempts could be made to dispose of sensations, of colors-as-seen, etc., I am at a loss to say. But it seems evident that the current ploys of latter day materialists such as J. J. C. Smart would have to be abandoned or drastically revised.

Returning now to the main point, note that the allegedly publicly observable objects and events so dear to some excessive empiricists – for example, to the behaviorists – are in the same boat with the matter of the materialist: insofar as they are observable, they are mentalistic and *not* public – insofar as they are public, they are *not* observable.

At this point, the empiricist surely can reply, 'Even if this absurd world view proposed by Maxwell is accepted, a perfectly consistent and only slightly amended sense can be given to "publicly observable". For example, a publicly observable object, in the amended sense, would be one which bears strong structural similarity to the sense impression (or what have you) which it causes under certain conditions. As a matter of fact, we don't even have to use the questionable notion of *structural similarity*. As is well known, we can easily give a public or intersubjective sense to, say, the color words. A red surface, for example, would be defined as one which, under standard conditions, produces a sensation (etc.) of red in a normal observer.'

I shall waive the familiar difficulties involved in explicating such notions as *standard conditions* and *normal observer* and grant that something like this can be done. I further concede that reports about the publicly observable in *this* new sense properly interpreted, are usually fairly reliable and that it is usually possible to obtain considerable agreement, considerable reproducibility, etc., concerning them. In short, I grant that for most purposes, the publicly observable, again in the amended sense, provides the *evidential basis* for our scientific theories. The crucial point, however, is that generally speaking, it is the *evidential base* only and *not* the subject matter – or at any rate, only a small portion of it. The subject matter, i.e. the entities and events with which our theories are mainly concerned and which are the referents of most of their terms are *not* publicly observable – not even in this modified sense. The instrumentalists have the matter completely reversed. Rather than our theories being mere instruments whose function it is to enable us to explain and predict concerning observables, the truth of the matter is that observables are, for the most part, mere instruments with which we test out theories.

Note that even in the explication of the modified notion of the *publicly observable*, the framework employed was highly theoretical. For example, in the 'new' definition of 'red', reference had to be made an unobservable, the external cause of the red sense impression – in this case a physical surface.

Let me now summarize the conclusions that I want to maintain and that seem to me supported by the preceeding considerations. First of all, of course, excessive empiricism fails as a world view – as a fundamental metaphysical and epistemological position. Thus if an excessive empiricist methodology for science is to be viably defended, it must be on some basis other than fundamental philosophical considerations – something like past success, I suppose – perhaps others. Now as far as the physical and the biological sciences are concerned, I strongly contend that no reasonable defense of such methodologies can be given. The successes here, even at the highly practical level of prediction and control, have been due in large part to theories about highly theoretical, completely unobservable entities (in *any* reasonable sense of 'observable'). [I have given arguments for this elsewhere as have many others – including even such empirically inclined philosophers as Carnap, Hempel, and Feigl. The arguments seem to me virtually conclusive.]

Now the fact that excessive empiricism cannot be supported by basic philosophical principles or by any principles applicable to general scientific methodology still leaves open the possibility that psychology and the social sciences have certain unique characteristics which do require that their specific methodologies be fashioned along excessive empiricist, say behavioristic lines. Indeed some methodologists have held such a view. Personally, I find their arguments singularly unconvincing, but this is not the question with which this paper has been concerned.

W. V. QUINE: *Comment.*

One central plank in Professor Maxwell's platform is that our knowledge of the external world consists in a sharing of structure. This is to my mind an important truth, or points toward one. Structure, in the sense of the word that is relevant to this important truth, is what we preserve when we code information.

Send a man into another room and have him come back and report on its contents. He comes back and agitates the air for a while, and in consequence of this agitation we learn about objects in the other room which are very unlike any agitation of the air. Selected traits of objects in that room are coded in traits of this agitation of the air. The manner of the coding, called language, is complicated and far-fetched, but it works; and clearly it is purely structural, at least in the privative sense of depending on no qualitative resemblances between the objects and the agitation. Also the man's internal state, neural or whatever, in which his knowledge of the objects in that room consists, presumably bears none but structural relations to those objects; structural in the privative sense of there being no qualitative resemblances between the objects and the man's internal state, but only some sort of coding, and, of course, causation. And the same applies to our own knowledge of the objects, as gained from the man's testimony.

I do think there is a substantial resemblance between our internal state, whatever it is, which constitutes our hearsay knowledge of the objects in that room, and the man's internal state which constitutes his eye-witness knowledge of the objects. This I find plausible on broadly naturalistic grounds. Here then I seem even to be in an odd kind of agreement with Maxwell's doctrine of the relative accessibility of other minds. But I must stress a distinction. What I just now conjectured is that between two men's knowledge of the same things there is a more substantial resemblance than between the knowledge and the things. But publicly observable bodies, still, and not other people's knowledge, are what our firmest knowledge is *about*.

Observation terms are the terms upon whose attribution all members of the speech community tend to agree under like stimulation. Observation terms are the consensus-prone terms, and they owe this trait to their having been learned mostly by ostension, or reinforcement in the presence of their objects, rather than by context or definition. What they apply to are publicly observable bodies, mostly, and not subjective entities, because the learning of language is social.

Thus I do not share Maxwell's doctrine that 'the external world . . . is unobservable'. On the contrary, the external world has had, as a theater of observation, few rivals. I disagree, too, when he denies bodies their color because they are collections of submicroscopic particles. Water remains water gallon by gallon, I say, even though its submicroscopic bits are rather oxygen and hydrogen; there is no paradox in this, and there is none in saying that a table top remains smooth and brown, square inch by square inch, even though its submicroscopic bits are discrete, vibrant, and colorless. The quality of being aqueous, also of being smooth and brown, are like swarming, or waging war: they are traits only of a congeries. This does not make them unreal or subjective. There is no call for a predicate to hold of each part of the things it holds of. Even a predicate of shape, after all, would fail that test. It is a modern discovery in particular that aqueousness, smoothness, and brownness resemble squareness and swarming on this score; but it is not a contradiction.

Maxwell's trouble, if he has one, is an unquestioning reification of sense data, Humean impressions, free-floating color patches. If you put the color there on a subjective *Vorhang* or curtain, of course you must leave bodies colorless; for, as Maxwell and I agreed, bodies and our knowledge of them are related only structurally and causally and not by a sharing of qualities. Also, if you keep the curtain, you understandably balk at acknowledging observation of bodies. But the curtain itself is a relic of the days when philosophy aspired to a privileged status, nearer and firmer than natural science. This, not behaviorism, is the excessive empiricism that wants exorcising. Neurath pointed the way, representing philosophy and science as in one and the same boat. Problems dissolve, some of them, when we view perception squarely as a causal transaction between external bodies and talking people, with no curtain to screen them.

K. R. POPPER: *Is there an epistemological problem of perception?*

The so-called epistemological problem of perception, to which the causal theory of perception discussed by Grover Maxwell is one solution, is, I believe, based upon a mistaken attempt to find foundations for knowledge, or sources of knowledge, in observation. And this in turn stems from the idea that *knowledge without foundations* is useless, or even impossible (because it would not be 'knowledge'). When naive realism was criticised, sense-data were introduced as the irreducible kernel of certainty for which our sense-organs are responsible. But sense-data, untheoretical items of information, simply do not exist. For we *always* operate with theories, some of which are even incorporated in our physiology. And a sense-organ is akin to a theory: according to evolutionist views a sense-organ is developed in an attempt to adjust ourselves to a real external world, to help us to find our way through the world. A scientific theory is an organ we develop outside our skin, while an organ is a theory we develop inside our skin. This is one of the many reasons why the idea of completely untheoretical, and hence incorrigible, sense-data is mistaken. We can never free observation from the theoretical elements of interpretation. We always interpret; that is we theorize, on a conscious, on an unconscious, and on a physiological level. Standard psychological experiments illustrate this. For example, a person may be shown a picture which is at first very unsharp, with its contours blurred, and which then becomes clearer. At first, the subject consciously tries to guess what it is. As it becomes clearer, at some point he suddenly *recognizes* it – the normal unconscious (perhaps even physiological) mechanism of interpretation takes over. We see from this the naivety of the usual attempts to justify our knowledge of the

external world by constructing it out of the 'data' which appear to
an epistemologist when he looks at an orange. We *cannot* justify
our knowledge of the external world; *all* our knowledge, even our
observational knowledge, is theoretical, corrigible, and fallible.
Here is not the place to argue that knowledge without foundations
is possible, and that we can solve the main problems of the theory
of knowledge in a non-justificationist way. It seems to me, however,
that Maxwell has taken the traditional approach to the problem
of perception too seriously. To call all our observational knowledge
theoretical and fallible is not to say that it is all false, as Maxwell
seems to infer from the causal theory of perception, according to
which our 'sense impressions' do not 'resemble' external objects
(in the usual sense) at all, but are merely caused by them.

A. J. AYER: *Are all our common sense judgements false?*

I have great sympathy and admiration for anyone who will come
right out and say that the common sense view of the world is just
untrue, but I am afraid that the way in which Professor Maxwell
does it leads him into an untenable position. When referring to
my views, he said correctly that I thought that what was required
of a philosophical theory of perception was that it should analyse
and justify our perceptual judgments; and on this he remarked
that this analysis presents no difficulty, since we have all been
conditioned from our infancy to adopt some form of naive realism,
and that since naive realism is false the answer on the point of
justification is that our perceptual judgments can not be justified.
    Now I am no friend to naive realism. But to suppose that it is
false in a sense which entails that all our judgments of perception
are false leads Maxwell into the same difficulty as beset the absolute
idealists who maintained that no judgement of any kind was altogether true. Let me illustrate this by an example. I can see Professor
Quine in the audience, that he is wearing a bow-tie and that he
is not wearing a top-hat. According to Maxwell, these statements
that I have just made are all false. I do not see Quine and *a fortiori*
do not see that he is wearing a bow-tie and not wearing a top-hat.

On the other hand, he would hardly wish to deny that the statement that Quine is wearing a bow-tie corresponds to the facts in a way that the statement that he is wearing a top-hat does not. Neither would he deny that our knowledge that one of the statements corresponds to the facts and the other not is based solely on the present evidence of our senses. But how is this possible if all such judgments of perception are false? If he does not want to say that any of them is true, at least he will have to allow that some of them are trustworthy and others not; for if we cannot make this discrimination, I fail to see how he can suppose that we are ever capable of testing any scientific theory. But then I wonder whether very much is to be gained by substituting the distinction between what is trustworthy, in this sense, and what is untrustworthy for the distinction between what is true and what is false.

W. C. KNEALE: *Secondary qualities and the causal theory of perception.*

Like the Chairman, I am puzzled by Professor Maxwell's thesis that our ordinary judgements of perception are all, or nearly all, false. It reminds me of some queer things Prichard used to say, and in particular of his assertion that we see colours but mistake them for bodies. I remember that when I was young we often pressed Prichard for a fuller explanation of this doctrine, asking 'Is it not remarkable that men should make this mistake naturally, if, as you go on to argue, a colour is not the sort of thing that could possibly be a body? And must there not in any case be a world of difference between this universal mistake which you allege and any ordinary mistake such as occurs, for example, when a man mistakes a stranger for a friend?' Prichard never produced a clear answer to these objections; and I doubt whether Maxwell could do better. For he too is committed, it seems, to the strange view that our basic use of colour words, that is our use of them in application to material things, is not merely wrong but necessarily wrong.

I am far from wishing to declare that all the common beliefs expressed by plain men in ordinary language are true, but it seems to me that there must be a serious error in any philosophical

doctrine which implies that the *primary* application of a simple
word such as 'green' is an *absurd* application. And yet that in
effect is what Prichard and Maxwell maintain. First they assume
that when we say 'The Chairman's necktie is green' we must be
using the word 'green' in precisely the same way as when we say
in some more sophisticated moment that a certain after-image is
green. And then, since it seems evident that nothing can be coloured
in the same sense as an after-image except another object of the
same status, they go on to conclude that it is impossible for a
material object such as the Chairman's tie to be green at all.
Unfortunately confusions of this sort have fogged the distinction
of primary and secondary qualities from the beginning. Even
Locke, who rightly described secondary qualities as powers to
produce sensations in us, fell into the absurdity of saying that
porphyry has no colour in the dark. It is true, of course, that
porphyry does not and cannot look-red in the dark, but it is grossly
misleading to talk as though it lost its colour at sunset. In the
only sense in which porphyry is ever red it is red in the dark as
well as in the light; for its redness is just its power to look-red in
appropriate conditions. Similarly, in the sense in which the Chairman's tie can rightly be said to be green, it can rightly be said
to be green even when lying in the remote recesses of his wardrobe.
And in order to distinguish that sense from the sense in which
an after-image can be said to be green, we need only remark that
it may sometimes be proper to say of the tie 'It is really green
though it looks-brown (and perhaps even looks brown) in this
reddish light' whereas for a green after-image there can be no such
possibility of looking-brown in exceptional circumstances.

Some understanding of all this is involved in our ordinary use
of colour words, and that is one reason why any satisfactory philosophical theory of perception must, in my opinion, be a causal
theory. But to say this is *not* to say that perception of material
things is always indirect. For the sense experiences produced in
us by the action of material things on our bodies are *not* a screen
between us and the material world; and if we are tempted to
suppose that they are, we should ask ourselves what it would be
like to perceive anything without having them.

GROVER MAXWELL: *Reply*.

A succinct and delightful characterization of what I have called *structural realism* is provided by the first three paragraphs of Professor Quine's comments, except for the very last sentence of the third one. I do not even find the agreement between us an 'odd' one. But the accord seems to end here; and I say 'seems' advisedly, for I think it likely that we are just at cross purposes about what it is to *observe* something. When Quine contends that '. . . publicly observable bodies . . . are what our firmest knowledge is *about*', he is not thinking about the kind of observation that I refer to when I contend that there *are* no publicly observable bodies. One notion of observation can be used such that at least some, perhaps most, of our firmest knowledge *is* about publicly observable bodies (see p. 159 of my essay), and a different notion may be introduced according to which, if structuralism is true, all that we observe is, in a sense, wholly within the mind. Now it is my view that virtually all of our usual notions of observation essentially involve both of these notions. In other words, observation, as usually conceived, is a naive realist concept through and through. Therefore, if structural realism is true, then, in any usual sense of 'observation', we observe neither public objects nor entities in our minds: we never observe anything at all. For example, if I have a dream, no matter how vivid, of seeing a white dog, I cannot be said to have observed a dog or, indeed, anything, since there existed nothing corresponding in any straightforward way to the ostensibly observed object. On the other hand, if I do what ordinarily could be called 'actually seeing[1] a white dog', then (again, if structuralism is true) I do not actually observe anything (or even *see* in the usual sense), for there *is* nothing external to me which is white in the usual, qualitative sense, or etc., etc.

But although, strictly speaking, I never *observe* anything, nevertheless when I dream of a white dog and also when I do what is inaccurately called 'actually seeing a white dog', there is something going on in me which, in each case, serves as an excellent clue to

---

[1] Forgive me, Professor Ryle.

information about external objects and events, provided these goings on are integrated with a world theory and certain reasonably good guesses about the rest of my environment and circumstances. When I have the experience corresponding to what we vulgarly call 'actually seeing a white dog', I make the guess, among several others, that my eyes, retina, etc. are involved in certain events which are among the causal ancestors of the experience, and then I infer with the aid of my world theory that what we would ordinarily call a 'white dog' is near. This is a reconstruction, of course. I actually make no such guesses about initial conditions, nor do I invoke any world theory at the conscious level; rather the world theory and the disposition to respond as if I had made such guesses are 'built into' me by means of genetics and my previous history. (See my essay, p. 157, and Popper's comments, p. 163.) Similarly, when dreaming of a white dog, if I made good guesses about environmental and other initial conditions, I would infer that whatever the causal antecedents of the dream experience might have been – too large a bedtime snack, etc. – they did not have among them anything that we would customarily call a 'white dog'. In each case there is a set of events causally connected with each other in various complex ways. In each case one member of the set is an experience identical with or very similar to what we vulgarly call 'seeing a white dog'. In neither case is there any *Vorhang* or screening curtain; there is the series of causally connected events, and that is all there is to it. In all of this it seems to me that I am merely agreeing with Quine that perception is a 'causal transaction between external bodies and talking people with no *curtain* to *screen* them', (p. 163, emphasis added) and, however that '[our] internal state, neural or whatever, in which . . . knowledge of . . . objects in . . . [the] room consists, presumably bears none but structural relations to those objects; structural in the privative sense of there being no qualitative resemblances between the objects and . . . [our] internal state, but only some sort of coding, and, of course, causation' (p. 161). The screening curtain is raised, I think, only by those who wish to maintain (inconsistently, I would hold) both a causal theory of perception and a direct realism, or, at best, a naive and qualitative representative realism.

In the face of what seems to be such strong agreement I am extremely puzzled by Quine's abrupt about face when he insists that 'a table top remains smooth and brown, square inch by square inch, even though its submicroscopic bits are discrete, vibrant, and colorless'. Apparently, he is attributing a simple 'fallacy of composition' to the critics of direct realism. It would be remarkable, though not unprecedented, if such acute thinkers as Russell, Poincaré, Dirac and others have been so easily misled. Let us see.

There are certainly some properties of which it is true to say that it is a modern discovery that they are 'traits only of congeries'. Among them are temperature and entropy and most other thermodynamic magnitudes. But I must contend against Quine that the case is quite different with smoothness and brownness. In this case, it is a modern discovery – a consequence of contemporary physics, psychophysiology, etc. – that the congeries that comprise tables and the like are *not* brown and smooth. Let me emphasize that I am talking about good old everyday, *qualitative* smoothness and brownness – properties with which we are directly acquainted, if we are directly acquainted with anything. Obviously, if 'brownness', for example, be given a new meaning such as 'the disposition to absorb certain frequencies and to reflect certain others' or, even, "the disposition, under appropriate conditions, to cause 'normal perceivers' to see brown (in the everyday sense of 'brown')" then the claim that physical objects are colored becomes true but completely irrelevant to this discussion. I shall now try once more to convince Quine that no table top is brown.

The argument assumes that certain tenets of common sense and of science are at the very least headed in the right direction – more specifically that an external or physical and physiological (i.e. non mental) *complete* account of all events which are in any way relevant to perception (for example, seeing a red surface) – any such account will be in terms of entities and events *something* like neural and brain activity, receptor sense organs, light quanta or electromagnetic radiation, molecules, atoms, electrons, neutrons and protons. Thus, a complete account of all nonmental aspects of perception would make no mention whatever of such things as colors, odors, tastes, sounds. (Again I must emphasize that I am talking about the

familiar colors, sounds, etc. as we actually see and hear them and
not, for example, of some reidentification of sound with some of
its causal antecedents such as certain vibrations of air molecules.)
Since, however, it is undeniable to me (and, I take it, to any candid
person other than perhaps philosophers) that I *do* directly experience colors, sounds, odors, etc. in the old-fashioned sense of
'color', etc., I am forced to conclude that instances of these properties exist wholly and only in the mind. Here, something of crucial
importance must be emphasized: the decisive point is *not*, as is
sometimes held, that it is meaningless or self-contradictory to think
of electrons, light quanta, etc., or atoms, molecules or even aggregates thereof as being colored; rather, it is that *even if such things
were colored it would make no difference.* Even if it made sense to
talk of a collection of blue colored molecules or atoms which
emitted blue colored light photons, such a 'blue' aggregate could
cause us to see the surface in question as a *red* one just as effectively
as a collection of red colored ones emitting red colored quanta;
the only relevant fact concerning the color we see is the amount
of energy per quantum, or, what amounts to the same thing, the
frequency of the radiation. So even if there are colored entities
– even colored surfaces as we ordinarily conceive them – in the
physical environment, we never see them and their being colored
plays no role in *any* process whereby we acquire or confirm knowledge. We thus have no more (perhaps less) reason for believing
that there are instances of color in the external world than we
do for believing in the existence of disembodied spirits.

I hope that I may now presume to return a favor and to diagnose
Quine's trouble, if he has one. I think that it is a hankering after
old-fashioned materialism, which, as I argued in my essay presupposes the truth of direct realism. I have found myself, however,
unlike Quine, I believe, forced to admit not only the existence of
experiences of sentient beings but also to recognize the full measure
of all of their qualitative richness. In the experiential events
themselves there inheres all that we can ever know of the qualitative.
Our knowledge of all other events and objects, whether these be
involved in causal chains terminating in perceptions or not, is
limited to the purely structural. I shall return to this point in

my reply to Quine's charge that I unquestioningly reify sense-data.

Before proceeding, however, I must make a few remarks about Quine's intimation that I would like to retain for philosophy 'a privileged status, nearer and firmer than natural science'. (Due to lack of space, they will have to be something of the nature of personal testimony and, I fear, somewhat dogmatic.) As far as I am concerned, there is no such thing as philosophy. On the one hand there are the formal sciences such as pure mathematics and logic, which by no means should be identified with most of the interesting and important activities of those who have been called 'philosophers'. All that remains on the other hand is natural science [1]. Among its assumptions, problems, and issues some are, in some sense and as a matter of degree only, more basic and fundamental and more indirectly connected with observation and experience than others [2]. These are the questions with which philosophers have, quite rightly, concerned themselves, although they have sometimes mistakenly considered themselves to be engaged in an autonomous discipline. I did try to make it explicit in my essay that it is physics (plus neurophysiology, psycho-physiology, etc.) and not some mysterious discipline such as 'pure philosophy' that falsifies direct realism. Thus again I seem to be in agreement with Quine and with Neurath, and especially with Popper, to whom I am indebted for liberating me from a number of silly views about the nature of philosophy.

In view of these considerations, the question with which Popper titles his comments, 'Is there an epistemological problem of perception?' receives the following answer: No, not if epistemology is conceived of as an autonomous discipline, completely logical or conceptual in nature. But if epistemology – as well as metaphysics – are taken, as they should be, to be continuous with, indeed integral parts of, natural science, the answer is: Yes, there are epistemological, metaphysical, *and* scientific questions about perception, but these are not happily classified as three distinct groups

---

[1] I omit consideration of ethics, aesthetics, etc. in this discussion.

[2] See my 'Philosophy and the causal theory of perception', *The Graduate Review of Philosophy* 6 (1964), pp. 9–21, for an earlier expression of these views.

of problems. Each question will be answered, if it is answered at all, in the same way: by adducing better *theories* of perception.

With Popper's contention that theories, or things very much like theories, are built into us at even the unconscious and physiological levels I not only agree but I think it such an important truth that it should be shouted from the housetops at frequent intervals. I was hinting, somewhat unclearly, at a similar view in my essay when I agreed with J. J. C. Smart that 'the tendency to conceive of the world in a naively realistic manner is "programmed into us" from birth' (p. 157). But this leads us to see immediately that, while our constitutional tendencies to 'theorize' along certain definite lines are necessary both for survival and for the increase in systematic knowledge, they are not an unmixed blessing. For those that are 'built in' the most firmly produce 'theories' that are so much a part of us that it is very difficult if not virtually impossible for us to subject them to the severe scrutiny and criticism that Popper quite rightly insists all theories should suffer (or enjoy). At any rate, I console myself with the rationalization that this is one of the main reasons for the generally hostile receptions that the views expressed in my essay usually encounter.

While it is likely that our innate tendencies, produced at least in part by natural selection, give rise to 'theories' which are among those best suited for our survival, we cannot, on pain of committing pragmatism, infer from this that these theories are true or, even, that they are likely to be closer to the truth than those we might be led to entertain after the full exercise of our critical facilities.

Since I have learned a large portion of what I have just said from Popper, I hope that I can convince him that I do not infer that what we customarily take to be our observational knowledge is false from the fact that it is theoretical and fallible. Rather, I conclude that it is false after subjecting it to detailed scrutiny and criticism both from within by turning it on itself and from without by means of what seems to be our best (or our least bad) contemporary science.

I can no longer escape the difficult and thankless task of considering sense data. Both Popper and Quine think that they are uncritically incorporated into my views, although the only time I mention them in my essay is to disavow them explicitly (p. 151). However, I am grateful to them for giving me the opportunity to try to remove the misunderstanding, which is almost certainly due to my failure to express myself clearly. Quine and Popper also see me as chasing the age old will-o-the-wisp, *certainty* or, at the very least, groping for a solid foundation for knowledge. Again, I must not only plead not guilty but insist that my position is entirely the opposite. In fact, I reject the attempt – quite fashionable today – to draw a sharp distinction between having an experience and knowing (or believing) something about the experience. The same skepticism applies to the putative act – object dichotomy. A certain amount of interpretation ('theorizing') is involved in every experience. All other events in us are lower-level physiological ones. Thus again I agree with Popper when he says, 'But sense-data, untheoretical items of information, simply do not exist.' Whether we conclude from all of this that sense data do not exist, full stop; or whether we say that they do exist but are very different indeed from what traditional sense data theorists conceived them to be is unimportant and largely a terminological matter. What is neither unimportant nor terminological is the necessity of avoiding the fallacy of inferring from the fact that traditional type sense-data do not exist, that the mind, or conscious experience, etc. has been thereby straightforwardly reduced to matter, or to behavior or similar fashionable but to me incomprehensible propositions.

Therefore, I am not at all concerned with a distinction between data and knowledge or between the corrigible and the incorrigible. The distinction that I do hold crucial is between our mental activity, in which I include both sense and intellect (they are essentially involved with each other anyway), on the one hand, and the external events that are causally connected (or connectable) with them, on the other. And again, this is because I believe that much light is shed on traditional problems of perception, the 'reality problem', etc. as well as on current issues in contemporary science, such as in quantum theory, by the recognition of the fact that our knowledge about the latter (the external) is limited to the purely structural, while in the former we are acquainted with all the richness of the qualitative.

The position defended here does not necessarily involve mind–body dualism. The claim is not that the external *has* only structural properties but, rather, that our *knowledge* can include only its structure. As Russell has put it (in somewhat different words) about the 'intrinsic' nature of the physical world we must remain epistemologically agnostic – except, a monist might add, for a small portion of what we vulgarly call 'the brain'. But such a monism bears little resemblance to traditional materialism or, even, to most contemporary varieties. The mental does not become any less mental by virtue of being identified with a subset of the entities or events that the physicist, neurophysiologist, etc. characterize only in purely structural terms.

Professor Ayer raises only one objection, but it is a crucial one, and again I must express gratitude for a valuable piece of criticism. Since everyone then present would have agreed that Quine was wearing a bow-tie and not a top-hat, he wonders how I can claim that *both* the proposition that he was wearing a top-hat *and* that he was wearing a bow-tie are false. Surely, he goes on to explain, '... the statement that Quine is wearing a bow-tie corresponds to the facts in a way that the statement that he is wearing a top-hat does not'; and with this I certainly must agree. I should like to take the time now to give Ayer's reply to his own objection that he very kindly related to me after the formal discussion had closed. Suppose that a certain primitive tribe worshipped a god named Mumba and that, in general, when the weather was bad they would say, 'Mumba is angry', and when it was fine they said, 'Mumba is pleased'. Now a statement to the effect that Mumba is pleased uttered by a native on an occasion of fine weather would correspond to the facts in a way that a statement that Mumba is angry on the same occasion would not, even though, as any true Christian knows, both statements would be false. While the example is a good one and very much to the point, I think that the proposition that Quine was wearing a bow-tie is in a little better shape *vis-à-vis* the facts than is the proposition that Mumba was pleased and that this can be explained in a fairly precise manner. I can only give a bare summary here: in the common sense, direct realist world story, the proposition that Quine was wearing a bow-tie is almost *structurally* identical with or, at any rate, structurally very similar to the proposition that would correspond to it and which would be true in a structural realist world story. Because of this strong structural similarity, it can be said, using a notion employed by Popper, that the proposition that Quine was wearing a bow-tie, although false, is *closer to the truth,* and thus more *trustworthy,* than the proposition that he was not, or that he was wearing a top-hat. Just as the proposition that I am six feet and four inches tall, though false, is closer to the truth and thus more trustworthy than the proposition that I am seven feet tall. (My height is six feet, three inches, plus or minus one half inch.)

It seems to me that these considerations *do* provide a 'clear answer' for the cases for which Professor Kneale tells us that Prichard always failed. And in replying to Kneale, I must stress again that I do *not* hold that our basic use of color words is *necessarily* wrong or *absurd* but, rather, that we see that its *contingent* wrongness is a consequence of certain discoveries of science and common sense, as explained earlier.

Kneale seems to feel that Locke was clearer on the subject of primary and secondary qualities than many other philosophers have been, and with this I am in strong agreement. In fact, I must defend Locke against Kneale. It seems to be often overlooked that Locke always had a tripartite division in mind: there are the primary qualities and the secondary qualities, both kinds of which inhere in the external objects, and, finally, there are the 'ideas' in us which somehow 'correspond' to the external qualities. As Kneale notes approvingly, Locke 'described secondary qualities as powers to produce sensations in us', – powers *of the objects,* we should add, again in accord with Locke, possessed by virtue of possession of certain of the primary qualities. Now it becomes a very subtle matter as to whether or not Locke fell into absurdity, as Kneale charges, when he said that porphyry has no color in the dark. It seems just as reasonable, and much more charitable, to suppose that when Locke spoke of color here he had in mind either an intrinsic ingredient of the experience corresponding to what we vulgarly call 'seeing something colored' or the power to produce such an experience, full stop, rather than the power to produce such an experience *in appropriate conditions*. On the first alternative Locke's claim is true, even trivially true; porphyry has no color in the dark because it has no color under *any* circumstances. (It might be charged that it is absurd to utter such a trivially true claim, and, moreover, misleading, since it might be taken to suggest that, although porphyry has no color in the dark, it does in the light. But Kneale obviously did not have this in mind.) On the second, that is that color is the power (simpliciter) to produce a certain kind of experience, again the claim is true; in the dark, porphyry has no such power. On the third alternative, that is, if Locke meant by porphyry's color its power, *under appropriate conditions*, to produce the appropriate experience, then Locke did fall into absurdity; for even when porphyry is in the dark it is still true that if it *were* in the light and other appropriate conditions obtained it *would* look red. Now Kneale obviously thinks that Locke, and all of the rest of us, are obligated to conceive of colors along the lines of this third alternative, except in a few extraordinary cases such as with after-images. He does not tell us why explicitly, but he seems to imply that it has to do with our ordinary use of color words. I am also interested in our ordinary uses of color words because I am interested in examining the theories – the world picture – that they presuppose so that they may be criticized and improved or replaced. And when I reflect on what I have meant virtually all of my life, and what I still mean in all but my most reflective moments when I say that something is red, I can find little of the sophisticated *dispositional* meaning that Kneale takes to be the primary sense of color words. Rather it seems to me that I intend to ascribe the color as I see it to the object as one of its intrinsic, *occurrent* qualities, and I strongly suspect that the same is true of my peers in the language community. In other words, I reach again the conclusion that our ordinary use of color words presupposes naive realism. Since the latter is false, it follows that, when engaged in attempts to construct theories that will be as close to the truth as we can make them, our ordinary use of color words should be abandoned.

Kneale explicitly opts for a causal theory of perception but at the same time insists that our perception of material things is, at least sometimes, direct. Whatever 'direct' can mean here, it cannot consistently mean 'not mediated by events and entities in the spatial interval between us and the material things and in our sense organs, our neural pathways, and our brains.' Once this is seen clearly, it becomes apparent again that we can assume no qualitative similarity between the material thing and our experience of it. And, once more, we see that an adequate causal theory of perception shows us how misconceived is the 'screening curtain' metaphor. Far from being a curtain between us and material things, our sense experiences are an essential part, though by no means the only part, of the conduit that gives us access to knowledge about material things.

A BUDGET OF PARADOXES IN PHYSICS [1]

WOLFGANG YOURGRAU

University of Denver

Since the beginning of this century, philosophers of mathematics
have been greatly interested in the paradoxes which, like the lions
in the fairy tale, block their paths to the coveted rock-bottom
foundations of set theory and thus of mathematics. Philosophers
of physics have so far shown little or no concern in the paradoxes
which arise in this realm. Their instinct may be sound: perhaps
the paradoxes of physics do not seriously threaten the various
theories, and are, for this reason, not worthy of earnest study.
Still, I doubt whether hitherto the question has been considered
at all.

The object of this paper is not to answer the question but simply
to undertake a first rough survey of this field. I shall merely collect
some of the more obvious of the so-called paradoxes of physics in a
bouquet, or in a basket, and not take umbrage if it turns out that
their attractions are nil, and that physicists and philosophers of
science will empty my basket into a bucket. In fact, I myself
suspect that something of this sort might easily happen. Be that
as it may, I should like to be a pioneer in these stony and barren
plains.

The occurrence of paradoxes is a refractory trait that has irritated
thinkers throughout the ages. And studies in paradox have acquired
a prominent role in logic, mathematics, and epistemology. Logical
paradoxes, in particular, tax our passion for ratiocinative exercises
to the point of tedium. Surprisingly, the existence of physical
paradoxes has never aroused an equally intensive curiosity among
'tough' logicians or epistemologists. The reason for this aloofness

[1] I am very much indebted to Karl Popper and Alwyn van der Merwe
for their valid criticisms and invaluable suggestions.

might well be that in physics, or rather in theoretical physics, we deal with apparently extralogical and, in a way, extralinguistic facts or data. Yet, contrary to what is commonly supposed, physical paradoxes need not merely be confined to an intra-physicist dialogue. They may even one day warrant attention by zealous logicians and so-called methodologists of science.

After this somewhat cumbrous preamble, and at the risk that occasionally I shall attempt to give answers to questions most philosophers do not care to ask, I shall turn to a summary description of my somewhat arbitrarily selected budget of paradoxes in physics.

1. What may be called the *first paradox of the kinetic theory* arises when one tries to understand the *slowness of diffusion of gases*. According to this theory, molecules move with tremendous speed. How can we explain then that direct observation does apparently not confirm this scientific fact? After all, the (macroscopic) slowness of the diffusion can be observed in the laboratory by any experimenter. For a while, this seeming paradox embarrassed the early protagonists of the kinetic theory. That this problem could soon be dismissed, and that the difficulty does not actually represent a real or genuine paradox, is a consequence of the appraisal (due to Avogadro and Loschmidt) of the unexpectedly gigantic number of molecules in a cm^3, the equally enormous number of collisions, and sheer thermodynamic reasoning.

2. Suppose we interconnect a number of vessels of different shapes and fill them with water. The result: the liquid column will reach exactly the same level in each vessel. Physicists once used to call this phenomenon, which they found startling, the *hydrostatic paradox*. It is now a commonplace that the most elementary principles of hydrostatics account fully for this experimental datum; but we should remember that these principles were largely inspired by the paradox. I wonder whether one ought to describe the above unexpected phenomenon as 'counterintuitive', and with it the principles designed to explain it. Indeed, such a decisive epithet might be better reserved for a stronger degree of discrepancy between theory and robust common sense.

3.   In our pursuit of some instructive physical paradoxes – and we shall leave it open whether or not they are 'apparent' or 'genuine' – we encounter a beautiful specimen issuing from Einstein's theory of Brownian motion and treated ingeniously by Ehrenfest. Let a very small sphere be suspended in a liquid medium. Assume that we can observe its Brownian motion. Further, select an instant when the sphere has a comparatively great velocity, e.g. upward. The question is: will the surrounding fluid move with the sphere or not? If we apply the statistical theory of the molecular movement to the *paradox in the theory of Brownian motion*, which emerges here, the answer is that such a common motion cannot occur. By contriving a very simple model as a reasonable analogy, however, Ehrenfest demonstrated that the forementioned answer can be convincingly challenged. He proved that *'there is no objection against* EINSTEIN's *assumption that a suspended sphere during its* BROWNIAN *movement imparts its motion to the surrounding fluid . . .'* [1]. In brief: it is possible to let a pair of points move in such a way that they remain close together and travel at the same time through great distances, and yet at every instant the velocity u_2 is independent of u_1!

Ehrenfest showed that the problem does not provide us with a real paradox, but can be solved in a plausible manner, provided that we do not try to furnish a positive proof that Einstein's assumption derives from the fundamental assertions of statistical mechanics. For such an approach will lead us into some hardly tractable difficulties.

4.   Another paradox, in an entirely different domain, was independently anticipated by Niels Bohr (1911) and by Miss van Leeuwen (1914). There are at least three distinct types of magnetization: diamagnetism, paramagnetism, and ferromagnetism. Now, in order to explain the observed magnetism, we have to compute the statistical average of the magnetic moment for an assembly of atoms in thermal equilibrium. Bohr and van Leeuwen neatly

---

[1]   P. Ehrenfest, *Collected Scientific Papers*, North-Holland, Amsterdam, 1959, p. 412.

and coercively argued that if we employ this method, the inevitable yet paradoxical result is that the average magnetic moment always vanishes. In other words, the *paradox of the classical theory of magnetism* states that it is theoretically impossible to explain the non-vanishing magnetic moment of matter in general by means of classical theory. After a little cogitation we come to realize that only a quantum theory of magnetism can be worked out in a consistent manner [1].

5. Einstein, obsessed with the indomitable spirit of unyielding inquiry, was not always patient when he recognized insuperable obstructions peculiar to his kind of search. Starting out from Bose–Einstein statistics for ideal gases, he developed an equation of state which, for sufficiently low temperatures, deviates significantly from the classical equation of state for ideal gases. Considering the mixture of two such gases, he was faced with what he himself described as 'a vexing paradox' (*ein ärgerliches Paradoxon!*), in consequence of his theoretically sensible procedure (1924).

Let us postulate N' to be the number of molecules of one type of ideal gas and N'' the number of molecules of a different ideal gas. Further, assume M' and M'' to be their respective molecular masses. Then: if $N = N' + N''$ and M' and M'' converge steadily towards the common value of M, one would expect the equation of state to go over, in the limit, into that of a single gas of N molecules with a mass M. Einstein was aware of this *suggestio falsi* and provided physically incontestable arguments for this paradox; nevertheless, he urged strongly that it be somehow resolved on first principles. P. Ehrenfest and G. E. Uhlenbeck (1927) were able to show that a wave-mechanical treatment of the statistics of ideal gases does not lead to *Einstein's mixing paradox* [2]. As far as I know, all attempts to solve the paradox without invoking wave mechanics have failed, and seem doomed to failure.

---

[1] L. Rosenfeld, *Theory of Electrons*, North-Holland, Amsterdam, 1951, pp. 46–47.

[2] P. Ehrenfest, op. cit., p. 576.

6.   There has been a good deal of vapid talk about a celebrated paradox conceived by Einstein, Podolski and Rosen (1935). They contrived an imaginary experiment that did not only question the customary interpretation of the formalism of the uncertainty relations: it raised grave doubts concerning the validity or even plausibility of the traditional exegesis of quantum theory proper. According to this *paradox of* EPR, neither matrix mechanics nor wave mechanics afford a comprehensive description of reality. If we accept the commonplace distinction between classical and wave-mechanical concepts as to the structure of matter, and if we furthermore disagree with EPR's criteria for physical reality and some of their highly 'unorthodox' assumptions, then the arguments in support of the paradoxical results inferred by these three authors will not at all be found to be impregnable.

I for one would but opt for the reasonableness of the critical objections leveled by theorists like Bohr, Bohm, Margenau et al., and not feel inclined to ally myself with Einstein's weird and debatable analysis of the ψ-function. The reasoning converging on the EPR paradox conveniently omits the physical possibility of interpreting their imaginary experiment within the boundaries of good old quantum theory! Bohm is right, I think, to stress that 'the one-to-one correspondence between mathematical theory and well-defined 'elements of reality' exists only at the classical level of accuracy'. [1] There is not a tittle of evidence, not an iota (or particle?) of substantiation that, at the quantum level, the mathematical formalism furnished by the ψ-function is in a one-one correspondence with the testable behaviour of a physical system: statistical correlation is all we can attain.

Popper's defense of the EPR paradox or rather of the actual intention of the authors, contains some valuable and sobering ideas. For example, many critics of the EPR paradox had ignored the relevant fact that Heisenberg had treated single particles in his uncertainty relations, whereas EPR discussed the problem of pairs of particles. Moreover, Popper pleads strongly, though im-

---

[1]   D. Bohm, *Quantum Theory*, Constable and Company, London, 1954, p. 619.

plicitly, for the necessity to retain a mechanical, even common-sense, viewpoint: if it is at all feasible to determine simultaneously positions and momenta of two particles with equal sharpness, then we ought to interpret the uncertainty relations in a manner compatible with our established methods or theories of measurement [1].

And yet, however thoughtful Popper's plea for the legitimacy of the EPR conception of sub-microscopic physics, the tenets of quantum physics do simply not allow for the existence of that specific occurrence envisaged in EPR's imaginary experiment. We have to acquiesce in the unwelcome fact that the physical interpretation of the uncertainty relations runs counter to common sense and classical mechanics.

7. Eddington once remarked in connection with the 'big bang conjecture' in cosmology that it is one of those conclusions from which there seems to be no logical escape, yet it suffers from the defect of being incredible. An analogous situation obtains in relativity theory (special and general): I am referring to the *clock paradox* and the *twin paradox*. It has been rightly claimed by Synge, Infeld, Bergmann et al.,[2] that the clock paradox – the twin paradox is no more than a somewhat jocular version of the clock paradox – is incorrectly if not absurdly called a paradox. None the less, since the seemingly paradoxical consequence from relativity theory is still occupying the fancy of physicists and laymen alike, we might as well mention it perfunctorily.

From Einstein's conception of simultaneity, the Lorentz transformation, time dilatation, and the stipulation of speeds approaching that of light follows conclusively that moving clocks do not run at the same rate as clocks remaining static in a laboratory: travelling clocks run slow. In other words, clocks of the same construction

[1] K. R. Popper, *The Logic of Scientific Discovery*, Hutchinson, London, 1959, pp. 445–453.

[2] J. L. Synge, *Relativity : The Special Theory*, North-Holland, Amsterdam, 1956, p. 16; L. Infeld, *Albert Einstein*, Charles Scribner's, New York, 1962, pp. 41–43; P. G. Bergmann, 'The special theory of relativity' in *Handbuch der Physik*, IV, Springer Verlag, Berlin–Göttingen–Heidelberg, 1962, pp. 124–125.

that are at rest in a given inertial frame of reference, run in a uniform rate; all moving clocks – irrespective of whether they are rod clocks, atomic clocks, biological clocks – run slow. Accordingly, we can perform a conceptual experiment with identical twins. Let one twin remain on earth, say, in his room. The other twin is supposed to travel out into stellar space, with a speed close to that of light. Then, relativistic reasoning tells us that the twin returning from his celestial venture will still be a young man in his prime, while the 'inertial', the phlegmatic twin, so to speak, will have aged considerably and perhaps become a delapidated old man. Biologically speaking, the heart (physiological clock) of the enterprising twin beat in a much slower rhythm than the heart of the sedentary twin who refused to loaf through the universe.

It can be shown that these strange consequences of relativity theory are not in direct conflict with experience; they are only strange if one remains a prisoner of Newton's concept of absolute time, which has come to be regarded as echoing common sense. When Ives (1938) performed an experiment with hydrogen atoms, which may be regarded as clocks whose rhythms are indicated by their spectral lines, he discovered that a moving hydrogen atom changes its rhythm precisely in agreement with the prediction by relativity theory.

8.   The search for paradoxes, even in physics, may become a compulsive habit. To wit, Schrödinger saw fit to christen an interesting physical phenomenon the *paradox of the Richardson effect* [1]. Granted, the theory which could account satisfactorily for so-called thermionic emission, i.e. the emission of electrons from incandescent metal surfaces, required some hard thinking, in particular because certain traditional assumptions with regard to the behaviour of free electrons proved to be wrong. Now, the electrons in a metal must be regarded as a Fermi–Dirac gas, rather than a classical gas. At a sufficiently high temperature, electrons emerge from the metal after overcoming a certain potential barrier (an obstacle that

---

[1]   E. Schrödinger, *Statistical Thermodynamics*, Cambridge U.P., 1952, pp. 72–73.

can be likened to a 'steep wall' at the surface of the metal). The strange fact is now that the electrons emitted display the classical Maxwellian distribution of velocities corresponding to the room temperature. A simple explanation, however, exists: the emerging electrons consist entirely of those possessing sufficient energy to surmount the exit barrier at the metal surface, so that we are effectively dealing only with the Boltzmann 'tail' of the Fermi–Dirac distribution.

Do we commit a serious error in refusing to treat this physical effect as a paradox? The answer is negative. After all, not every apparently unexpected situation or state of affairs that is refractory and therefore challenging, should be dubbed paradoxical.

9.   Can we accept without cavil, after the preceding remarks, the validity of our claim that physics generates paradoxes? The following two illustrations should certainly clarify the issue. When Boltzmann propounded his famous H-theorem in thermophysics, two formidable objections were raised against its 'truth'; the theorem was said to lead to paradoxes. I shall not attempt a detailed evaluation but merely present a very cursory and rough orientation as to some of the problems involved.

The H-theorem explains, in mechanical terms, the irreversible approach of macroscopic systems towards equilibrium. The quantity H which can be regarded as the negative of the entropy of a gas, is always decreasing or remains constant, provided the velocity distributions of molecules colliding in pairs are assumed to be uncorrelated. But now we recall that the classical equations of motion are held to be invariant with respect to a substitution of $+t$ by $-t$. Thus it becomes clear that if we conceive of the H-theorem as if it were an exact law depicting an individual system, it is no doubt in sharp contradiction to the laws of classical mechanics. This is the *Umkehreinwand*, or *reversal paradox*, first advanced by Loschmidt. How then can one possibly account for irreversible processes by means of equations that characterize reversible processes?

Technically speaking, Boltzmann correlated entropy with his H-function and the concept of thermodynamic probability, and thus demonstrated the purely statistical nature of the second law, whereas in traditional, i.e. phenomenological, thermodynamic theory it is held to be not a statistical but a deterministic or a dynamic law – a law commanding exceptionless validity. If we treat the H-function in a 'classical', that is, dynamic manner, then it is decidedly inconsistent with the stipulation that it should be invariant with respect to time reversal. Yet, in fact, the H-theorem not necessarily implies that dH/dt is a continuous function of time; its value is subject to abrupt changes caused by molecular collisions. However, the notion of molecular collisions is associated with that of molecular chaos, and thus the expression for the H-theorem, viz. $dH/dt \leqslant 0$, becomes tenable only if one interprets dH/dt in terms of statistical mechanics. Once we realize the statistical nature of the H-theorem, we can easily consent that it is definitely invariant with respect to time reversal. Hence: suppose the system is in the state of molecular chaos right now at this moment; consequently we have $dH/dt \leqslant 0$ in the next moment. Analogously: assume that there is molecular chaos in the next instant, then we get $dH/dt \geqslant 0$ right now. Viewed from a microscopic standpoint, the value of H fluctuates symmetrically, though irregularly.

The advent of Boltzmann's H-theorem created a situation bizarre in the extreme. Loschmidt's arguments are, at first glance, quite persuasive. The H-theorem selects a certain preferred (privileged?) direction of time. Thus, it is inconsistent with the principles of Newtonian mechanics, which do not permit any distinction between past and future times. And this reversibility appears to be contradicted by the H-theorem. It is clear that in Loschmidt's interpretation of the theorem we have $dH/dt \leqslant 0$ *at all times*. Had he applied statistical arguments, he would have realized that the H-function does indeed generally decrease, but that it occasionally increases too. The condition of reversibility is thus satisfied and Loschmidt's demand actually fulfilled!

The gravest objections against Boltzmann's H-theorem can be found in the *recurrence paradox (Zermeloscher Wiederkehreinwand)*. It is based on a theorem propounded by Poincaré in 1890, and it was invoked by Zermelo in 1896 against Boltzmann's kinetic theory; Poincaré's theorem was rigorously proved by Carathéodory in 1919. The theorem implies that a conservative dynamical system in a finite space will, after a sufficient but finite length of time, revert to a state, or phase, arbitrarily close to its initial state. To repeat: any system possessing a finite energy and confined to a finite volume will always, after a sufficiently long time, recover any given initial state to an arbitrarily chosen degree of approximation. Translated into physical jargon the theorem asserts that 'every finite isolated mechanical system is very nearly periodic, if not strictly periodic' [1]. Of course, the recurrence time (i.e. of the Poincaré cycle) of a sufficiently large system will be 'prohibitively' long, and in reality one will be unable ever to observe a recurrence of the initial state – the real physical systems we treat in our experiments are not truly closed due to never ceasing weak and often even strong external influences. Let us pause and examine the claim that we cannot expect numerical verification of the theorem.

By way of illustration (not of proof): the time interval between two (small) similar fluctuations represents a Poincaré cycle; assume that such a cycle is of the order of 10^N (N being the total number of molecules in the gaseous system chosen), that is, if we take N to be 10^{23}. What is the necessary, and not even trite, conclusion? Well, if one bears in mind that the age of the universe is approximately a shabby 10^{10} years, one might be inclined to entertain the idea that the theorem of Poincaré–Zermelo–Carathéodory, in spite of its physico-mathematical rigour, foregoes its empirical significance and has very little to do with thermophysics being a science describing events that occur in the real world.

A reconciliation of the opposing standpoints, i.e. the H-theorem and the two paradoxes, is found in the *Stosszahlansatz* or the collision number hypothesis, which introduces a probability aspect into Boltzmann's proof of the H-theorem. And by appealing to the principle of microscopic reversibility, we can defend the plausibility of the H-theorem against the advocates of the two paradoxes. In current thermophysics, one employs without any qualms the

---

[1] Yourgrau, van der Merwe and Raw, *Treatise on Irreversible and Statistical Thermophysics*, The Macmillan Company, New York, 1966, p. 95.

quantum-mechanical version of the H-theorem, which mollifies, though not completely satisfies, most of its critics. In brief: the H-theorem tells us something about the average, the probable rather than the actual, behaviour of the physical system; it holds in the mean but not necessarily in the individual case. (It is worth noting that fluctuations actuate observable effects such as scattering light; for instance, the blue of the sky.)

To summarize: stochastic methods explain the concept of irreversibility and its apparent incompatibility with classical mechanics. I have tried to indicate that the above two paradoxes are far from conclusive and that especially the Poincaré–Zermelo objection has some features of mathematical fiction and lacks physical meaning at least for macro-systems. It is always dangerous to extrapolate from a state of partial knowledge to conceptual regions too far remote from physical data! On the other hand, I admit that there is a host of reasons to which one can appeal if one wishes to adopt a critical attitude towards the H-theorem; moreover, this theorem has never been rigorously derived and the range of its validity is therefore far from clear.

10.   We next turn to the often-cited *Gibbs entropy paradox* or *discontinuity paradox of Gibbs*, which also arises in the domain of thermophysics and is 'parasitic' on Boltzmann's entropy equation. Envisage two separated vessels containing different gas molecules, that is, of the species A and the species B. For the sake of convenience we assume the two volumes to be equal, to have the same pressure, and hence to contain equal numbers of molecules. The entropy of gas A is S_A and that of gas B is S_B. From some established equations we can then derive the entropy of the mixture, if gases A and B are assumed to be ideal: $S_{AB} = S_A + S_B + 2Nk \log 2$, where N is the number of molecules. Verbally expressed: the entropy of the mixture of the two ideal gases exceeds total entropy of the separated gases by a factor $2Nk \log 2$. Workers in this field, reflecting adequate acquaintance with the topic, would express the main argument more lucidly by using the physicist's vernacular in the following way.

In phenomenological thermodynamics the final entropy of a

mixture of two different yet chemically noninteracting gases S_{AB} must, in concordance with the second law, be greater than the initially given entropy $S_A + S_B$ of the unmixed gases. For the entropy of mixing we get $\Delta S = S_{AB} - (S_A + S_B)$. Now, we posit that the two gases A and B are different but have the same number of molecules N. Therefore: $\Delta S = 2Nk \log 2$, for $A \neq B$. And the increment ΔS is positive, as was to be expected.

Unfortunately, there is that spoil-sport qualification 'on the other hand'! The preceding equation becomes absurd when the gases A and B become identical. Logically, application of the above equation for the entropy of mixing would induce us to expect, even in the case of equal numbers of *identical* molecules, an increase of entropy by a quantity $2Nk \log 2$. Physical considerations as well as empirical evidence, however, show that the diffusion of a gas into itself is not associated with a change in any of its thermodynamic parameters – the entropy included. For gases of the same type, we thus have to write $\Delta S = 0$, if $A = B$. The Gibbs paradox then states that for different gases, however similar they may be, we get $\Delta S = 2k \log 2$, independently of any degree of dissimilarity. But for similar, that is, identical gases, $\Delta S = 0$.

Gibbs attempted to avoid the paradox, which stems from Boltzmann's entropy equation, by modifying this equation. Yet this 'tampering' with the original equation violates some of its crucial assumptions and hence destroys the internal logic of the original argument.

Let us attack the problem from an unambiguous angle. If one holds that the mixing entropy ΔS can assume the values $2Nk \log 2$ or zero only, this entails that ΔS remains finite and constant as long as there is any distinction between the gases of species A and species B. But ΔS drops *abruptly* to zero as soon as A and B become identical. But according to Boltzmann's theory, the equation for the entropy of mixing is not dependent upon the identity or difference of the species of gases. Should we therefore not arrive at the same increase of entropy, namely $2Nk \log 2$? Could it be that the entropy of a gas is plausibly contingent upon the 'history of the gas'? Was not the entropy always thought to be a function of the thermodynamic state alone?

Bridgman submitted an operational solution of the paradox [1]. He reasons as follows: when $A \to B$, the set of physically significant operations by which we distinguish A and B becomes gradually less performable. Yet once we have reached the limit $A = B$, the whole picture changes abruptly. In consequence, the protagonists of the operational solution of the Gibbs paradox regard the discontinuity of ΔS at $A = B$ as a primitive, elementary, and fundamental premiss. This solves for them the paradox. But in my opinion the whole operational argument is tantamount to resorting to a subterfuge.

The various attempts to resolve the Gibbs paradox have been flawed or vitiated for one reason or another. It was only the brilliant insight of von Neumann, later developed by Landé, that led to a satisfactory solution of the paradox [2]. Quantum mechanics teaches us that the atoms (particles) of any given kind are intrinsically *indistinguishable*. In contrast, classical mechanics demands, for the sake of consistency, that the particles have to be *distinguishable*. Using quantum mechanical considerations, we are in the position to dismiss the objectionable discontinuity and all the implications deduced from it. The paradox ceases to be physically insolvable when one accepts the existence of different quantum states A and B of the *same* kind of particle. To demonstrate the gist of von Neumann's powerful method: the value of the mixing entropy ΔS decreases continuously from $2Nk \log 2$ to zero, as a clearly defined quantity varies from zero to unity. Mathematically, one has to introduce a certain factorial in order to treat the indistinguishability of identical molecules (or atoms) in a formally *and* physically adequate manner. By thus adjusting the basic, the crucial assumptions of Boltzmann's and Gibbs' equations, he as well as Landé and M. J. Klein established convincingly the predicted continuous variation of ΔS with a precisely defined quantity which represents the degree of similarity of A and B.

The theoretical solution of the paradox, offered by von Neumann,

---

[1] P. W. Bridgman, *The Nature of Thermodynamics*, Harvard U.P., Cambridge, 1943, pp. 168–169.

[2] A. Landé, *From Dualism to Unity in Quantum Physics*, Cambridge U.P., 1960, pp. 24, 27, 38.

can hardly be buttressed by (macroscopic) facts. It made, however, an enormous impact on thermophysics, so that we have now a new comprehension of the whole area in which the paradox emerged. Still, there are some queries that baffle us. For instance, how can we explain that ΔS is not contingent upon the size of the molecular mass or any other permanent quantity? It seems that whenever we achieve greater sharpness of focus of a perplexing issue, different questions become urgent and need be answered. And thus it is not surprising at all that further and often almost unrelated inquiries are suggested from time to time by the solutions of our puzzles. Some theorists refuse to be overly impressed by positive results for reasons such as these.

Indeed, a countersuggestion against the proposed solution of the Gibbs paradox was made by R. Rosen who readily concedes that there is undoubtedly what he chooses to call a principle of indistinguishability in current physics, but he claims that we cannot tell when to apply it [1]. Consequently, there exists no genuine solution of the paradox! With Bridgman, Rosen is of the opinion that the entropy paradox amounts de facto to an operational problem that has to be dealt with correspondingly. He then formulates the paradox in a generalized way and argues that in certain circumstances, analogous to situations in physics, it simply cannot have any resolution at all. To cut the Gordian knot of the problem, he utilizes various set-theoretical concepts, equivalence relations, semi-groups, Kleene's notion of dictionaries D with unsolvable word problems, and so forth. The gist of his unorthodox procedure can readily be stated: the relation between physical and recursive processes may be close enough to allow for the conjecture that distinguishability in physics is not even in principle a solvable problem. Where the mathematical model fails, the physical analogue will hardly do better.

11. I should also like to mention *Turing's paradox* in quantum mechanics, which seems to be little known even among physicists [2].

---

[1] R. Rosen, 'The Gibbs' paradox and the distinguishability of physical systems', *Philosophy of Science*, **31**, No. 3, July 1964, pp. 232–236.

[2] I wish to thank Dr. Robin Gandy, University of Manchester, for having

Suppose a quantum-mechanical system occupies the eigenstate $|q\rangle$ at time $t = 0$, q being an eigenvalue of some observable Q. Let observations of Q be made subsequently at the instants $1/n, 2/n, \ldots, n/n$ throughout a unit interval of time.

The probability per unit time that the system will undergo a transition to neighbouring states $|q'\rangle$ is, according to perturbation theory, equal to a time-independent quantity, say $2C$. Naturally, C depends on the Hamiltonian and the density of the states $|q'\rangle$. The probability for a transition to have occurred at $t = 1/n$ will be $C(1/n)^2$; therefore the probability that the observed value will again be $|q\rangle$ is

$$P_1 = 1 - C/n^2.$$

This result is an approximate one and requires n to be sufficiently large.

It follows that at the end of unit time, Q will still have the value $|q\rangle$ with the probability

$$P_n = (1 - C/n^2)^n.$$

But, by the binomial theorem,

$$\lim_{n \to \infty} (1 - C/n^2)^n = 1.$$

In other words, the system will permanently remain in the state $|q\rangle$ provided Q is sufficiently often – say, *continuously* – observed! [In writing down the penultimate equation we have admittedly ignored transitions of the kind $|q\rangle \to |q'\rangle \to |q\rangle$, but these will only increase P_n and thus leave the ultimate result unchanged.]

In order to arrive at the foregoing paradox, one tacitly invokes Schrödinger's wave equation when giving the expression for P_1. But we know that the wave equation holds only for an undisturbed system, whereas in fact we disturb the system infinitely often by our observations. Herein may lie the resolution of Turing's paradox.

12.   As the last paradox I wish only to mention the famous and much discussed divergencies appearing in quantum field theory.

drawn my attention to this neat paradox; the presentation given here deviates a little from Turing's original formulation.

They are particularly shocking to the mathematician who has learned from Cantor that for any infinite number α, the sum of α and any finite number equals α itself, and that, *vice versa*, the subtraction of α from such a sum is not an operation with any definite result. But it is just such impossible sums and differences with which quantum physicists have worked most successfully, thereby scandalizing all mathematicians! The problem has been so often debated that I hesitate to add anything here. I only mentioned it because I could not very well omit it altogether from this 'budget'.

One must be singularly imperceptive not to notice the utter confusion, the total absence of any systematic appraisal in many of these attempts to cope with physical paradoxes. That there is no universal, rigorously formulated, theory, is only a demerit for those who suffer from the temptation to rigidify and overformalize at any price. We know that there *are* physical paradoxes and it seems to me that not all of them can be banished from physics. But is it really possible to subsume them under any one of the various types of paradoxes with which we are so much better acquainted and about which we talk with such effortless eloquence, and occasionally even with knowledge? Without forgetting that we do not yet understand rationally the main 'symptoms' that physical paradoxes have in common or even whether they have anything in common that is significant, we shall briefly visit the familiar terrain of logical, mathematical, and semantic paradoxes and also glance at some of the more recently discovered antinomies whose interpretation is still in *statu nascendi*.

Contrary to what one might expect, terminology and classification reveal rather a cavalier attitude to paradoxes in general. Although Ramsey's division of paradoxes into logical (mathematical) and semantic (epistemological) antinomies draws a demarcation line between certain important types or species of paradoxes, there still exist imprecisions and casual formulations. Let us first pass under review some of the well-known logical paradoxes.

Zeno's four paradoxes – dichotomy, Achilles, arrow, stadium – have been customarily, though perhaps wrongly, looked at as being logical antinomies. Russell's paradox and other antinomies in set theory which were conducive to the development of a rigorous axiomatic set theory, are instances of a different though somewhat related category. The Skolem paradox ordinarily qualifies for a logical paradox, no less than the paradoxical results discovered by Hausdorf, Banach and Tarski. We owe Shen three interesting set-theoretic paradoxes. Cantor's paradox about the greatest cardinal number and that of Burali–Forti were often treated as genuine mathematical antinomies. The paradox of the Greek lawyer and his pupil and its closely related Nile paradox, as well as the Möbius paradox of one-sided surfaces, are also sometimes regarded as logical antinomies!

One issue here is that we have to make up our minds whether or not we conceive of set theory as belonging to the realm of logic or that of mathematics; alternatively, whether we accept any fundamental distinction between logic and mathematics at all. Hao Wang avoids this terminological tortuosity by simply adopting with slight modifications Ramsey's proposal and refers to *logico-mathematical* antinomies [1].

I am not quite happy with Quine's contention that the contradictions in set theory which actuated researches like those by Russell, Zermelo, and so forth, are 'implicit in the inferential methods of uncritical common sense ...' [2]. However, I think that the canons of naive common-sense reasoning are indeed involved in the very heart of the semantic antinomies. Their paramount property is that they invoke common-sense notions like truth or designation. I do not pretend to know them all or even most of them. Hence, let me mention a few, such as the Epimenides (there are many versions of it), the paradoxes of Berry, Grelling, Jourdain, König and Richard. The amusing yet highly perplexing aporia, namely, the famous riddle of the barber (also known as the man of Alcalá) has been repeatedly shown, especially by Quine, not to be a genuine paradox, but merely a *reductio ad absurdum* proof

---

[1] Hao Wang, *A Survey of Mathematical Logic*, North-Holland, Amsterdam, 1963, pp. 384–388.

[2] W. V. O. Quine, *Mathematical Logic*, Harvard U. P., Cambridge, 1947, p. 166.

that such a barber cannot possibly exist [1]. Quine himself propounded a very neat and instructive semantic paradox and also demonstrated how to resolve it [2]. What do all these semantic paradoxes lead us to conclude? Obviously, that unsophisticated handling of references is a source of trouble!

There are thinkers who insist that the propositions controverted must be either right or wrong. This viewpoint may turn out to be imprudent in the cases of some of the classical antinomies. First of all, our classificatory schema does not hold in certain instances. Thus, Shen's paradoxes about provability are a borderline case where one cannot decide whether the antinomy pertains to the logico-mathematical or to the semantic-epistemological category. Besides, once we succeed in achieving strict formalization of some semantic paradoxes, they lead to unambiguous results and cease to be antinomies. A further example: Martin has shown that the Skolem paradox is not actually a paradox in the sense of being a formal contradiction, but merely in the somewhat vague sense of pointing at an unexpected and startling situation [3].

The spectrum of paradoxes seems to be inexhaustible. O'Connor has adduced some so-called pragmatic paradoxes ('I remember nothing at all', or 'I never speak English', etc.). They are not formally self-contradictory but cannot be conceived to be true under any circumstances. Hempel tried to demonstrate that both verifiability and falsifiability are affected by the 'asymmetry-paradox' as well as by the 'tacking-paradox'. Kant's 'space-paradox' can easily be resolved and was based upon his urging us to consider space as three-dimensional in an absolute, or rather, apodictic sense.

That the method of linguistic analysis can, on occasion, solve a certain type of logical paradox has been correctly emphasized by Popper, though I think that some of the pragmatic paradoxes rather than the truly logical paradoxes reveal the property of

---

[1] W. V. O. Quine, *From a Logical Point of View*, Harvard U. P., Cambridge, 1953, p. 133.

[2] Ibid., p. 139.

[3] R. M. Martin, *Truth and Denotation*, Routledge and Kegan Paul, London, 1958, p. 292.

reflexivity or self-reference. The decision depends, I suppose, upon one's formal definition – explicit and not contextual! – of 'self-reference' [1]. That some antinomies derive from symbolic fallacies and not from intrinsic logical contradiction has been established by Hao Wang when he examined several variants of the liar paradox [2].

Rousseau reportedly stated: 'A paradox is a truth that has come into the world a century too early.' Well, linguistic analysis appeared on the scene much earlier, but unfortunately bore a freakish child, namely, the paradox of analysis. Carnap has very precisely sharpened the concepts involved in it and shown how it can be resolved in a very simple manner [3].

At present, there is no unitary theory dealing satisfactorily with the antinomies or paradoxes in the respective domains. Russell's theory of types was developed as a method of evading 'paradox' or 'contradiction'. But, it has the embarrassing consequence that some of his inferences lead to counterintuitive results.

Russell says somewhere that a great many philosophical questions are, in fact, scientific questions with which science is not yet ready to deal. Physical paradoxes, far from depending on the existence of semantic paradoxes, stand clear of mathematical paradoxes altogether and seem to require one or perhaps many autonomous methods of treatment. We are still on the threshold of a clear understanding of the many facets physical paradoxes display so generously. So far we were merely able to deal with single problems and our solutions leave us still with further and deeper questions. When Russell attempted to eliminate paradoxes, because he regarded them as meaningless pseudo-statements, he certainly did not have paradoxes in theoretical physics in mind; yet Heisenberg and some philosophers tried to apply the idea to Heisenberg's uncertainty relations.

What was in the past a paradox might now be one no longer, but one or other irritating and perplexing question may newly

---

[1]   K. R. Popper, op. cit., p. 17.
[2]   Hao Wang, op. cit., p. 387.
[3]   R. Carnap, *Meaning and Necessity*, Chicago U. P., 1947, pp. 63–64.

arise, so that we cannot stay smug and self-righteous and enjoy our ephemeral victory.

In many cases, we are able to evade the paradoxes without solving them. Whether only a meta-theory can do the adequate and ultimate job, is a moot point. We employed throughout this paper terms like 'may', 'might', 'perhaps', and so on. It is arguable but far from convincing that modal methods might therefore help us. I personally do not see any decisive advantage in invoking modal logic in order to resolve paradoxes. Indeed, one could show that most of the arguments raised by Quine against the myth of logical advances due to modal concepts are also valid here, and that we might get more paradoxes if we use modal logic rather than less.

It seems as if there is a tendency to almost cultivate the growth of paradoxes. This trend may be tantamount to courting the absurd, the weird. During the last years, the literature has been flooded with a very torrent of new paradoxes, e.g. the paradox of the preface, of self-deception, of omnipotence, of unexpected examination, of prediction, in addition to further set-theoretic antinomies, biological paradoxes, and so forth. Perhaps the preoccupation with paradoxes is a sign of sophistication – perhaps it is an indication that one has reached the cognitive limits of a specific domain. Be it as it may, so far any attempt to arrive at a comprehensive theory of paradox, formal or informal, has failed.

How do the foregoing observations affect the main subject under review, the paradoxes in physics? Their significance will undoubtedly pale in the light of those numerous antinomies and puzzles that have been mentioned before. First of all, some of our twelve physical paradoxes can be so easily explained and eliminated that they need not bother us. In fact, in these cases the term 'paradox' proved to be no more than a misnomer – they are not authentic or genuine paradoxes at all. One might call them 'paralogisms', that is, simply errors in reasoning. However, the question may well be raised whether there is a clear demarcation between 'genuine' and 'non-genuine' paradoxes. Could it be that insolvability is the criterion of genuineness? And with regard to the demarcation between logical (or semantic) and physical paradoxes, will it contribute much to any clarification of the issue if we decide that reflexivity or self-reference is the crucial, distinguishing factor?

The linguistic aspect so relevant in many of the traditional logical and semantic paradoxes is hardly an important aspect when one examines the nature of paradoxes in physics. Now, most of these paradoxes occur in assertions which are embedded in some physical theory. But here we encounter a new possibility. If we regard any physical theory as an interpretation of some formalism, then the paradoxes appearing in a theory might be shown to be anchored within the foundation of a particular mathematical discipline. This could be of great interest, even if it would lead us to withdraw the claim that there are 'true' paradoxes in physics proper!

Well, I do not contend that any of the twelve paradoxes in physics cited in this paper could reasonably be reduced to any known classical mathematical antinomy. And this means, implicitly, that not even any system of axiomatic set theory – e.g. Zermelo's formal system ZF or Quine's system NF – could be applied to a solution of physical paradoxes. Russell's theory of types does not seem to help either. I once hoped that Zermelo's axioms of separation, of the power set, and of the sum set in the Fraenkel–Hao Wang formulation might be of some value to our problem, but so far it looks as if (*pace* Rosen) *no set-theoretic considerations have any bearing upon physical paradoxes*. The question whether or not we admit entities that are not sets becomes a fundamental one, and either alternative answer poses new difficulties, if not new paradoxes. Hao Wang's assistance in illuminating the above-mentioned axioms so vital for our issue was *via* set theory altogether. Moreover, all the defects of current set theory, i.e. in their axiomatic foundations, would affect any treatment of our paradoxes by means of some brand of set theory.

Furthermore, let us investigate the more realistic conjecture that physical theories tell us something about the world, that is, inform us about facts that are either true or false. In this case, some may appeal to one of the many semantic paradoxes and so attempt to treat at least one of our physical paradoxes within a known and tractable frame. Others may perhaps think in this connection of Grelling's paradox that introduces the distinction between autological and heterological words; it leads to the irritating result that 'heterological' is heterological if, and only if, it is not heterological! A word is autological if it refers to itself. Thus, 'polysyllabic' is polysyllabic, while 'Russian' is not Russian. Yet it seems that Ramsey's proposal to equate semantic with epistemological paradoxes is unsatisfactory, for Grelling's antinomy, in contrast to a paradox in physics, does not tell us anything about the physical universe. Physics ought to increase our knowledge about the external world – we want to *know* about motion, energy, particles, etc.

Physical paradoxes seem to escape any precise analysis in terms of our customary criteria and techniques in dealing with other paradoxes. There exists though a definite pattern among many of the paradoxes in physics: they appear within a theory as 'necessary' contradictions to a familiar, plausible argument or proposition. Now, either we dismiss the plausible argument as incorrect or we change (or extend) the given theory. True, statements of physics contain variables and constants and we can therefore express certain physical paradoxes in a formalized manner. However, what do we gain by such a procedure? No more than using the logical tilde to indicate a negation or contradiction! And yet, the presence of paradoxes in physics may warrant deeper efforts on our part to work towards an autonomous theory that would adequately account for their occurrence.

It is interesting to note that it was Bolzano who pondered over the existence of physical paradoxes. But he was unable to arrive at any significant conclusion – which was to be expected by reason of the fact that physics at this time had not yet attained a high level of sophistication. Before he became a Wittgensteinian, Schlick held that some questions are intrinsically incapable of being answered. Do paradoxes in physics belong to that category? I should like to argue that, although many philosophers of science and theoretical physicists have chased many subjects – paradoxes in physics were too seldom among them.

DISCUSSION

W. V. Quine: *Comment.*

The word 'paradox' is commonly used in an inclusive sense, for any plausible argument from plausible premisses to an implausible conclusion. Paradox in this broad sense can be a casual affair. A little scrutiny may show that a premiss was subtly false, or a step subtly fallacious, or that the conclusion was more plausible than we thought; and so the paradox may be resolved without violence to firm beliefs.

Some philosophers have used the word 'paradox' in a narrower sense, reserving it for cases that compel revision of deeply rooted principles. Such is the usage of those who say that Zeno's paradoxes, the barber paradox, the paradox of the condemned man, Skolem's paradox, and Gödel's incompleteness theorem are not genuine paradoxes. But there is already an established word for paradoxes in the narrow sense; viz., 'antinomy'. So the easier line is to accept the common inclusive use of 'paradox' and then distinguish the crisis-engendering species as antinomies.

Russell's paradox is for me a prime example of antinomy. For Yourgrau it is not, I gather; anyway he does not agree that it contravenes principles 'implicit in . . . common sense'. The question on which we differ is whether there being a class for every formulable membership condition is a principle implicit in common sense.

In any event, both the broad quality of paradox and the narrower quality of antinomy are temporal. What premisses and what steps of reasoning are persuasive though faulty, and what conclusions are implausible though true, will vary with the sophistication of the individual and the progress of science; and so, therefore, will paradox. Within paradox, again, the special quality of antinomy will in turn depend on whether what is challenged is a firm tenet of the individual at the time. Besides varying with time and person, moreover, the qualities of both paradox and antinomy are matters clearly of degree and not of kind.

If already within mathematics and semantics a certain vagueness thus attaches to the concepts of antinomy and paradox, we must expect these concepts to run vaguer still in physics. Consequences or purported consequences of existing physical theory are, I suppose, entitled to the name of paradox when they are surprising; and they are entitled to the name of antinomy when they are so surprising, and the attendant argument is so plausible, as to spark a major crisis in physical theory. It will be noted that two of the physical paradoxes in Yourgrau's impressive budget are called 'objections': there is an *Umkehreinwand* and a *Wiederkehreinwand*. They are felt simply as objections to the theory of the time. Surely there is no hope of a common recipe for the treatment of paradox in such a sense, in physics and elsewhere, beyond what there may be for the treatment of scientific perplexity generally.

Among the antinomies of set theory and semantics there is indeed a family resemblance, namely a certain air of self-application or circularity. It is shared also by some paradoxes which are not antinomies, notably Gödel's theorem, the barber paradox, and the paradox of the condemned man, and indeed it is present wherever there is a diagonal argument, with or without an air of paradox. It is not easily read into Skolem's paradox, and it bears none on Zeno. But it is so characteristic of paradoxes at their most vivid and of antinomies at their most virulent that perhaps self-application, rather than antinomy or paradox as such, is what wants closer scrutiny and deeper understanding.

For we encounter somewhat this same pattern of self-application also at significant points outside the bounds of logic, set theory, and semantics. A case in the philosophy of science is the paradox of Laplace's sage undertaking to falsify his predictions. Much the same problem takes a serious turn in economics, where a predicted state, e.g. a price in the stock market, is disturbed by the prediction of it. To cope with this predicament was a central motive of the theory of games. In physics we find an analogy in Heisenberg's indeterminacy principle, which turns on the disturbance of the observed object by the observation of it. If we ever find a unified solution of the antinomies of set theory and semantics, along more natural lines than are now known, these analogies tempt us to expect repercussions in other domains.

K. R. POPPER: *On so-called paradoxes in physics.*

1.   I wish to make a slightly critical remark on Wolfgang Yourgrau's paper, a criticism which, I expect, he will be very willing
to accept.

Yourgrau speaks at several places about physical paradoxes – in
a manner with which I completely agree – by stressing that his
examples may have little in common, and that the term 'paradox'
has no very clear meaning. Now my main criticism is that he
does *not always* speak in this manner: at times his words seem
to imply that there exists, or that there perhaps exists, a sense of
using the term 'paradox' which would apply to at least several
of his twelve examples and which might also have a fairly clear
and unambiguous meaning.

I doubt this; and I wish to strengthen those passages in Yourgrau's paper in which he hints that he too is sceptical, by pointing
out some stark ambiguities of the word 'paradox' in its application
to the so-called clock paradox.

2.   The so-called clock paradox is nothing more than a straightforward theorem of the special theory of relativity which happens
to clash with untutored common sense. It is no more paradoxical
than hundreds of assertions of physical theory – such that in a
dark room there may be rays of (invisible) light. The clock paradox
was first so-called by relativists themselves who liked to point to
what is for common sense a most unexpected and indeed shocking
consequence of their theory. Hence 'paradox' meant here at first
nothing more than 'unexpected, and for this reason worth pointing
out'. Then anti-relativists took up the name 'paradox'; but what
they meant was 'shocking and therefore obviously untrue – an
attempt by clever people to bluff and impress us'.

Ultimately it was used in a third sense by some anti-relativists;
that is, in the sense of 'a theorem which does follow from the theory
but which, at the same time, contradicts the principles of the very
theory from which it follows (more precisely, the principle of
relativity of motion), so that it establishes an antinomy or a contradiction within the theory, and thus refutes the theory'.

Thus *in this one single case of the clock paradox*, the word 'paradox' was used in at least three different meanings: (a) an unexpected and therefore interesting result; (b) a shocking attempt to bamboozle us; (c) an antinomy or contradiction which arises within the theory and thus refutes it.

Of course I agree with Yourgrau that the anti-relativists are just mistaken: the clock paradox is not a paradox in either sense (b) or (c). It does not refute relativity but shows that common sense always needs to reform itself. However, I find that Yourgrau uses the term 'paradox' more often in the senses (b) or (c) than in the sense (a) in which, for example, Einstein used it; and he seems to do so under the influence of the discovery of the so-called paradoxes of logic and of set theory.

But I doubt even more than Yourgrau that paradoxes such as those of set theory – Russell's paradox, say – exist in physics, or in physical theory. For the discovery of such a paradox would simply refute the theory in which it is discovered. The ensuing situation would be this: either the discovery of the paradoxes can be shown to be mistaken, in which case the whole argument collapses; or else the discovery is genuine, in which case the physical theory in question collapses; that is, it must be more or less severely modified.

3.   This was, in my opinion, the case with Loschmidt's and Zermelo's objections against Boltzmann's original theory. They discovered contradictions – and the theory had indeed to be modified. This point is not, in my opinion, sufficiently clearly brought out by Yourgrau.

But Yourgrau is far from alone here. It seems to me that a simple clear discussion of the situation is urgently needed, and that it has not yet been supplied, not even in the famous and beautiful monograph by Paul and Tatjana Ehrenfest.

4.   Let me put the original phenomenological problem in the crudest terms. If I open a bottle of air in an air-evacuated box, or if I puncture a blown up bicycle tyre, the air will escape. This may be called the fundamental effect of phenomenological gas

dynamics, just as the flow of heat from a hotter to a colder body is the fundamental effect of phenomenological thermodynamics. Both together constitute the main explicanda (or, in Lakatos's terminology, the 'naive conjectures') which the kinetic theory wants to explain, essentially by deducing them from molecular dynamics.

Now Loschmidt's and Zermelo's objections show, I think conclusively, that this cannot be done; you cannot deduce from a theory like molecular dynamics which is symmetric with respect to the two directions of time a theory like Boltzmann's original theory which is not. But Boltzmann's original theory and the two fundamental effects are emphatically irreversible.

This was the end of Boltzmann's first attempts. But he revised his *theory* and at the same time also his *problem*.

The revision of the *theory* was very obvious: the revised theory was indeed *completely symmetric with respect to past and future*. Accordingly, the two objections of Loschmidt and of Zermelo were completely met by the revision.

The revision of the *problem* was much less obvious, because the problem had not been put in the crude form of the naive conjecture in which I put it.

As a consequence we are faced with a degenerating problem situation in Lakatos' sense: the problem of explaining (or deducing) the two naive conjectures is replaced by the related problem of showing that a closed molecular system left to itself will almost certainly be for most of the time in a certain state of equilibrium (Maxwellian velocity distribution, etc.).

A close study of the relation between the original naive problem (the conjectures) and the new or degenerate problem would be enlightening.

W. Yourgrau: *Reply.*

I. Reply to Quine.

Pater peccavi! Quine is quite right in making a systematic distinction between paradoxes and antinomies. Although one can always argue about terminology and nomenclature, it seems to me that his classification is not an arbitrary one. He provides good reasons for it, and hence I do not see any purpose in taking issue with him.

However, I still cannot accept his flirtation with the idea that paradoxes and antinomies contravene common sense. Paradoxes in general and antinomies in particular are *logical* labels and apply to 'formal' categories. In the domain of common sense, our reasoning is 'informal'. I realize, of course, that any dogmatic separation of the realms of (informal) common sense and (formal) logic is open to controversy. But once we accept this division, violations of common sense too must be of an informal nature. In consequence, neither paradoxes nor antinomies obtain in the field of common sense – merely perplexities, surprises, quandaries, difficulties, troublesome situations.

Further, my remarks about Russell's paradox were plain and unambiguous, at least so I hoped. I therefore fail to understand how my friend Quine could possibly gather that I do not consider this paradox 'a prime example of antinomy'. I only wished to register my protest against his contention that it does violate principles inherent in common sense. Can Quine seriously maintain that it is common sense to ask oneself whether or not a class can be a member of itself?

The fact that we can translate $(\exists x) \cdot [(x \in x) \equiv \sim (x \in x)]$ into English does in no way involve common sense. Terms such as 'class', 'membership', 'element', and so forth, are *logical* designations. If Quine concurs with this interpretation of set-theoretic terms, then his objections to my standpoint can be outright refuted. In this connection, one is reminded of Philipp Frank's claim – a view to which Einstein also subscribed at one time – that physical theory is no more than refined, sophisticated common sense. I have to register a protest against all these attempts to eliminate metaphysical snares by regarding common sense as the primal source in logic and scientific theory. On a metaphorical level such an approach may be plausible, yet on the argumentative plane it is impermissible. In other words, the front of common sense has to be narrowed rather than widened in order to be meaningfully defended.

Quine is correct in asserting that 'the qualities of both paradox and antinomy are matters clearly of degree and not of kind'. I must however confess my repugnance to his contention that these qualities vary with time and person. In a trivial sense all knowledge is a function of at least those two variables. But would he deny that it is the singular aim of any logical inquiry to arrive at findings that are free from temporal and personalized 'impurities'? Depersonalized results may not satisfy the student of history – they are definitely indispensable in logical studies.

Indeed, if the paradoxes and antinomies in logic, mathematics, semantics, and so forth, cannot be subsumed under a single characteristic law or treated in a uniform manner, then paradoxes in physics will *a fortiori* display vagueness and heterogeneity. It should none the less be stressed that difficulties or perplexities encountered in physical theory are of different nature than those met in common sense experience and that objections to certain assertions in physics are dubbed 'paradoxes'! I shall have occasion to refer to the reversal (Loschmidt) and recurrence (Zermelo) paradoxes mentioned by Quine when I turn to Popper's comments.

Let me refrain from the deplorable practice of trying to score debating points while the issue under discussion is still in an incipient stage. Besides, with most of Quine's remarks I find myself in agreement; e.g. with the appraisal of the role of self-application or circularity. My only reservation is that he sometimes casts his net much wider than he should, and as a result pulls in a richer catch than he can land. To wit, the concepts of paradox, antinomy, or self-application do not apply to Heisenberg's uncertainty relations. A cautious physical interpretation of the indeterminacy principle shows that the perplexing, the unexpected is a trait pertaining to nature, or rather, to certain aspects of physical theory. In a very loose sense, one might call this state of affairs 'paradoxical'. But if this term is so emptied of even a measure of precise content, I cannot see why we should care to retain it at all.

In the last sentence of his reply, Quine adopts a somewhat prophetic stance; I find his guarded optimism not only interesting but also stimulating. But, as I pointed out in my paper, it is doubtful whether set-theoretic progress will ever aid us much in our understanding of physical paradoxes. Quine, the logician, graciously admits that we have no unified theory covering all varieties of paradoxes and antinomies. Is it possible that logic will never be able to 'map' them? . . .

II.   Reply to Popper.

Popper is quite right when he criticizes me for having at times drifted into the convention of using the term 'paradox' in a misleading manner. It appears that its validity or applicability was feasibly assumed before I bid adieu to it. And for the sin of having given a wrong impression concerning the main thesis of my paper, I feel contrition – *mea culpa, mea maxima culpa*. May I be permitted, after my confession of guilt, to advance some extenuating circumstances of reasons which will explain why I seemingly took the wrong path?

In common (academic) parlance one talks of physical paradoxes. Rather than minting a novel terminology of my own, I resorted to *usance* – as the commercial traveler in Vienna and Berlin put it. Only after having tabulated some of the fundamental conundrums concerning these so-called paradoxes did I attempt to show how intrinsically implausible the view is that the term 'paradox' has any precise meaning. In other words: I did not wish to commit myself from the outset of my investigation to the conclusion that there are no genuine physical paradoxes or that they cannot even conceivably exist! Besides, one cannot simply ignore the fact that the label 'paradox' is appended to some vexing difficulties or seeming incompatibilities occurring in physics. I hope that Karl Popper, my brother-in-scepticism vis-à-vis physical antinomies, does not accuse me of glamorizing terminological confusion and employing deceptive interpretation. Of course, one could have entitled the paper: 'On not-appreciating the misnomer "paradox" when dealing with perplexities in physical theory'. I chose to recount blatant violations of 'untutored common sense' – if not in full, then at least in some salient cases – and used the prevalent nomenclature. And thus I deliberately invited Popper's mild opprobrium for having enumerated wrongly labeled juxtapositions *before* demonstrating the sequiturs and non sequiturs of the twelve instances selected in my budget of physical 'paradoxes'.

Since my discussion of the clock paradox in relativity theory was rather sketchy, I welcome Popper's incisive comments with which I agree without reservation. In fact, he has improved on the somewhat aphoristic nature of my exposition by effectively cutting off all possibility of retreat to a pre-relativistic (or non relativistic) position.

Popper's chief concern in his reply appears to be that I did not do justice to Loschmidt's and Zermelo's objections to Boltzmann's original formulation of his H-theorem. Indeed, the discussion under item $\neq$ 9 is a little shorter than the analysis of the Gibbs entropy paradox under item $\neq$ 10, because I did not elaborate on the essential, cogent implications from these celebrated 'paradoxes'. My motive for this omission was that recently several workers in this field have dealt with them quite systematically [1].

Popper's remarks do not warrant a pedantic rejoinder – he is certainly aware of the deficiencies in the original formulation of the H-theorem. But there is always the risk that by trying to be a *purist* in the interpretation of a physical theory, one can easily succumb to 'galactic' generalizations. And although both Popper and I are cognizant of this danger, I should perhaps add a few comments.

In the perfunctory discussion of Boltzmann's H-theorem, I intended to show that it is possible to remove *somehow* the incompatibilities between the original 'classical' version of the theorem and Newtonian mechanics. Yet whenever we treat gaseous systems, we have to adduce a number of conjectures, often slippery *ad hoc* hypotheses, and thus the conceptual neatness of the theorem becomes impaired. I can only repeat what I stated in my paper

---

[1] To mention only a few: A. Münster, 'Prinzipien der statistischen Mechanik' in *Handbuch der Physik*, III/2, Springer Verlag, Berlin–Göttingen–Heidelberg, 1959; K. Huang, *Statistical Mechanics*, John Wiley and Sons, New York, 1963; W. Yourgrau, et al., *Treatise on Irreversible and Statistical Thermophysics*, The Macmillan Company, New York, 1966.

(and Münster definitely concurs with this claim): There does not exist any rigorous derivation of the H-theorem! Even its quantum mechanical interpretation does not eliminate some essential criticisms. It can only be demonstrated by means of coercive arguments that the theorem is valid for the mean, but not *a priori* for each individual case. None the less, its significance does not pale, not even in the light of the most recent investigations.

The most dyed-in-the-wool physicist will acknowledge that Popper's suggestion at the end of his reply is a basically sound one. And does it matter if the results of the proposed study may turn out to be devastating in that there is no uniform, consistent, elegant theory which will account comprehensively for the naive *and* the degenerate problems (situations, conjectures)?

FORMAL LOGIC AND THE DEVELOPMENT OF KNOWLEDGE

ROMAN SUSZKO

University of Warsaw

Formal logic is considered here not as a logical calculus but as the theory of logical properties and relations like for example the relation of consequence and the property of inconsistency. Formal logic in this sense is a metatheory and it is identical with the syntax and semantics of formalized languages. Semantics is meant here as the theory of models built by A. Tarski and other mathematicians (A. Mostowski, J. Łoś, L. Henkin, J. G. Kemeny). It is important to point out that formal logic does not consider any pragmatical questions concerning language and thinking. Pragmatics is meant here in the sense of Charles Morris [1].

A theory of knowledge and of its development built within formal logic is an abstraction. Indeed, here I pass over many important features of human knowledge and of its real change and development.

The problem is: can formal logic tell us something about the development of knowledge? I think it can. I think, to use a suggestive terminology, that we can build something like a *diachronic* formal logic as opposed to the *synchronic* formal logic of today [2]. It must be added that diachronic logic can only be simply an application of notions, theorems and methods used in synchronic logic to the problem of change in human knowledge. I will use

---

[1] '. . . it is a sufficiently accurate characterisation of pragmatics to say that it deals with the biotic aspects of semiosis, that is, with all the psychological, biological, and sociological phenomena which occur in the functioning of signs.' C. W. Morris, 'Foundations of the theory of signs', *International Encyclopedia of Unified Science*, i, No. 2, Chicago, 1938, p. 30.

[2] Compare the distinction between synchronic and diachronic linguistics made by Ferdinand de Saussure, *Cours de linguistique générale*, Lausanne, 1916.

here, for example, the notion of set-theoretical limit, the notion of submodel, and the operation of relativizing of bound variables.

The basic ideas of diachronic formal logic were published by me in Polish eight years ago [1]. At that time I explicitly used the notions mentioned above.

There is a philosophical background behind diachronic logic, but it is a long story and I will not say much about it. It will be enough to mention the *Evolutionstendenzen der Begriffsapparaturen* considered by my late master Kazimierz Ajdukiewicz in his paper on so-called radical conventionalism [2]. On the other side diachronic logic has some distinct connexions with general ideas of dialectical materialism.

1. When considering in formal logic the phenomenon of knowledge we take into account the ordered pairs (S, M) called *epistemological oppositions* or, shortly, E-oppositions. The first member S is called here *the subject* or the mind and the second member M is called *the object* or the world for the mind in the given epistemological opposition. Both members are intricate structures which will be described below. The main component of the subject is a formalized language L and the object M correlated with the subject is a model of L.

I consider here only so-called standard formalized languages and their classical (i.e. two-valued) models which are known e.g. from Tarski's book *Undecidable Theories* (Amsterdam, 1953).

Strictly speaking every model of a language is a function of a special kind. It assigns to the variables a non-empty universe of discourse U and to every (non-logical) constant C a suitable denotation $d(C)$ which is a set-theoretical entity (an individual, a set, a relation or a function) in a certain sense over U.

According to another terminology, a model is just the set-theoretical structure $(U; d(C_1), d(C_2), \ldots)$ which is composed of the universe U and of all denotations $d(C_k)$ assigned to the constants

---

[1] 'Logika formalna a niektóre zagadnienia teorii poznania', *Myśl Filozoficzna* 2/28 (27–56), 3/29 (34–67), Warszawa, 1957.

[2] 'Das Weltbild and die Begriffsapparatur', *Erkenntnis* **4** (1934), pp. 259–287.

by the model in the former sense. I use here the second terminology. The models in the first sense may be called *modelling-functions*.

I assume it as known that given a modelling-function or, equivalently, a model for a language one can define the notions of satisfaction, of denotation, and of truth and falsity.

The subject, or language, is supplied with a certain relation of consequence and with the corresponding set of tautologies. We know that the theory of models allows us to define in a given language L a relation of consequence Cn which according to Gödel's completeness theorem is identical with the consequence-relation generated in L by the well-known classical logical rules of inference. We write $Cn(X)$ for the set of all sentences which follow from the set X of sentences. The set $Cn(\emptyset)$ where $\emptyset$ is the empty set, is just the set of tautologies i.e. theorems of the classical logical calculus.

2. The modelling-function and the secondary semantical relations (satisfaction, denotation, truth, falsity and so on) constitute the epistemological link between the subject and the object as seen in formal logic. One may say that in an E-opposition the subject is speaking or thinking about the object and its components, through semantical relations between subject and object. For instance, the subject is making assertions about the object. The set T of asserted sentences, which may be called *theorems*, is a component of the subject.

We may assume that the set T is quasi-finite. This means that it is composed of a finite number of sentences and of a finite number of schemes of sentences. A more important assumption concerning the set T is as follows: T is a consistent and incomplete set of sentences, i.e. $Cn(T) \neq L$ and for some sentence α neither α nor its negation $\sim \alpha$ belongs to $Cn(T)$. Consequently, the sets T and $Cn(T)$ do not equal the set $Ver(M)$ of all sentences which are true with respect to the object M. Note that we do not assume that $T \subset Ver(M)$: we allow the subject to make mistakes.

Now, we have to take into account in some way the distinction between *analytic* and *synthetic*. One may say that the subject is supplied with certain *principles of thinking* which are the source of analytic theorems. The logical part of the principles of thinking is comprised just by the consequence relation Cn. In this way the set T of asserted theorems may contain some logical truths i.e. tautologies, which may be obtained by pure logical reasoning. The non-logical principles of thinking may be represented by a certain set A of assertions. The sentences in A may be called *axioms*. We assume that the set A contains no tautology. It may also be assumed that the set A is quasi-finite.

Later, I will make a certain essential assumption concerning the set A. It follows from that assumption that A is a subset of T. Consequently, the set A, like the set T, is a consistent and incomplete set of sentences. It also follows from that assumption that every sentence in A is true, that is $A \subset Ver(M)$ or equivalently $Cn(A) \subset Ver(M)$; and the sentences in A behave as the extralogical principles of thinking. Consequently, the set $Cn(A)$ may be identified with the set of analytic sentences in the given E-opposition. The set $Cn(A)$ includes, of course, all tautologies.

The E-oppositions appear now as quadruples of the following form: $((L, A, T), M)$ [1]. I would remind you that structures similar to some extent to our quadruples were called *semantical systems* by Carnap. It is easy to see that given an E-opposition as above, the expressions of the language L have certain intensions and extensions in Carnap's sense [2]. Thus we can develop the theory of intension starting with the pair $(L, Cn(A))$. On the other hand the corresponding theory of extension must take into account the object M or at least the complete set $Ver(M)$ of all true sentences. The extensions may be identified with sets and relations which are definable with respect to L and M [3].

---

[1] I omit the consequence-relation Cn and further secondary components of the subject.

[2] R. Carnap, *Meaning and Necessity*, Chicago, 1958 (Enlarged Edition, Second Impression). For a simplified and generalized version of Carnap's theory see my 'An essay in the formal theory of intension and extension', *Studia Logica* **20** (1967), pp. 7–34.

[3] One may enlarge the model M by adjoining to it all extensions in the above sense (generalized denotations). The result of this enlargement might be called the semantical closure of the model M. It seems more natural to identify the object with the semantical closure of some model of the corresponding language in the subject.

3. The remarks made above concerning the E-oppositions belong to synchronic formal logic. To proceed further we need some diachronic ideas. We consider in diachronic formal logic the transformations of E-oppositions. The transformation of the E-opposition E into the E-opposition E^* will be represented in symbols as follows: E/E^*, or in a more detailed form

$$((L, A, T), M)/((L^*, A^*, T^*), M^*).$$

We want to make precise which transformations of E-oppositions may be called steps in the development of knowledge. The development of knowledge is conceived here as *a process of knowing more about more*. This process may proceed in many ways. I intend to discuss here only some general features which may be found in the development of knowledge, and illustrated by elementary transformations of E-oppositions.

4. Let us consider the simplest case in which the object does not change: $M = M^*$. Consequently, the language does not change either: $L = L^*$. So we have to consider the following transformation: $((L, A, T), M)/((L, A^*, T^*), M)$. Transformations of this kind are characteristic for *the evolutionary process of inquiring into the given object*.

Let us distinguish the subcase when the axioms do not change: $A = A^*$. There are many ways in which the set T may be transformed into a new set T^*. These transformations are studied in the methodology of particular sciences and I will not mention them. We are interested here in general and formal properties of transformations of assertions. Unfortunately, I cannot find any general formal feature of the transformation T/T^* which would be characteristic for the development of knowledge. Notice that the subject may correct old errors and commit new ones.

The problem is not quite hopeless, however. We need only consider a possible infinite sequence of transformations:

$$T = T_0, T_0/T_1, T_1/T_2, ..., T_n/T_{n+1}, ...$$

where $T_n \neq T_{n+1}$. This is an idealisation, of course. But now we can formulate an assumption which says that the subject is searching for the truth. Namely, we assume that every possible infinite sequence of transformations as above is a limiting process and its set-theoretical limit is just the set of all true sentences: $\lim_{n\to\infty} T_n = Ver(M)$. This means that (1) every false sentence belongs at most to finitely many sets T_n, and (2) every true sentence belongs to almost all sets T_n (with the exception of finitely many of them) [1].

It is easy to realize that we cannot select any convergent sequence of transformations as above and command the subject to behave in this prescribed way. On the contrary, we must provide the subject with certain sets of possibilities for its epistemological behaviour. So we state that the subject is supplied with a nonempty family Φ of infinite sequences of possible sets of assertions: $\Phi = \{T_n^\lambda\}$. The sets T_n^λ are consistent and incomplete and fulfil the condition: $T_n^\lambda \neq T_{n+1}^\lambda$. The family Φ has the structure of an infinite tree which may be represented by the following diagram.

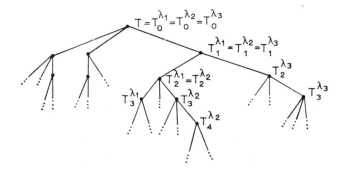

We assume that every sequence in Φ i.e. every branch of the tree as above starts with the set T of actual asserted theorems and converges to the set $Ver(M)$.

The E-oppositions have now the form $((L, A, T, \Phi), M)$ and the

<hr />

[1]   Every error will be corrected for ever and every truth will be grasped for ever. In a more precise formulation: (1) for any finite set X of false sentences there exists a number p such that for every n greater than p the sets X and T_n are mutually exclusive and (2) for any finite set Y of true sentences there exists a number q such that for every n greater than q the set Y is included in the set T_n.

transformations which we consider now

$$((L, A, T, \Phi), M)/((L, A, T^*, \Phi^*), M)$$

consist simply in that $T^* = T_1^\lambda$ for some λ and Φ^* equals the subtree which begins with T_1^λ. This process may run ahead *ad infinitum* And we can say no more about it.

Now we can formulate the condition mentioned above concerning the set A of axioms. Namely, we assume the following inclusions:

$$A \subset \hat{\Phi} \subset Cn(A),$$

where $\hat{\Phi}$ is the common part of sets in Φ i.e. the set-theoretical intersection of all sets $T_n{}^\lambda$. This condition characterizes the sentences in A as certain principles of thinking. Our inclusions mean that the sentences in A will be asserted in every possible process as above and that no sentence which does not follow from the axioms can be actually asserted for ever in any process as above.

The last inclusions and the condition of convergency imply that every axiom is true $A \subset Ver(M)$. Consequently, $Cn(A) \subset Ver(M)$, i.e. every analytic sentence is true. It follows that the errors, i.e. the false asserted sentences, may be found only within the difference $T - Cn(A)$.

The evolutionary process of inquiring into the given object (M and L being constant) comprises also the case when the axioms change: $A \neq A^*$. The set of axioms may change in the development of knowledge. But the axioms may change in a special way only. They cannot be refuted [1] in any process in which the object does not change. An axiom may cease to be an axiom and it may even not be asserted at next stage. However, it must surely be capable of being asserted. Hence, we assume that the axioms may change (A/A^*) in a way such that the following inclusion holds: $A \subset Cn(A^*)$ or equivalently $Cn(A) \subset Cn(A^*)$. This means that analyticity is a persistent property.

It may happen that $Cn(A) = Cn(A^*)$ i.e. the sets A and A^* are equivalent. In this case we have a *systematisation of axioms*.

---

[1] Refutation of a sentence means assertion of its negation.

If the sets A and A^* are not equivalent $[Cn(A) \neq Cn(A^*)$ and $Cn(A) \subset Cn(A^*)]$ then we have a *strengthening of axioms*. It may happen for example that certain true sentence in $T - Cn(A)$, which is asserted but not analytic, changes its epistemological character and becomes an axiom. The transformations of this kind have been pointed out by conventionalists and especially by Ajdukiewicz, with his radical conventionalism. There may be also a combination of two steps: a sentence which is not asserted will be asserted in the next stage and then it will be converted into an axiom.

5. The evolutionary process of inquiring into the given object corresponds to a stage of normal science (in the terminology of T. S. Kuhn's book *The Structure of Scientific Revolutions*, Chicago, 1962). It is important to note that the formal description of the development of knowledge recognizes not only the evolutionary processes mentioned above but also certain *revolutionary* steps.

In the evolutionary process (M and L being constant) we have observed the convergence of sets of assertions and the persistence of analytic sentences, i.e. the retention of axioms. On the other hand, in the revolutionary process there is no convergence, and the potential retention of axioms (the persistence of analytic sentences) holds in important cases only in a limited way.

We have now to consider the transformations of E-oppositions in which the object changes: $M \neq M^*$. It is clear that there is only one reasonable general assumption which can be made concerning the change of the object within the development of knowledge. It is the assumption that the former object M is *a submodel* of the later object M^*. We say also that the model M^* is *an extension* of the model M and we write: $M \subseteq M^*$.

The notion just introduced is a precise one but it is somewhat complicated and I will give here only a short informal description of it. If $M \subseteq M^*$ then the model M^* is in some sense composed of two parts: $M^* = M_1 \oplus M_2$. The first part M_1 corresponds with respect to its structure to the former model M but is in a sense greater than it. For instance, the universe U^* of the model M^* is always an overset in comparison with the universe U of the model M: $U \subset U^*$, the equality being allowed. The second part

M_2 of the new model M^* contains new sets and relations which do not correspond to any expression in the old language L. It follows that if the second part of the new model is not empty then the new language L^* is greater than the old one.

So, from the assumption that the old object M is a submodel of the new object M^* it follows that the old language is a sublanguage of the new one: $L \subseteq L^*$.

Every transformation of an E-opposition, or development of knowledge, in which the object changes has the following form [1]:

$$((L, A, T), M)/((L^*, A^*, T^*), M^*),$$

where $M \subseteq M^*$ and $L \subseteq L^*$.

One may study several relations which hold between two E-oppositions transformed in this way. We may consider for example the sets $Ver(M)$ and $Ver(M^*)$ of true sentences. It must be noted here that it may happen that a sentence of L true in M is false in M^* or conversely. There are many other relations concerning for instance satisfaction, definability and so on, which are known in the semantics of submodels. But I will not go into details.

Truth and falsity are not the most important points here because the set of true sentences is not a component of the subject. We are interested more in the sets of assertions and of axioms. We ask what general formal conditions concerning these sets are satisfied in one-step-move-ahead in the development of knowledge in which the object changes?

When extending the object truth may be converted into falsity as remarked above. But the subject is searching for the truth. Therefore the subject will change its assertions. Unfortunately again, it is impossible to find any general formal property of this change. But I do think that the subject retains the axioms in a certain limited way at least. The assumption that the old object is a submodel of the new one allows us to formulate this supposition in a precise way.

---

[1] In the description of the subject I omit here the trees of sequences of possible sets of assertions.

6. One may distinguish several special ways in which a model M is a submodel of a model M^*. I mention here only two general cases.

In the first case the universe does not change: $U = U^*$. It follows that the denotations of constants of the old language L do not change too. Therefore the first part M_1 of the new object is identical with the old object. Consequently, the second part M_2 is not empty and the new language L^* contains new constants.

In this case, the sentences of the old language L do not change their truth-value. The old axioms were true in the former object and they are also true in the later object: $A \subset Ver(M)$ and $A \subset Ver(M^*)$. Therefore we may assume that $A \subset Cn(A^*)$ or equivalently $Cn(A) \subset Cn(A^*)$. This is *the principle of potential retention of axioms* i.e. of persistence of analytic sentences. This is the condition which we may impose on the sets of axioms in the case when the universe does not change. It is, of course, the same condition which we have imposed on the evolutionary process in which the object does not change at all.

The axioms and analytic sentences behave here ($U = U^*$, $L \in L^*$, $L \neq L^*$) as in the evolutionary transformations. However, the subject is catching now certain new properties and relations in the given constant universe and new notions are emerging in the subject. This may be seen as *a weak revolution* in the subject.

The second case which we consider here has a strong revolutionary character. The universe is growing now: $U \subset U^*$ but $U \neq U^*$. I suppose that among the new constants of the new language L^* there is a constant φ, a monadic predicate which denotes (according to the new modelling-function) the old universe: $d(\varphi) = U$. Subsequently, we take into account the operation of relativization of bound variables to the predicate φ. It consists in the replacement of unlimited quantifiers $\bigwedge\limits_{x}$, $\bigvee\limits_{x}$ (for all x, for some x) by corresponding quantifiers limited to the predicate φ:

$$\bigwedge\limits_{x} [\text{if } \varphi(x) \text{ then} \ldots] \qquad \bigvee\limits_{x} [\varphi(x) \text{ and} \ldots].$$

The operation of relativization of bound variables allows us to formulate the principle of limited potential retention of axioms.

If α is a sentence of the former language L true in the former object M then (as may be proved) the sentence α_φ which is the result of relativization of bound variables in α is true in the later object M^*. One may perform this operation on the whole set A of former axioms. They have been true in M i.e. $A \subset Ver(M)$ and the sentences in the relativized set A_φ are true in M^* i.e. $A_\varphi \subset Ver(M^*)$. On the other hand the later axioms are also true in the later object M^*: $A^* \subset Ver(M^*)$ or equivalently $Cn(A^*) \subset \subset Ver(M^*)$.

Now we may assume that $A_\varphi \subset Cn(A^*)$. This is the principle of limited potential retention of axioms which we impose on the transformations of E-oppositions in which the object changes in such a way that the universe is growing. This is a condition concerning the set A of new axioms. It means that the subject assumes only such new axioms as allow him to prove the old axioms when they are restricted to the old universe of discourse [1].

The revolutionary character of the step just considered consists in the following. As observed above, some sentences change their truth-value. Therefore, the subject which is searching for the truth rejects some of its assertions, including some axioms. The set of axioms is being completely rebuilt and this is *a strong revolution* in the subject.

7. I have tried to present certain basic ideas of diachronic logic. The topic is somewhat technical and therefore I must omit some important points. To be brief I did not give any illustrative examples [2]. Instead I would like to conclude with some general remarks.

We have built a formal framework for certain abstract structures and some relations between them. This formal framework may be

---

[1] There may be further conditions satisfied by the set A^* of new axioms. For example, it may be assumed that the sentences

$$\bigvee_x \varphi(x), \qquad \bigvee_x \text{not } \varphi(x),$$

are among the new axioms.

[2] There is in preparation an extensive paper about diachronic logic, including its philosophical background and certain applications.

studied in itself without any epistemological interpretation. Indeed, the mathematical business connected with formal logic is very important. However, the interesting and important thing which I would like to point out here is just the epistemological interpretation of the formal framework.

To apply contemporary formal logic to classical philosophical problems has been the quite conscious leading idea of Ajdukiewicz. My point of view is somewhat simpler. I think that formal logic, i.e. the syntax and semantics of formalized languages, is simply an abstract and formal and, of course, narrow theory of the epistemological properties of the human subject and of its relations to reality. In particular, the model-theoretic notion of truth is in my opinion just the classical philosophical notion of truth as agreement between thought and reality.

Proceeding in this way, one may interpret Gödel's two non-derivability theorems (together with his completeness theorem), and Tarski's theorem concerning the non-definability of the notion of truth, as certain features of the subject. We could present them in our framework if we supplied the subject with some sort of *self-consciousness*. Namely, we allow the subject to speak or think about itself through suitable Gödel numbering, or through an elementary syntax built into it. The subject can contain some partial semantics of itself (compare Montague's semantically closed theories). But according to theorems mentioned above, the subject cannot state in full generality the fact that it is speaking about the object.

If we pass now to diachronic logic we may ask what the subject supplied with semantical notions concerning itself can say about its earlier and future stages. Problems like this seem to be interesting and the solution of them may give some insight into how we see the past and the future of our knowledge.

Finally I must say something concerning applications of the epistemological scheme presented here. I am a little sceptical at this point. I think that diachronic logic can give only some general information concerning the development of human knowledge. This is a simple consequence of the very nature of formal logic. Formal logic, synchronic or diachronic, is an abstract theory which does not consider non-formal or pragmatical aspects of human knowledge. We may try to apply the formal scheme of diachronic logic to the development of mathematics or of natural science. But the results will be, I think, only general and approximate.

But I am not unhappy about this. It will be enough to have a clear formulation of what the development of knowledge is and to recognize certain general formal features of the process.

W. V. QUINE: *Definability in enlarged universes.*

Dr. Suszko has noticed two respects in which the model may be enlarged: its universe of discourse U may be enlarged to U^*, and its primitive sets and relations may be supplemented with a new lot M_2. This latter enlargement depends, as he says, upon an enlargement of the language L to L^*; new primitive predicates are added. The former enlargement, U to U^*, requires no enlargement of language. Now I want to stress a point that does not stand forth in Suszko's account, though he is probably aware of it. It is that the mere enlargement of U to U^*, involving no enlargement of L, can cause subsets of the original U to be definable which were not definable before. Thus let N be the set of all natural numbers, let K be a set of other things, and let the elements of U comprise all the elements and some of the subsets of $N \cup K$. Suppose that $N \in U^*$ but that every element of U that has N as subset has K as subset. Then the open sentence:

$$(y)(0 \in y \cdot (z)(z \in y \cdot \supset \cdot z+1 \in y) \cdot \supset \cdot x \in y)$$

of L determines N when the universe is interpreted as U^*, but determines at best $N \cup K$ when the universe is U. N can be undefinable in L as long as the universe is U.

J. GIEDYMIN: *Revolutionary changes, non-translatability, and crucial experiments.*

Professor R. Suszko compares (p. 217) evolutionary growth of science discussed in the first part of his essay with what Thomas Kuhn calls 'normal science'. He claims in the second part of his essay that certain revolutionary changes can also be studied with the help of his formalism. But it seems to me that the 'revolutionary changes' which Suszko analyses are by no means revolutionary in Kuhn's sense, and that on the contrary they could all occur within Kuhn's 'normal science'.

Suszko defines as revolutionary those transformations of the system $((L, A, T)M)$ in which the object of study, or model M, changes so that $M \neq M^*$. But he immediately adds that 'there is only one reasonable general assumption which can be made concerning the change of the object within the development of knowledge. It is the assumption that the former object M is a *submodel* of the later object M^*' (p. 217). From this assumption it follows that the original language L is a sub-language of the new language L^*, so that "Every transformation ... in which the object changes has the following form: $((L, A, T)M)/((L^*, A^*, T^*)M^*)$ where $M \subseteq M^*$ and $L \subseteq L^*$" (p. 218). Suszko distinguishes two cases of such transformations: (1) 'weak revolution', where the universe of the model remains unchanged, i.e. $U = U^*$, so that $A \subset Ver(M)$ and $A \subset Ver(M^*)$, therefore $A \subset Cn(A^*)$; and (2) 'strong revolution', where the universe of the model 'expands', i.e. $U \subset U^*$ but $U \neq U^*$, so that $A_\varphi \subset Ver(M^*)$, where A_φ is the set of statements which result when we relativize the bound variables of the original axioms A to a predicate φ of L^* denoting the original universe U.

Now it seems to me that changes which Kuhn would regard as revolutionary, such as the transition from Ptolemaic to Copernican astronomy, or from Newtonian corpuscular to the wave theory of light, are neither 'weak' nor 'strong' revolutions in Suszko's sense, since they do not satisfy the general requirements that $M \subseteq M^*$ and $L \subseteq L^*$.

Moreover, Kuhn would presumably reject Suszko's 'principle of limited (potential) retention of axioms', based on the operation of relativizing bound variables to a predicate φ of L^* which denotes the original universe U of the original model M. Some philosophers of science (e.g. Philipp Frank) have used similar methods to show classical mechanics to be a special case of relativistic mechanics. And Kuhn has criticised this [1] as a neo-positivistic device designed to render rejected theories 'special cases' of current ones, and thus to create the illusion that the growth of science is cumulative, and

---

[1] See his *The Structure of Scientific Revolutions*, 1962, pp. 97–8.

to conceal the truly revolutionary disruptions (involving discontinuity of language) in its history.

Thus Suszko tames scientific revolutions by imposing upon them
the assumptions $M \subseteq M^*$ and $L \subseteq M^*$ so that both the language
and the object studied are merely *extended*, and we have accumulation of knowledge. For Kuhn, on the other hand, revolutions are
pretty uncontrollable. In several places in his book, and in his
paper at this conference, he uncompromisingly insists that during
revolutionary periods scientists who favour rival 'paradigms' use
different languages, that they mean different things even when
they use the same words (e.g. 'mass', 'time', 'particle'), and that
as a consequence they 'speak over each other's heads'. But if
crucial experiments (however provisional) are at all possible and
if any role is to be attributed to them in the development of science,
then there must be at least partial understanding between scientists
who favour rival paradigms. Kuhn does seem to acknowledge at
least the possibility of crucial experiments by saying that falsi-
fications in Popper's reconstruction of science have a role similar
to anomalous effects in his, though he stresses that incompatibility
with observed facts is not usually sufficient for the rejection of a
paradigm. This qualification, therefore, seems to refer to the *weight*
of the result of a crucial experiment and not to its *intertranslatability*
in the languages of the rival paradigms. If so, then at least the
assumptions underlying the proposed crucial experiments (e.g. 'If
light is wave-like, then it is diffracted; if light is corpuscular, then
it is not diffracted') must be implied by the postulates of the
languages of the rival theories. This would mean that there are
changes in science such that $L \cap L^* \neq 0$ and $A \cap A^* \neq 0$ and
$M \cap M \neq 0$.

On the other hand, the history of phlogiston, of ether, and of
other such scientific objects shows that there are also changes in
science from M to M^* such that not every object of M is a member
of M^*. Should it be objected that only 'physically real' objects
may belong to the models of scientific (empirical) theories, an
obvious rejoinder would be that the concept of model would be of
doubtful use in philosophy of science if the construction of a model
of a theory were to depend on an unknown criterion of 'physical

reality', a criterion independent of the theory itself. Besides, it seems that even 'physically real' objects, properties, and relations are occasionally dropped from models because they are no longer believed to be relevant. If so then there are changes such that $M \neq M^*$ and $\sim (M \subseteq M^*)$.

Thus it seems to me that while Kuhn is too radical in judging the extent of changes in the language of science during revolutionary periods, Suszko is not radical enough.

One of the objections which might be raised against the assumption that in some changes in science $L \neq L^*$ and $\sim (L \subseteq L^*)$ and $L \cap L^* \neq 0$ is connected with a result published by K. Ajdukiewicz in 1934 [1]. It has been shown convincingly by Ajdukiewicz that two closed and internally connected languages based on axiomatic, deductive and empirical meaning rules [2] are either intertranslatable or else have no meanings in common, so that either there is a one-to-one correspondence between their postulates or else none of their axioms are intertranslatable. Two such mutually non-translatable languages were called by Ajdukiewicz different conceptual (or scientific) world-perspectives; in some of his pre-war articles [3] he wrote that as long as we use one of two mutually non-translatable languages we cannot deny any of the propositions belonging to the other language, and that it is even doubtful whether we can assert the falsehood of any of them. If A and A^*

---

[1]   'Sprache und Sinn', *Erkenntnis* **4** (1934), pp. 100–138.

[2]   A language is *closed* if it is *not open*. A language L_1 is *open* in relation to L_2 if L_1 may be extended to L_2 by adding new expressions (L_2 then becomes a closure of L_1) without altering the meanings of any of its previous expressions. A language is internally *connected* if it has no isolated part i.e. no set of expressions unrelated by meaning rules to other expressions of the language. A language L is based on axiomatic *meaning rules* if its axioms are implicit definitions so that they cannot be rejected without altering the meanings of the terms occurring in them. Similarly, deduction in a language L is based on deductive *meaning rules* if it is not possible to accept a sentence in this language and to reject a logical consequence of this sentence without altering the meanings of logical terms.

[3]   'Das Weltbild und die Begriffsapparatur', *Erkenntnis* **4**; 'Die Wissenschaftliche Weltperspektive', *Erkenntnis* **5** (English translation, 'The scientific world-perspective', in *Readings in Philosophical Analysis*, ed. by H. Feigl and W. Sellars).

are two axiom-sets of two such different scientific world-perspectives, then their intersection is always empty i.e. $A \cap A^* = 0$. This result seems to support either Suszko, who only discusses open languages and considers their extensions, or Kuhn, if Kuhn's rival paradigms are similar to Ajdukiewicz's different scientific world-perspectives.

This objection is correct, *provided* the language of empirical science is reconstructed as based on axiomatic and empirical meaning rules. But the fact that this reconstruction renders crucial experiments impossible may be regarded as an argument *against* it. And there are other arguments against it, e.g. that the theoretical and hypothetical character of some observation statements cannot be preserved in this reconstruction.

In fact Ajdukiewicz himself considers [1] the possibility of constructing languages without axiomatic and deductive meaning rules, in connection with the problem of empiricism and the defensibility of extreme empiricism.

R. Suszko: *Reply.*

The idea of my paper is to combine the theory of extensions of models with the theory of human knowledge and its development. Professor Quine's remarks are placed within the first field. Dr. Giedymin considers the second one. Firstly, I shall consider the point mentioned by Quine.

Let L be a language and let M_1 and M_2 be two of its models such that M_1 is a submodel of M_2. Suppose that $U(M_1)$ is a proper subset of $U(M_2)$, where $U(M_i)$ is the universe of M_i.

(I) It may happen as shown by Quine that some subset of $U(M_1)$ which is M_1-undefinable in L is M_2-definable in L. The converse case (II) may hold too.

(II) It may happen that some M_1-definable subset of $U(M_1)$ is M_2-undefinable. To show this take the language with only two non-logical predicates denoting addition and multiplication of

---

[1] 'Logic and Experience', 1947 (English translation in *Synthese*, VIII, 6/7); 'The problem of empiricism and the concept of meaning', *Studia Filozoficzne*, 1964.

numbers. Suppose that $U(M_1) =$ the set of rational numbers and $U(M_2) =$ the set of real numbers. The set $U(M_1)$ is M_1-definable and M_2-undefinable.

Case I is not surprising. On the other hand one may regard case II as being inconsistent with the general idea of diachronic logic. Indeed, to avoid case II I assumed in my paper that when the universe is growing a new monadic predicate φ denoting the old universe, appears in the new language. It follows from this assumption that every set which is M_1-definable (by a sentence α containing one free variable) is M_2-definable (by the relativized sentence α_φ).

Now I pass on to the questions raised by Giedymin. First let me say that my formulation containing the reference to Kuhn's book is not precise and it may cause certain misunderstandings. It was not my aim to *compare* my formal construction with Kuhn's descriptions of the development of science. I only wanted to present a simple formal framework of the development of knowledge, and I used comparative terminology simply to provoke further inquiries into the relation between the framework I presented and the history of science. Thus Giedymin's comment is the first such comparative study stimulated by my paper.

The essential point is the difference between formal logic and pragmatics. Formal logic is an abstract theory. It does not consider human individuals or collections of individuals, and their psychological or sociological properties and relations. Speaking figuratively, one may say that formal logic considers pure mind, and pure epistemological relations between mind and the world. The syntactical and semantical properties and relations which are studied in formal logic may be, and as a matter of fact are, applied in methodology, philosophy of science, and history of science. However, science is embedded in the whole social activity of human individuals. There is a sensory and practical contact of human beings (physical subjects) with reality, and a communicating interaction between them. Human individuals and the social collections of them are not uniform. They may use different languages, face different models, and assert different axioms and theorems. These differences are connected usually with different ideological and methodological valuations. Thus there are many pragmatic phenomena in science and its history which cannot be described in terms of formal logic.

Because of this, logical evolution and logical revolutions in the development of knowledge are to be distinguished from pragmatic normal science and pragmatic scientific revolutions. There is no simple connection between them.

It is possible, I think, to find a logical revolution within pragmatic normal science. This may happen when scientists are methodologically highly conscious and are not tied by any ideological trend. On the other hand there may be a strong intellectual fight between two schools of thought (two groups of scientists) which use the same language and the same axioms, but which assert different (inconsistent) inductive generalisations. This intellectual fight is part of the logical evolution of science.

There may be another kind of pragmatic antagonism between two schools of thinking. To describe it let us represent two schools of thinking by the E-oppositions:

$$E_1 = ((L_1, A_1), M_1), \qquad E_2 = ((L_2, A_2), M_2).$$

Suppose that $L_1 \neq L_2$, $M_1 \neq M_2$, and $U(M_1) = U(M_2)$ or at least $U(M_1)$ and $U(M_2)$ have common elements. This means that both schools speak about (in part) the same objects but they 'see' (in part at least) different properties and relations of these objects and use (in part at least) different notions and different principles of thinking. Then there is a pragmatic antagonism between E_1 and E_2 i.e. between corresponding schools and they 'speak over each other's heads'. However (L_1, A_1) and (L_2, A_2) may be logically compatible, in the sense that both can be extended to (L, A) where $L_1 \subseteq L$, $L_2 \subseteq L$, and $A_1 \subset Cn(A)$, $A_2 \subset Cn(A)$. It is clear that neither the transformation E_1/E_2 nor the transformation E_2/E_1 are steps in the logical development of knowledge. But I think that the pragmatic antagonism between E_1 and E_2 is resolved in either of the two transformations E_1/E and E_2/E, where $E = ((L, A), M)$ and M_1 and M_2 are submodels of M. The last two transformations are, of course, revolutionary steps in the logical development of knowledge.

The case considered above suggests an important distinction
which should not be overlooked. We must distinguish between the
logical development of human knowledge in my sense, which is
cumulative (E_1/E, E_2/E), and the historical changes of science
(E_1/E_2 or E_2/E_1).

If we understand science and its development as being developing
knowledge in the logical sense (i.e. as true and logically interconnected theorems about the world), then we must describe it
by means of E-oppositions and their transformations. The description of an actual situation in science as an E-opposition is a
scientific hypothesis which must be proved and tested in the usual
scientific way. But this raises a very difficult point. For it is not
at all clear what is the 'empirical' basis for proving and testing
hypotheses concerning logical (especially semantical) properties and
relations in science and its change. The 'empirical' basis in question
must, I think, be given by pragmatics. However, the mutual
relation between pragmatics and formal logic is today quite unclear.

Let me now come to Giedymin's remark concerning 'phlogiston'.
We may always assume that the old language is a sub-language
of the new one. In particular, we may suppose that the expression
'phlogiston' belongs to contemporary scientific language, that its
denotation is the void set, and that the nonexistence of phlogiston
is lastingly asserted. Such an assumption is like the assumption
of the existence of a void word in the theory of concatenation,
and does not imply any undesirable consequences.

Giedymin calls attention to the papers of K. Ajdukiewicz published in 1934. These papers do indeed contain very deep ideas and
are important for the theory of knowledge and philosophy of
science. However, I will not discuss Giedymin's remarks concerning
this topic. Ajdukiewicz wrote the papers in question when the
semantical theory of models did not exist. The semantical reformulation of Ajdukiewicz's notions and theses is still a worthwhile
task. But it cannot be carried out without entering into the difficult
problem of the relation between formal logic and pragmatics.

EPISTEMOLOGY AND EXPERIMENT:
THE CASE OF MICHAEL FARADAY

L. PEARCE WILLIAMS

Cornell University

It is a commonplace today to describe the first half of the nineteenth century in England as a period in which the philosophy of Sir Francis Bacon became the accepted philosophy of the intellectuals and his brand of empiricism permeated every sphere of investigation. The appeal to the collection of facts in place of *a priori* reasonings was made in political economy, in meteorology, astronomy, hydrography and terrestrial magnetism [1]. This characterization has recently been attacked by Dr. Walter F. Cannon who has succeeded in pointing out that there was a considerable and weighty opposition to 'Baconian empiricism' which can no longer be neglected [2]. At the same time, there were many who felt that the Baconian philosophy was peculiarly English, exceptionally effective and indispensable to the progress of science.

---

[1]   Walter F. Cannon, 'Scientists and broad churchmen: an early Victorian intellectual network', *The Journal of British Studies* 4 (1964), p. 75. Cannon uses this fact and the activities of what he calls the Cambridge Network (members of which were anti-Baconian) in forming these factual collections to argue that they were not inspired by Baconian empiricism. This argument seems weak to me; when writing philosophy, the Network attacked Baconian principles but it is significant that their philosophy was of little practical use in their science. Whewell is the great example here for he quite clearly rejected the Bacon–Locke epistemology and the method which flowed from it yet could not escape from it when he did his scientific work. His work on tides would have gladdened Verulam's heart. For a discussion of the 'Baconian revival' see George A. Foote, *A Study of Attitudes Toward Science in Nineteenth Century England* 1800–1851, unpub. Cornell Univ. Doct. Diss., 1950. Bibliography of question.

[2]   Ibid. See also Walter F. Cannon, 'The normative role of science in early Victorian thought', *J. Hist. Ideas* 25 (1964), p. 487; 'History in depth: the early Victorian period', *Hist. of Sci.* 3 (1964), p. 20.

Maxwell, it is true, could state in 1856 'I find I get fonder of metaphysics and less of calculation continually, and that my metaphysics are fast settling into the rigid high style, that is about ten times as far *above* Whewell as Mill is *below* his . . .' [1] but it should be well noted that he chose to say it in private. In public, such utterances were uncommonly rare. We should be reminded that the public face of science *was* Baconian. In 1854, Thomas Huxley did lay out in public *the* method of science.

'. . . The methods of all [sciences] are identical; and these methods are:

1. *Observation* of facts – including under this head that *artificial observation* which is called *experiment.*

2. That process of tying up similar facts into bundles, ticketed and ready for use, which is called *Comparison* and *Classification*, – the results of the process, the ticketed bundles, being named *General propositions.*

3. *Deduction*, which takes us from the general proposition to facts again – teaches us, if I may so say, to anticipate from the ticket what is inside the bundle. And finally –

4. *Verification*, which is the process of ascertaining whether, in point of fact, our anticipation is a correct one' [2].

Huxley graciously acknowledged his source, well aware that everyone knew it from the mere reading of his four points. 'Save for the pleasure of doing so', he wrote, 'I need hardly point out my obligations to Mr. J. S. Mill's *System of Logic*, in this view of scientific method' [3]. Before this audience, I need go into no

---

[1] Cited in Cannon, 'History in depth . . .', p. 24, from Lewis Campbell and William Garnett, *Life of James Clerk Maxwell*, 2nd ed., London, 1884, p. 178.

[2] T. H. Huxley, 'On the educational value of the natural history of sciences', in *Science and Education, Essays by T. H. Huxley*, New York, 1894, p. 52.

[3] Ibid.

further detail but I should like to underline a few points in Huxley's (and, by extension, Mill's) scientific method. The first is one upon which commentators on Bacon have insisted for centuries. It is the purely mechanical nature of the early stages of the scientific quest. The scientist is a recorder – 'I am a camera' might well be his motto – and his primary goal must be the clear and accurate apprehension of the facts of the natural world. Experiment – *artificial observation* – is merely a human device for eliciting facts from nature, which facts, like those of observation, await their turn to be bundled and ticketed. Deduction from the bundles follows straightforward rules of logic which, once mastered, leave little room for error. The verification of these deductions seems intended primarily to check the logic of the bundles. What Huxley does not give us is the rules for bundling and this is, of course, the crux of the whole problem. Huxley implies that it is all rather easy; you simply put 'similar facts into bundles'. Similarity will be determined by the mind acting like a stereoscopic microscope comparing the ballistic marks on two bullets and matching up ideas as the microscope matches the marks made by the lands. Again, the simile is a mechanical one; the mind can be replaced by a recording instrument, a mechanism by which 'signals' can be compared and grouped together, and a computer operating upon these groups of signals. The glory of this kind of vision of science lies precisely in the fact that it *is* mechanical. Any number can play once their mental instruments have been properly cleaned, oiled, and tuned to the right signals [1].

---

[1]   Undoubtedly a large volume could be written on the reasons for this hypocrisy in early Victorian science for the number of creative scientists who actually *did* science in this fashion must then have been almost infinitesimally small. Yet most felt obliged to pay some kind of lip service to it. One reason I would suggest for this is that, on a low level, allegiance to this method gives one the illusion of doing science whereas one is merely preparing the way for someone who may contribute the flash of genius that no amount of mere collecting of data will supply. Thus, in fields where there are so many variables that it was almost impossible to keep track of them before the advent of computers-meteorology, research on tides, terrestrial magnetism, social statistics, for example – the collection of data offered activity to those who might otherwise have despaired. Also, the

In opposition to this view of science was the one which guided Faraday throughout his life. It must have infuriated his contemporaries that the foremost experimentalist of the nineteenth century rejected the prevalent theory of experimental method. Not only did he reject it, but he kept making fundamental discoveries (of fact!) that escaped everyone else, no matter how arduously he observed, bundled and ticketed. To account for this, recourse was had to all kinds of epithets. In his public eulogy of Faraday, John Tyndall would have been lost without reference to Faraday's profound physical 'intuition'. Just precisely what this meant, Tyndall left unsaid. In private, he referred to Faraday as 'the great, mad child'. Sir George B. Airy, Astronomer Royal, remarked, 'I have always known Faraday as a mystic' [1], although, once again, what this means in physics is not clear.

Faraday, I am sure, would have been quite confused by all this. To be sure, he felt strongly the harmony of the universe, but few scientists have ever been deeply convinced of its inherent chaos. The unity and convertibility of forces which guided his researches for many years appeared to rest on solid epistemological arguments far removed from intuition or madness. In fact, Faraday's scientific career was founded upon a rather simple, but fundamentally important, concept of the mind and its faculties. It was on this concept that he erected *his* experimental method which led him down paths that others had failed to see, perhaps because their bundles blocked their vision.

From the earliest records of his life comes evidence of his fascination with epistemology and the structure of the mind. I have elsewhere recounted how while delivering newspapers he debated with himself over the existence of an outside world of things. His musings then were rudely interrupted by the sudden opening of

---

very democratic nature of this vision of science provided an important weapon to those who identified science with liberalism (in the twentieth century sense) and progress. Behind Huxley's passionate pleas for the inclusion of science in higher and secondary education lay the conviction that everyone, in fact, could play and the larger the game, the better the world must ultimately become.

[1] Cited in Cannon, 'Scientists and broad churchmen ...' p. 84.

a door which crashed into his nose [1]. Later, while continuing his self-education at the Royal Institution, he composed two essays on the mind and its faculties which revealed the germ of his later, more mature, view. In his *Diary*, as well, he dropped little hints that, taken with other writings, permit us to reconstruct the very simple psychology to which he held [2].

The mind consists of basically three faculties – the senses, the judgment and the imagination. The senses provide the mind with the raw material for its operations but this is not automatic or mechanical. The mind has to be carefully trained in the reception of sense impressions or else it will err in its judgments.

'Our sense perceptions are wonderful. Even in the observant, but unreflective infant, they soon produce a result which looks like intuition, because of its perfection. Coming to the mind as so many data, they are stored up, and without our being conscious, are ever after used in like circumstances in forming our judgment; and is it not wonderful that man should be accustomed to trust them without examination. Nevertheless, the result is the effect of education: the mind has to be instructed with regard to the senses and their intimations through every step of life; and where the instruction is imperfect, it is astonishing how soon and how much their evidence fails us' [3].

Note the subtle difference here between Huxley and Faraday. Both are within the Lockean tradition but the emphasis is not the same. In Huxley, the process is even and uninterrupted from observation through classification to general laws. The implication is that when the proper procedure is once learned, the process is almost guaranteed to lead to truth. With Faraday, however, the process was dialectical and constantly in need of examination. The judgment constantly needed to be honed between the senses and its own conclusions drawn from sensory data. The road to truth did not depend solely upon accurate observation and correct logic

---

[1] L. Pearce Williams, *Michael Faraday, A Biography*, London, 1965, p. 80.

[2] Ibid., pp. 80 ff. See also pp. 336 ff.

[3] M. Faraday, 'Observations on mental education', in *Exptl. Res. in Chem. and Phys.*, London, 1859, p. 463.

although these were necessary; judgment was required as well. It was the judgment, educated through years of experience in discriminating, composing, and selecting amongst the data of the senses that gave to this data a certain *interpretation*. The interpretation was *not* a product of mechanical sortings but ultimately found its justification in the sense of completeness, of aesthetic harmony and of satisfaction that it created in the person whose judgment was being exercised. It is at this point that Faraday begins to look different from the Lockeans and the Baconians.

The difference can best be illustrated by giving another citation.

'I should be sorry, however', he wrote, 'if what I have said were understood as meaning that education for the improvement and strengthening of the judgment is to be altogether repressive of the imagination, or confine the exercise of the mind to processes of a mathematical or mechanical character. I believe that, in the pursuit of physical science, the imagination should be taught to present the subject investigated in all possible, and even in impossible views; to search for analogies of likeness and (if I may say so) of opposition – inverse or contrasted analogies; to present the fundamental idea in every form, proportion, and condition; to clothe it with suppositions and probabilities, that all cases may pass in review, and be touched, if needful, by the Ithuriel spear of experiment. But all this must be *under government*, and the result must not be given to society until the judgment, educated by the process itself, has been exercised upon it.' [1]

The point was put more forcefully in his Diary. 'Let the imagination go, guiding it by judgment and principle, but holding it in and directing it by *experiment*.' [2]

A number of points are worth noticing here. The interactions of the three constituents of the mind now seems clear. The senses report on the outside world, which data are recorded in the mind. The judgment acts upon these data to discover similarities or, as Huxley suggested, to tie up data into bundles. Here Huxley stops

[1] Ibid., p. 480.
[2] Thomas Martin, ed., *Faraday's Diary*, 8 vols., (London, 1932–6), **7**, p. 337.

but this is really where Faraday begins. The imagination delights in making odd bundles guided, and this should be underlined, by a whole host of different motives. It may simply be fancy, or aesthetic pleasure, or delight in the juxtaposition of the unusual. The result is an *idea* or an *hypothesis* and is *prior* to experiment. Now the judgment must really begin to work and its function is essentially critical. In its examination of the ideas presented to it by the imagination, it may find logical inconsistencies which lead it to reject the idea. In many cases, however, because of the very unusual nature of the combinations produced by the imagination, it will be unable, by itself, to judge without further inquiry. This is where experiment and the senses come in. Experiment is used by the judgment to test the flights of the imagination. It is, in short, *not* an instrument of discovery but the best critical tool at the disposal of the scientist. Thus Faraday's theory of the mind gave him the base from which he could attack the orthodoxy of his day. As we shall soon see, the attack was devastating.

Another point worthy of our attention is the fact that Faraday's theory of the mind destroys the democracy of Baconianism. In Faraday's theory, any number *cannot* play for the imagination is not a faculty that can be educated. The material upon which it feeds can be enlarged by widening the circle of experience, but the actual *operation* of the imagination is an intensely personal and inherent activity which, like artistic creativity, can only be admired not inculcated. Thus radical new departures in science are not inherently or logically necessary. They depend upon the richness of imagination of rare individuals who have the courage and the ability to dream of other worlds than those of accepted science. Finally, true creativity is thus restored to scientific activity. The scientist does not *uncover* nature but interprets her. There is, of course, an objective element in this interpretation but it is only an element. As Faraday was to show so dramatically in his creation of field theory, the facts of physics need not be seen exclusively as the result of particles acting at a distance upon one another. The same facts could as easily be interpreted in terms of a field and the value of a variety of interpretations was that it enlarged the scientist's views and refined his judgment as he proceeded further,

I should like to conclude by briefly illustrating the use Faraday made in his own researches of his own ideas on the mind and the place of experiment in scientific research. Two examples will, for lack of time, have to suffice. The first concerns his work on the relation of gravity, heat, and electricity which was rejected for publication in the *Philosophical Transactions*. As is well known, Faraday carried on a long series of experiments to try and detect the existence of some 'force' produced by the raising of a large weight. He felt positive that such a force must appear or else the principle of the conservation of force would be violated. The results were all negative yet Faraday sent the paper in to the *Philosophical Transactions*. One immediately wants to know why since it is a rather detailed record of constant failure. I would suggest that Faraday was simply trying to follow his own advice in the *Diary*. He had let his imagination go and it had suggested an effect. He had been unable to find it experimentally but the year was 1859, he was 70 years old, and his mental powers were failing rapidly. Could not his last *Experimental Research* simply pass on the fruits of his imagination in the hopes that others, unable to soar so high, might, nevertheless, control the critical apparatus of experiment sufficiently to find or to rule out the effect he saw in his mind's eye?

A more dramatic, and less conjectural example, is that offered by his rejection of action at a distance in electrical phenomena. It was in his search for the identity of electricities that Faraday first observed the electrolytic decomposition of a substance without there being any obvious poles involved. What Faraday was after, however, was simply evidence that static electricity, like voltaic electricity, could decompose chemical compounds. That he went so far as to entertain the idea that action at a distance, emanating from poles, could not operate here is an indication of the fertility of his imagination for such a position to the majority of his colleagues was literally unimaginable. But from this flight of speculative fancy, Faraday was able to devise experimental set-ups to test his first, tentative, challenge to orthodox physics.

It is in the years following 1833, during which Faraday successfully laid siege to the accepted theory of electrical action, that we can observe what I think may be considered as the most extended use of experiment as an instrument of destruction in the whole history of science. Given the idea that electricity did not act at a distance, Faraday proceeded to devise experiment after experiment to prove that it did not. For six years, theory after theory fell before him until, by 1839, the old system was in ruins. In Faraday's judgment, it must be rejected and it was his rejection of action at a distance that was to guide him later in his epoch-making researches in magnetism. Faraday's contemporaries, unable to follow the interplay of his judgment, imagination, and experiments, by and large, rejected his conclusions. The writing on the tags of their bundles was indelible and ineradicable. Faraday knew this and refused to invade so personal a domain by resorting to polemics. He was content to write his epitaph:

'The *laws of nature*, as we understand them, are the foundation of our knowledge in natural things. So much as we know of them has been developed by the successive energies of the highest intellects, exerted through many ages. After a most rigid and scrutinizing examination upon principle and trial, a definite expression has been given to them; they have become, as it were, our belief or trust. From day to day we still examine and test our expressions of them. We have no interest in their retention if erroneous; on the contrary, the greatest discovery a man could make would be to prove that one of these accepted laws was erroneous, and his greatest honour would be the discovery.' [1]

---

[1]   M. Faraday, 'Observations . . .', p. 469.

G. J. Whitrow: *Faraday and mathematics.*

Faraday is generally regarded as one of the greatest masters of experimental science. Dr. Pearce Williams has shown us that he was also a fertile proponent of new hypotheses and theories. In fact he describes him as the leading theorist of the nineteenth century. However, it would be interesting to see how his lack of mathematics influenced his method. For, although his concept of lines of force was adopted by Clerk Maxwell as the foundation of field theory and so became an essentially mathematical idea, Faraday himself had a definite distaste for mathematical formulation. A remarkable example of his weakness in this respect is provided by his failure to recognize clearly Ohm's law when he obtained the empirical evidence bearing upon it. Indeed, it was probably Faraday's lack of mathematics that prevented the significance of his ideas of lines of force from being fully appreciated before Maxwell took up the subject.

M. Bunge: *The various functions of experiment.*

I was very much impressed by Dr. Pearce Williams' competent analysis of the intimate intertwining of Faraday's epistemological and scientific ideas, as much impressed of course as by the remarkable consistency of these two sets of ideas in the case of Faraday. Faraday, one of the most productive experimentalists of all time, was not an operationalist, whereas many high-brow theoretical physicists think modestly that all they are doing is to package empirical data: they follow in this regard Thomas Huxley's example – so vividly reconstructed by Pearce Williams – of bowing to a philosophy of science contrived by people without scientific experience. Now I am sure Pearce Williams would like to supplement his analysis of Faraday's epistemology with an examination of the role certain metaphysical ideas may have had in Faraday's research work. I have in mind the idea of a *plenum*, the old Aristotelian and Cartesian hypothesis that the universe is full – an idea whose rich history has been so brilliantly told by A. O. Lovejoy in *The Great Chain of Being*.

As we all know, this hypothesis seems to have played an important role in Faraday's thought and, like every other metaphysical idea, it was double-edged: on the one hand it did facilitate his invention of the field concept, but on the other hand it may have prevented him from realising the quantum nature of electric charge. If we look at his own laws of electrolysis we feel that he was just on the brink of discovering the quantization of electric charge, and that only a bias in favour of continuity obscured his sight. The moral for us is clear: 'Don't be afraid of metaphysics as long as it is fertile – only, state it as explicitly as possibly and keep it under control, for otherwise it won't play its heuristic role'. But I understand that Pearce Williams discusses the ontology of Faraday in his comprehensive work, and I look forward to seeing his forthcoming discussion of Ampère's philosophical ideas and the influence they may have had on his scientific work.

Now I wish to comment briefly on Pearce Williams' idea of scientific experiment. This seems to be the Popperian thesis that the function of experiment is solely critical. I don't think this is quite fair on the experimentalists. I believe experiment performs several functions in addition to testing hypotheses and systems of hypotheses, i.e. theories. The experimentalist gathers data, doesn't he? And experiment does suggest problems – namely the problems of explaining how the experimental effects come about. Finally it suggests certain low-level hypotheses, and indeed in two different ways. Firstly, without having too many ideas in your mind you may just ask what will happen if A is the case: you ask nature or society as it were, and watch for the reply. If the answer is 'B', you have got a new hypothesis: 'If A, then B' – which you will have to retest and link to the available body of knowledge. Secondly, a set of data of a given kind may suggest an inductive jump – e.g., one of the so-called empirical curves.

To be sure, every experiment involves some ideas: both the experimental design and the reading or interpretation of experimental results require one or more scientific theories. But the point is that *the guiding hypotheses need not be those which are being tested*. In other words, every experiment presupposes a body of ideas that are used but not questioned, i.e. not tested in the course of that particular experiment. Thus an atomic experiment uses classical mechanics and classical optics even if its purpose is to test a hypothesis that conflicts with that background. And even the most thoughtless experiment in psychology takes physics and chemistry for granted. In short, in every experiment we must distinguish the ideas that are being subjected to test (if any) from those which help us to conceive and to interpret the experiment: while the latter are always present, the former may be absent in the early stages – and this was, precisely, the case with many of Faraday's experiments. For Faraday's ideas, let us not forget, remained in an embryonic state until Maxwell completed them and made them precise with the help of mathematics. While Faraday could only ruin the action-at-a-distance theories, he had no proper theory to offer in place of them. It was only Maxwell who, on the basis of Faraday's semiqualitative ideas, built the first nonmechanical field theory of electromagnetism. To this end he had to evolve a whole new mathematical theory, the theory of vector fields, without which there would be no Faraday–Maxwell electromagnetic theory.

In sum, I would say that experiment fulfils at least four different functions: (1) to gather data; (2) to generate hypotheses – low-level conjectures to be sure; (3) to suggest new problems; (4) to test hypotheses and systems of hypotheses. In no case is experiment done in a conceptual vacuum, but sometimes it is done in order to get new ideas rather than to criticize available hypotheses.

K. R. POPPER: *Mathematics, observation, and physical thought.*

I would like to begin by saying how much I liked Pearce Williams' talk. Details about Faraday have been sadly missing in the history of the theory of matter. Perhaps owing to Tyndall [1] he is usually thought of as the great experimentalist, the empirical scientist who

---

[1]   John Tyndall, *Faraday as a Discoverer*, 5th ed., 1894, p. 184.

established the facts on which Maxwell built the theory. Faraday's speculative ideas have not been seriously discussed; it was sometimes even hinted that they were a kind of mental aberration. Some remarks of Einstein [1] on Faraday show that he, at least, recognized the importance of Faraday's speculations. And Maxwell saw [2] the connections between these speculations and the ideas of Boscovich. A discussion of Faraday as a theoretician was much needed, and Pearce Williams has provided it.

Whitrow has argued that Faraday's lack of mathematics hampered his work. I wonder whether it was not as much a stimulus as a hindrance. As the excellent mathematician Schwartz has pointed out [3], with his tongue in his cheek, mathematics can have a pernicious influence on science. For to express a proposition mathematically can make things look too easy, and conceal very serious problems. In some ways, of course, Faraday's lack of mathematics was a hindrance. But it also helped, by forcing him to see things clearly in a purely imaginative or intuitive way. Faraday made terrific efforts to clarify his intuitive theories – without these efforts, Maxwell's mathematization of the theory might not have taken place.

The pernicious influence of mathematics is particularly strong nowadays. It is expressed in the view that we cannot think in physics, or *understand* physical theories, because we only have formulae and no intuitive models. This doctrine that you can only think with models, not with formulae, is mistaken. However, a standard method of mathematical physics has become: don't think; but tinker with the formulae to make them 'work' better, or to get better 'fits'. This may occasionally be very valuable, but it is not a substitute for trying to think, and to understand your formulae. Finally, I would like to say how much I welcomed Pearce Williams' stress on the negative role of experiments. One cannot start an

---

[1]   *The World As I See It*, p. 153.

[2]   'Atom', *Encyclopaedia Britannica*, III 9th ed.

[3]   See J. Schwartz, 'The pernicious influence of mathematics on science', *Logic, Methodology, and Philosophy of Science*, Proceedings of the 1960 International Congress, Stanford, 1962, eds. E. Nagel, P. Suppes and A. Tarski, pp. 356–360. One of his best examples is the pernicious influence of the Birkhoff Ergodic Theorem on statistical mechanics.

experiment without a theory: as Darwin said '. . . all observation must be for or against some view . . .' [1]. You may want to test your theory, and the experiment you perform may not even be a test of your own theory, but of some other competing theory. However, I know of no experiment which did not have, among other roles, the role of checking or of criticizing.

Incidentally, this role may not be apparent if you merely ask experimentalists what they are doing. What answers you get will depend on whom you ask, and where you ask: in some laboratories, only the head of the laboratory knows why certain experiments are being performed, and the others just carry out his instructions. Socio-psychological investigation of experimenters may not shed much light on the role of experiments.

In science we always operate with a *multiplicity* of competing theories or hypotheses [2], which always guide our observations. We are not observers, (as even Faraday's psychology implies) but *thinkers*. A man does not *see* more or better than a hawk, he *thinks* more. And he has developed, outside his skin, language, and in particular, argumentative language in addition to purely descriptive language. Science is an argumentative debate in which experiment plays a vitally important role. This debate goes on between schools, between individual scientists, and, as the case of Faraday illustrates, within the scientist himself.

L. PEARCE WILLIAMS: *Reply.*

The comments of Bunge, Whitrow and Popper have touched upon a number of extremely important matters which it is impossible

---

[1]   Francis Darwin, ed., *More Letters of Charles Darwin*, I, 1903, p. 195. See also J. O. Wisdom, *Foundations of Inference in Natural Science*, 1952, p. 50, and Nora Barlow, *The Autobiography of Charles Darwin*, 1958, p. 161. Darwin at least was very clear on these matters, and Thomas Huxley, who was quoted by Pearce Williams as an illustration of the primitive empiricism prevalent in Faraday's time, should have learned from his great friend Darwin.

[2]   Thomas Chrowder Chamberlin, the American geologist, formulated this as the 'Method of multiple working hypotheses', *Journal of Geology* 5 (1897), pp. 837–848, reprinted, 34 (1931). The idea is due to Aenesidemus.

to discuss here in any detail. I should like, however, simply to indicate how I view these issues so that the exact areas of disagreement can be seen precisely.

In my biography of Faraday, I have tried to show how Faraday's commitment to the idea of a *plenum* was made in quite specific terms, namely those of Boscovich's atoms. It is worth remarking here that this gives rise to a rather peculiar kind of *plenum* for there are points in space where literally nothing exists. These are the null points on the Boscovichean curve. They are of fundamental importance for they mark a point of *physical* discontinuity in a mathematically continuous function. The great power of Boscovich's theory, it seems to me, lies precisely in this ability to combine continuity and discontinuity in this fashion. For the physicist, it is the continuity that counts; for the chemist it is the discontinuity; it is the null points which determine the stability, instability and chemical properties of the chemical elements. Field theory, today, is securely within the boundaries of physics; in the 1830's when Faraday was struggling to clarify his own concepts, he was attacking the problem from within the framework of chemistry.

In 1834 when Faraday published his new theory of electrochemistry he was perfectly aware of the 'quantization' of electric charge and wrote: . . . 'if we adopt the atomic theory or phraseology, then the atoms of bodies which are equivalents to each other in their ordinary chemical action, have equal quantities of electricity naturally associated with them.'[1] What he was not willing to accept was that the electrical 'force' had to be embodied in a material particle. This does not seem to me to be attributable to a 'bias in favour of continuity' although such a bias could lead to the same position Faraday took. As he later spelled it out, it was an epistemological problem and his personal inclination was simply to reject a material substratum for force.

As my remarks on Popper's comments will show, I agree with Bunge on the nature of experiment in general but I disagree with him on the nature of experiment as Faraday used it. This is a

---

[1] M. Faraday, *Experimental Researches in Electricity*, I, London, 1839, p. 256.

minor point, but perhaps worth stressing here before an audience of philosophers of science for it reveals an interesting and important difference between historians and philosophers. I must confess to being an inductivist when it comes to the writing of history. That is, I work in terms of individual cases leaving the universal rather carefully alone. Thus my remarks on Faraday's use of experiment were meant to apply only to Faraday. I believe they do and I should like to ask Bunge to give me the specific evidence that Faraday used experiment in the ways he outlines at the end of his remarks. By generalizing, the supreme goal of the philosopher, Bunge has come to a conclusion on the function of experiment which he feels I hold, but which, in fact, I do not.

Finally, as regards Bunge's comments, I should like to take sharp issue with his statement that Faraday's ideas remained 'embryonic' until Maxwell turned them into a proper theory, and that all he (Faraday) could do with them was to make life un-comfortable for proponents of action at a distance. I shall only say here that these 'embryonic' ideas led Faraday from fundamental discovery to fundamental discovery throughout the course of thirty years. Some embryo! I do not see why a theory whose logical consequences led Faraday to the discovery of specific inductive capacity, the laws of electrochemistry, the rotation of the plane of polarized light in a magnetic field and diamagnetism is any more 'embryonic' than a mathematical theory which led Hertz to the discovery of electromagnetic radiation. I will agree that it was more acceptable to physicists when put into mathematical language and that it gained in precision by this translation but, with very few exceptions, the *physics* of classical field theory is as Faraday first saw and expressed it. Maxwell was always the first to insist upon this point.

This brings me logically to the consideration of Whitrow's remarks. What difference did Faraday's lack of mathematical training make in his development as a theorist? This is, of course, an impossible question but there is a clue which may lead us to a partial answer. It is to be found in the dispute between Ampère and Faraday which I have discussed in some detail on pages 154ff. of my biography of Faraday. The essence of the problem consists in the nature of the 'force' surrounding a current-carrying wire. To Faraday, it was simple; the 'force' was circular. Here was born the idea of the line of force for Faraday later went on to show how the combination of these circular lines of force could produce the lines traced out by iron filings in a magnetic field. This was inadmissible to Ampère. The circular line of force *had* to be the resultant of central forces emanating from current elements in the wire. Note that in Ampère's view, the 'line of force' is of no consequence; it is always a straight line in its most primitive manifestation. The observed lines can simply be analyzed into central forces acting in straight lines. The reason for Ampère's rejection of Faraday's idea is instructive. If the *primary* line of force were circular then, Ampère pointed out, it could not be subjected to mathematical analysis. This was sufficient reason for Ampère to consider it impossible. Ampère's analysis of electrodynamics, therefore, followed strictly orthodox lines. So did everyone's until Faraday showed that physical reality could be viewed from a different perspective. I suspect, but of course cannot prove, that Faraday would never have been able to see nature as he did if he had been thoroughly grounded in mathematics. It should not be forgotten that the vision of field theory came first; the mathematization of it second. The fact that a circular line of force created formidable mathematical difficulties caused Faraday no anxiety. I suspect that most mathematically trained physicists have the tendency to equate mathematical difficulty with physical improbability, at least they seem to have done so in the nineteenth century, and this subtle influence made it extremely difficult to see the world in any terms but those which mathematical physics had already made familiar. Thus, I would suggest that if Faraday had been Senior Wrangler he might have played Weber to Ampère, but I strongly doubt that he would have been the architect of field theory.

I find it difficult to answer Sir Karl Popper. I consider myself a Popperian but not, I think, in the same sense as Sir Karl is a Popperian. In my comments on Kuhn's paper, I have already indicated that I do not believe that *every* experiment is and must be a test of an hypothesis and cited the history of spectroscopy as evidence. I doubt that I have persuaded Popper and rather than belabor the point, it seems to me that it might be of some interest simply to point out the dimensions of my adherence to Popper's philosophy of experiment. To me, as an historian, the immense service that Popper has done is to force the historian to think and to look behind the 'official' views published by scientists on the nature of the scientific quest. How simple and how easy life would be if only Huxley were right and science consisted of tying up and labelling bundles. Most of Faraday's biographers have contented themselves with following Huxley; the great debt historians owe to Popper is that he has made it impossible for them to be content with Huxley's approach. Now, the historian *must* dig into the manuscript record, examine the intimate details of the genesis of experiments and their evolution, read the private correspondence of scientists who, sometimes, reveal their innermost thoughts on their scientific problems in letters to friends. This is where the hypotheses to be tested often lurk. Thus, I think we must all start as Popperians and we will often be rewarded by the discovery of satisfyingly rich lodes of precious metal. In this way, Popper's philosophy provides both a vital stimulus to historical research in depth and a valuable guide to be followed in this research. But, we must also be aware that it can be detrimental to the attempt to recapture historical reality. It is possible (and my own efforts in the work I have done in the history of spectroscopy provide me here with an example) to explore in depth and to follow Popper's critical philosophy faithfully only to find that it has led to a dead end. At this point, continued adherence to the rule that *all* experiments *must* be tests will only serve to becloud the historical investigation. The historian then has two choices; he can insist that the real evidence to prove his Popperian point is missing or he can indulge in fanciful and ingenious exercises to show that experiments which are *not* tests but, say, simple mapping operations, *really* are testing something even if the scientist being studied didn't know it. Both courses seem to me rather sterile. I prefer simply to continue to be grateful to Popper for what he has given me and to admit that the essence of his philosophy is a brilliant insight, not an eternal law.

THE GENERAL THEORY OF RELATIVITY – CASE STUDY
IN THE UNFOLDING OF NEW PHYSICAL CONCEPTS [1]

P. G. BERGMANN

Syracuse University

Let me state first what I conceive to be the purpose of my talk
to a group of people who are engaged professionally in philosophy
of science, when I am obviously not a philosopher of science. From
this morning's discussion I could give a very pat answer to the
effect that I am here to test a hypothesis, to wit that this programme
booklet's statements are true, provided that you apply a time
translation of approximately twenty minutes. Aside from this
newly-hatched purpose, I can see, on a more serious level, my
objective as this: that it ought to be one of the main sources of
stimulation for philosophers of science to investigate, as far as
possible at first hand, or at least as closely as possible, case histories
of scientific hypotheses, so as to test not so much the correctness
of a programme but to be stimulated in conceiving of, and testing,
hypotheses as to the dynamics of scientific enquiry.

The advantage that a physicist, let us say, has over a philosopher
is that, whereas physicists would not dream of permitting non-
physicists to express opinions about technical matters in physics,
they take it for granted that they will have opinions and views
on philosophy, whether or not they are qualified and competent
by their own training to render such judgments. I am mentioning
this only because in presenting some case histories of my own I
want to acknowledge the fact that I am not at all a blank sheet
that represents raw material, but rather an opinionated sheet. To
this extent, of course, the evidence presented may well be slanted.
It has the redeeming virtue of being first-hand. I should like to

[1] The author's attendance was made possible by a travel grant from
the National Science Foundation.

249

talk to you about two complexes of ideas within my own field, that of general relativity, not so much because this audience is tremendously interested in the subject matter for its own sake, but simply because I have been somewhat associated with the formation of these two complexes. Hence my evidence, even though coloured, is at least first-hand, and I am offering this not as an apology, really, but merely as part of the record, which I consider unavoidable in any case.

Before coming to the two main topics that I am to discuss, the notion of observables, which was formed about ten years ago in general relativity, and a critique of the concept of world point, I should like to give you just a few pieces of background.

When, after the formulation of the special theory of relativity in 1905, Einstein was led to the exploration of gravitation, he reminded himself of a fact that had been well known previously for about 300 years but which had not been further analysed. I am referring to the equality of the two kinds of masses that enter into the Newtonian structure of physics. There is, first of all, the so-called inertial mass, that is the property of the body that determines the extent to which a given force will accelerate it. The inertial mass of a body is defined as the ratio between force and acceleration. The other role of mass is more specialized in the Newtonian structure; the mass also acts as the source of gravitational attraction. It does so in exactly the same manner in which the electric charge serves as the source of electric repulsion or attraction. In fact the mathematical forms of Newton's and Coulomb's laws, one for gravitational forces, the other for electric forces, are, as you know, in all respects identical. Only the respective sources are in one case the electric charge, in the other the gravitational mass.

Newton knew that as a matter of experience these two kinds of mass, which served totally different functions in his theory, are in fact numerically equal. Or, if you want to be finicky about units, you may prefer to say that there is a universal factor of proportionality between them. It does not matter: the two formulations are equivalent. And, moreover, both formulations are equivalent to the statement that the accelerations experienced by all test bodies are the same in a given uniform gravitational field; that is to say, the acceleration depends only on the strength of the field, but not on the chemical composition or any other characteristics of the test bodies employed to plumb the gravitational field.

This fact then, that test particles of different compositions will exhibit the same acceleration in the same uniform gravitational field, leads automatically to equating for phenomenological purposes the so-called inertial acceleration, such as centrifugal and Coriolis' accelerations, with gravitational accelerations. And this equality, in turn, is responsible for the inability on the part of the physicist to separate by local experiment alone gravitational and inertial forces. In fact, phenomenologically the nearest approximation to what in Newtonian mechanics is known as an inertial frame of reference in the presence of a gravitational field is a freely falling frame or reference. Consider Einstein's famous 'elevator' (in American English), 'lift' (in British English), in which an intrepid observer, far from worrying what will happen to him when he reaches the bottom of the shaft after the supporting cables have broken, goes about making experiments. Regardless of the philosophical and scientific implications, the observer's actions show a high measure of moral virtue. Of course, nowadays we can actually perform what were originally conceptual experiments by sending people out into orbit where they are also freely falling whenever they turn off all sources of rocket power. The result of these experiments was essentially a foregone conclusion, except for the physiological effects, and by now we know a good deal about those.

This, essentially, was the situation of gravitational theory, which had not been fully analysed prior to the formulation of general relativity. Einstein made an extrapolation from this set of facts by postulating as a hypothesis the *principle of general covariance*. The general theory of relativity is that theory of gravitation which incorporates this principle in the simplest possible mathematical structure. According to the principle of general covariance, any system of space and time co-ordinates that assigns to any given event (the 'event' being considered as something that is localisable both in space and time) a set of four numerical data for identification, and so that the geometric notions of neighbourhood are faithfully reflected by this assignment of numerical data up to a certain finite degree of differentiability, is as good as any other frame of reference.

Since I have just come from a congress on general relativity where this and other points were also discussed, let me say that I, at least, conceive of the principle of general covariance not as merely stating that all laws of nature, all conceivable laws of nature, may be represented in terms of arbitrary co-ordinate systems. This statement is true, but I think it is a truism. Rather, the principle of general covariance is a 'principle of impotence', in Whittaker's language [1]. It states that it is impossible to select from among all curvilinear co-ordinate systems a subset (such as the inertial frames of reference) that on a global scale would be more suitable for the formulation of the laws of nature than the remaining curvilinear co-ordinate systems. Even this formulation is not without its pitfalls [2], but I cannot enter into this aspect if I am to get to the first main topic of my talk. What I want to impress on you is that, for better or for worse, the general theory of relativity incorporates this principle of general covariance. In fact one speaks of a whole class of physical theories, which go beyond the theoretical description of gravitation alone, as *general-relativistic theories*, which incorporate this principle of general covariance.

The adoption of a general-relativistic theory results in the breakdown of the notion that there is a natural and specified rigid relationship between the world points of the space-time four-dimensional manifold, which is expressible either in terms of the Galileo or Newton structure, or in terms of the Minkowski structure. The only remaining *a priori* assumptions are, first of all, the existence of world points as such, and then the assumption that the manifold of space-time is a topological set of such world points, and there are relationships of neighbourhood, separability, and what have

[1] E. T. Whittaker, *A History of the Theories of Aether and Electricity*, Nelson, London, 1953.

[2] E. Kretschmann, *Ann. Physik* IV, **53** (1917), p. 575; P. Havas, *Rev. Mod. Physics* **36** (1964), p. 938.

you; in short, the totality of topological relationships and assumptions that are usually summarised by the statement that the manifold is locally Euclidean (not in the metric but in the topological sense of that term). Any other relationships are to be subject to the dynamical laws, and therefore not universals but particulars of the given physical situation.

With this as a background let me try to proceed first to an explanation of how the notion of observables came about historically [1]. As you know, probably, one of the large bodies of theoretical structure in physics is quantum theory, both in the form of quantum mechanics and quantum field theory. To this day the theory of gravitation has not been successfully quantised, that is, it has not been incorporated in the general conceptual framework that we call the quantum description of nature. It has remained a classical theory ('classical' here not in the sense of pre-relativistic but of non-quantum). It appears an important programme that we should explore the possibility, and in fact try very hard to achieve, the quantisation of the theory of gravitation. This programme represents a sort of testing process internal to theoretical physics. The attempt might be successful, and thereby provide a significant step toward achieving organic unity of the major fundamental theories of physics; or it might fail, in which case we should hope that the nature of the breakdown of the attempt will have educational value in itself, and perhaps help us to proceed in more successful directions [2].

In the course of the quantisation programme relativity was first cast successfully into the so-called Hamiltonian formulation simultaneously by two groups, A. Schild and F. A. E. Pirani and our group at Syracuse [3]. Pirani is the Felix Pirani at King's College here in London, who was then a graduate student at Carnegie Institute of Technology in the United States, and Alfred Schild was his thesis adviser. This was approximately sixteen years ago; the Hamiltonian formulation was further perfected by Dirac in

[1] P. G. Bergmann, *Nuovo Cimento* 10, 3 (1956), p. 1177.

[2] P. G. Bergmann, *Helvetica Physica Acta*, Suppl. 4 (1956), p. 79.

[3] A. Schild and F. A. E. Pirani, *Phys. Rev.* 79 (1950), p. 986. Bergmann, Penfield, Schiller and Zatzkis, *Phys. Rev.* 80 (1950), p. 81.

1958 and 1959 [1]. Thus there is now available a formulation of the (non-quantum) general theory of relativity as follows. There are a set of field variables, twelve altogether, which are canonically conjugate and which satisfy standard Poisson bracket relations in the classical sense. These twelve variables, however, at any one time t_0 may not be chosen freely but are subject to four conditions at each point of space. If they fail to satisfy these so-called constraints, they describe a non-physical situation. In other words, there is some redundance in these field variables, which is reduced by the constraints. Remarkably, these constraints are not accidental. It can be shown that in any general-relativistic field theory the occurrence of this minimum set of constraints at every space point is unavoidable. This is because these constraints are, in the Hamiltonian sense, the generators of infinitesimal co-ordinate transformations. And as infinitesimal curvilinear co-ordinate transformations are essential to the fundamentals of general-relativistic theories, these constraints will appear if a Hamiltonian formulation of the theory is feasible at all. Moreover, as these constraints are the generators of co-ordinate transformations, they automatically include the possibility of generating the transition from one three-dimensional manifold to a neighbouring three-dimensional manifold.

This function of providing orderly progress from one three-dimensional manifold to another is normally assumed by the Hamiltonian in both classical mechanics and classical field theory. Hence the four constraints that appear in any general-relativistic theory, and whose explicit form has been worked out in its most convenient version by Dirac, take over the duties of the Hamiltonian; they are usually referred to as the Hamiltonian constraints. A theory may also contain other constraints for a variety of reasons, but if it is general-relativistic, then it must contain at least these four Hamiltonian constraints. Accordingly the Hamiltonian of general relativity, of any general-relativistic theory, is necessarily zero. And this fact carries a number of implications. We became aware of the most obvious consequences when we proceeded to

---

[1]   P. A. M. Dirac, *Proc. Roy. Soc.* **A246**, London, (1958), p. 333. *Phys. Rev.* **114** (1959), p. 924.

apply the newly gained knowledge to our attempt at quantising general relativity.

If you have a Hamiltonian, then normally the Schrödinger equation of ordinary quantum theory takes the form

$$H\psi + \frac{\hbar}{i}\frac{\partial\psi}{\partial t} = 0.$$

If the Hamiltonian is a constraint, then our theory must also satisfy the condition

$$H\psi = 0.$$

From this condition we conclude immediately that $\partial\psi/\partial t$ vanishes as well:

$$\frac{\partial\psi}{\partial t} = 0.$$

As we are dealing here with what is known technically as the Schrödinger picture, and as this last equation is normally a relationship pertaining to the Heisenberg picture, we conclude that in a general-relativistic theory the Schrödinger picture and the Heisenberg picture are identical and indistinguishable.

We can then formulate the condition on ψ (which is presumably a functional over the space of the configuration variables) by saying that any ψ that is physically admissible must satisfy the constraints. H is an arbitrary linear superposition of the four Hamiltonian constraints $\mathscr{H}_s$, $\mathscr{H}_L$ at each point of the three-dimensional space-like surface

$$H = \int d^3x(\eta^s\mathscr{H}_s + \eta^L\mathscr{H}_L)$$

and the coefficients η^s, η_L, which are completely arbitrary, determine the manner in which we want to propagate the surface, and on the surface the co-ordinates. Remember that in a theory that is not general-relativistic this propagation is far from arbitrary. Unless we move rigidly along the pre-ordained time axis, the form of the theory will change, whereas the essential fact about general-relativistic theories is that no matter how we proceed to a neighbouring hypersurface, the form of the theory will remain unchanged.

So that is why these coefficients η^s, η_L are arbitrary, and why you must have Hamiltonian constraints in a general-relativistic theory. The Hamiltonian is a constant of the motion; how can any functional or integral with arbitrary coefficients be a constant of the motion unless the coefficients are multiplied by vanishing quantities? Of course, every statement that I have made can be verified by arithmetic, but it is one of Bergmann's lemmas that whenever you try to do a calculation in general relativity that you do not understand from its group-theoretical or invariant-theoretical point of view, then you are bound to make more mistakes than you will ever be able to eliminate again.

Because the human mind is not perfect, it is important, when you proceed by so-called pure reasoning, that you can verify your results by arithmetic, but the reverse is, for practical purposes, equally important. Unless you understand your results, you should not believe them. What I am getting at is that this theory has some very nasty consequences. If a number of variables, all these Hamiltonian constraints, when operating on any permissible wave functional Ψ are to be zero, we can also re-state that fact by saying that any permissible wave functional Ψ is the simultaneous eigen functional of a large number, in fact an infinite number, of constraints (there is an infinite number of points on the three-dimensional initial-value surface). Ψ must be the simultaneous eigen function of all of these operators. If the canonical commutators are expected to hold, then from the very beginning we are doomed to find that a very large number of other functionals, almost all of the dynamical variables, can never have sharp values. At most they possess expectation values, but in general expectation values with infinite variances, and that means, of course, that you can predict nothing. It was this formal dilemma that indicated to me that one should not simply try to apply the usual kind of Hamiltonian quantisation.

As almost all of the dynamical variables turn out to be unpredictable, you ask yourself whether they should be predictable physically, and if so, how the theory should be modified so that it produces reasonable results? I should perhaps say not the theory but the mathematical machinery. Alternatively, perhaps these quantities should not be predictable? Further analysis indicated to me that these variables should not be predictable. As I have indicated before, the Hamiltonian constraints determine the transition from one co-ordinate system to another. If a quantity fails to commute with the Hamiltonian constraints, that means that it is not an invariant, that its numerical value will be different in different co-ordinate systems, and this is a very common property of almost all physical variables that we know. But as co-ordinate systems are merely a mode of description and not something existing in the real universe, it is impossible to predict the value of any quantity whose value will depend on the choice of co-ordinate system. As a result you must exclude from prediction all variables, all physical quantities, whose value is not entirely independent of the choice of co-ordinate system. Such quantities are normally called invariants; I have called them observables, I suppose partly for psychological reasons. A physicist will consider an invariant a rather stodgy affair, whereas observables are obviously the kind of quantities that any scientist must go for. An observable, by its very name, is the antithesis to the worst name of all, metaphysics.

Well, this is how some of us have arrived at the conclusion that in any quantum theory of gravitation, if there is to be one, the only operators, and hence the only physical variables forming part of the theory proper, will be the observables. I shall give you three definitions for observables. The three are equivalent, but they emphasise different aspects. An observable may be defined as a quantity, or as a functional, which has vanishing Poisson brackets with all Hamiltonian constraints. This is one way of stating what an observable is. The second definition is to the effect that an observable is a quantity invariant under all conceivable curvilinear co-ordinate transformations. The third definition, and perhaps the most startling formulation, is that an observable is a constant of the motion. This is so because propagation along the time axis is one possible co-ordinate transformation; in view of the fact that the time axis is not rigidly defined but something that we can, within wide limits, set up at our pleasure, any co-ordinate transformation can be composed of backward and forward steps along various time-like directions. Hence a constant of the motion is *ipso facto* an invariant in a general-relativistic theory. Even though it is easy to show formally that all these three definitions are equivalent, it is perhaps not too surprising that it is the third definition that has given rise to the most controversy, whereas the other two have been accepted without contradiction.

How would one go about constructing observables? That is a problem that has been solved 'in principle' in a variety of ways; but so far no programme has fully succeeded in producing a complete set of observables which would describe a physical situation completely but not redundantly. We do have complete systems of observables now [1], but they are highly redundant, that is to say, a large percentage, almost all of them, can be obtained from a subset, a non-redundant subset has not yet been delineated in a useful way. The search for observables remains a challenging technical problem, which, like all technical problems, leave you with the lurking suspicion that there may be more than technicalities involved; it may turn out to be a profound problem.

If I may summarize the first point, it is that very late in the history of general relativity a fundamental concept has been crystallized out of a programme that was aimed at something totally different, the unification of quantum field theory with general relativity, a programme that is still far from concluded. The new concept appears to be useful in analysing a variety of physical situations that arise within the framework of general-relativistic theories, without in itself having found as yet its definitive technical form. All of this, I might add, represents a case history of the development of a concept without the benefit of any experiments. None of the experiments actually performed has any bearing on the concept of observables. All experiments that anyone has proposed, or carried out, to date, deal with the conventional aspects of the general theory of relativity. So here we have a partly creative, but mostly analytical intramural achievement of the theorists. It may be useful for philosophers of science

---

[1]   P. G. Bergmann and A. Komar, *Phys. Rev. Letters* **4** (1960), p. 432.

to consider occasionally this type of case history involving the evolution of a new physical concept.

Let me spend the remaining few minutes on a critique of the point concept. I mentioned fairly early in my talk that the general theory of relativity leaves us with the notion of a locally Euclidean topological four-dimensional manifold, but that the metric relations between the constituent points have become part of the dynamics. What has remained intact is the notion of the point itself. I should like to tell you in what little time remains why I think there is some evidence, as yet far from conclusive, indicating that the point concept also may eventually be eroded and disappear from physics.

First, it has been well known in quantum field theory, far away from general relativity, that whenever you try to confine things too much, if you try to localize particles by putting them into too small a cage, then you are forced to invest an enormous amount of energy; this is presumably true in the real physical world as well – close confinement means large energies. Formally this implies that any attempt, not only in general relativity but in any conventional quantum field theory, quantum electrodynamics and the like, to describe a physical situation on a point basis rather than in terms of normal modes, leads to divergences. If there were no points, and hence no theoretical possibility for close confinements, perhaps our divergence problems would be ameliorated – I say 'perhaps' because so far all attempts to proceed along these lines and to formulate non-local field theories have resulted in ills worse than those for which the cure had been intended.

From the vantage point of general relativity there is some evidence that the point concept may perhaps not die but, like old soldiers, fade away. The evidence is purely theoretical; essentially it is as follows. In constructing the invariance group of general-relativistic theories, which formalizes the fact that world points may be identified by arbitrary quadruplets of numbers, one usually is thinking of the transformations in which the new co-ordinates of a point, say x^2, are functions of the original co-ordinates of the same world point only, and do not depend on the physical fields that may be present at that world point. Through this kind of transformation the point as a point is simply given a new label.

This set of transformations froms a group (or at least a groupoid), and this group is usually meant by the term of curvilinear co-ordinate transformations. General relativistic theories are, however *ipso facto* invariant with respect to a much larger group of transformations in which the new co-ordinates may depend both on the original co-ordinates of a world point and on the total physical situation. In general relativity the total physical situation is summarized by the metric field. Imagine a number of possible physical situations, all of which are subjected to the same (new-type) co-ordinate transformation, that is to a transition to a new description. In each of these diverse physical situations the world point which originally had a certain label, say $\bar{x}^\varrho$, a set of four numerics goes over into some new world point, but a different point in each of the different physical situations. This is clearly a more general class of transformations than the one that I discussed previously, and one which still carries over world points into world points but in a manner dependent on the total physical situation.

Finally there is a class of transformations with respect to which the theory is also invariant, the canonical transformations generated by arbitrary observables. These transformations include those generated by linear combinations of the Hamiltonian constraints, but go beyond them. If we adopt an arbitrary observable as generator, then we are led to transformations in which points are no longer transformed into points, no matter how liberally we are ready to interpret that term. Here we have the germ of a theoretical possibility, whether we like it or not, which may point the way to the eventual elimination of the notion of world points altogether. All of us who are actively engaged in the formulation, the exploration, and analysis of physical theories are well aware of the fact that not every clue encountered leads to new knowledge.

Testing clues within their theoretical sphere is just as important as testing by experiment. The notion of observable already has proven its worth, even though it is not completely established in every respect. As for the eventual disappearance of the world point from the scene of our physical theories, this is a hunch in which I myself do not passionately believe – it is something that ought to be kept in mind as a possibility. But it may never prove to be useful.

G. J. WHITROW: *Principle of covariance or principle of impotence?*

I should like to add a footnote to what Professor Bergmann has said about the principle of general covariance. This principle must be sharply distinguished from the principle of equivalence. The latter is a definite physical hypothesis concerning the equivalence (for the description of physical phenomena) of a uniformly accelerated frame and a frame in a uniform gravitational field. The principle of general covariance, however, asserts that any law of nature may be expressed in the same mathematical form whatever the frame of reference. This has been called by Bergmann 'a principle of impotence', in Whittaker's sense, but I do not think that this is correct. A principle of impotence makes an assertion about the nature of the physical world, for example that no experiment can enable us to measure the absolute motion of a body. It is conceivable that such a principle is false. On the other hand, the principle of general covariance is more in the nature of a rule of procedure, a kind of scientific command – express the law in this form! If we are sufficiently ingenious we can always comply. But the principle can be given empirical content if we go on to assert that the laws of nature are those that are particularly simple in their general covariant formulation. Einstein's law of gravitation arises in this way, whereas Newton's law does not. On the other hand, other laws of nature have not been derived by following this rule – so it may only hold for gravitation.

M. BUNGE: *Material frames and imperceptible 'observables'.*

I have just two questions, one on co-ordinate systems, the other on invariants.

(1) Is it not necessary to distinguish between a co-ordinate system, which is a concept, and a reference frame, which is a

material thing such as a laboratory or our planet? Whereas co-ordinate systems are arbitrary, reference frames have certain physical properties with which we cannot tamper – for example, they can move relatively to one another whereas co-ordinate systems cannot. Moreover, one and the same reference frame can be mirrored by infinitely many co-ordinate systems: e.g., by cartesian, cylindrical, spherical, etc. co-ordinate systems. Now if we wish our co-ordinate systems to mirror possible reference frames then it becomes necessary to impose certain restrictions on them, i.e. to select a subset of all the co-ordinate systems – as proposed by Hilbert in 'Die Grundlagen der Physik' (1915–16). For instance, one will choose the components of the metric tensor in such a way that two events lying on a time-like line could not become simultaneous upon a co-ordinate transformation. In other words, one chooses physically admissible co-ordinate systems and thereby also physically admissible co-ordinate transformations. Otherwise no sensible physical interpretation of the mathematical formalism is possible: in fact unless such restrictions are imposed practically anything becomes possible – e.g., that when observed in a certain way a person might turn out to have been born at the same time as his son.

(2) Can data be frame-free? I think this is impossible, for every observation requires the choice of an observation platform – a kind of physical reference frame. The invariant distance, the invariant matter tensor, and other frame-independent quantities are not observed but hypothesized; at most they could be reconstructed out of frame-dependent data. This gives a powerful argument against remaining on the observational level – for we want quantities and relations that are independent of the contingencies of observation. It is the same with covariant relations, e.g., covariant field equations: one can think them up but not look at them. In short, all invariants and covariants are constructs. This does not mean that they are fictions: they do have physical referents all right, but the referents are empirically inaccessible pieces of reality, or rather they are only partially accessible, and only to a very sophisticated experience informed by a lot of theories. Consequently, to use the word 'observable' to designate physically

interesting invariants is epistemologically unjustified. Why not call every physically interesting invariant an absolute or intrinsic magnitude? If by 'physical' one means 'observable' in the epistemological sense, or 'measurable' in the sense of directly measurable (rather than measurable via a heap of theoretical formulas), then invariants deserve to be regarded as metaphysical. Yet they are at the heart of physics, as Professor Bergmann himself has so eloquently shown. If so, let us change our view of metaphysics – and our view of observation.

P. G. Bergmann: *Reply.*

I. Reply to M. Bunge.

In replying to Professor Bunge, I shall deal with his remarks one by one: First I shall comment on the notions of *frame of reference* and of *co-ordinate system*, and then I shall have some further remarks concerning the concept of *observables*. In both instances I consider the issues raised more verbal than basic. If I have not misunderstood Mario Bunge, all that needs to be done is to attempt to remove possible sources of misunderstandings, and we shall find ourselves in full agreement.

1. To my mind the notion of the *frame of reference* is intuitively plausible but not very clearly defined. A laboratory, or a planet, convey a rough picture of the terms of reference of our description. But as neither the laboratory nor the planet are rigid bodies, and as neither penetrates throughout the interior of the physical apparatus, such frames of reference must be considerably supplemented, and in fact idealized, before they are suitable to describe unambiguously the where and the when of any given physical process. I should tend to call such a perfected frame of reference a *co-ordinate system*.

Whether one should restrict oneself to co-ordinate systems in which a specified axis is time-like everywhere, whereas the remaining three axes are space-like is not so much a question of principle but of expediency. There are manifolds imaginable in which globally complete space-like three-surfaces do not exist, and such manifolds have been investigated by relativists. We cannot afford to deny ourselves the luxury of fitting co-ordinate systems to the task in hand. Many of us believe that locally, at least, a manifold ought to be Minkowskian, that it should possess in the neighborhood of each world point a decently shaped light cone of directions, though others question the validity of such a requirement. In any case, whether a given manifold has this property can be ascertained by an algebraic examination of the metric tensor, regardless of the choice of co-ordinate system.

Perhaps I may summarize as follows: There are no doubt sensible restrictions to be imposed on the space–time manifolds to be considered by physicists, though what these restrictions ought to be in detail is not completely settled. The choice of co-ordinates to be used in working with physically admissible manifolds is, however, not a matter of physics but of convenience.

2. I have borrowed the term 'observables' directly from the prevailing usage in quantum mechanics, and I certainly have no wish to imply that this term denotes quantities that can be observed 'directly', i.e. quantities that are the analogs of 'sense data'. Rather, my 'observables' are quantities that can be observed 'in principle', indirectly, to be sure, and only within a certain conceptual and theoretical framework; in this sense they are, most assuredly, constructs.

How do 'observables' differ from other variables in physics? They differ in that other variables are, in principle, not subject to observation, directly or indirectly. That is to say, unless a quantity is an observable within the definition proposed by me, its value has no physical significance but is coincidental to an arbitrarily chosen mode of describing a physical situation. A typical example of a non-observable in electrodynamics is the numerical value of an electromagnetic potential, an example of an observable the value of a field strength. Through a gauge transformation we can change the former at will but not the latter. In electrodynamics observables are not necessarily constants of the motion, nor are they absolute invariants, as they are still subject to Poincaré transformations; in general-relativistic theories observables are both invariant and constants of the motion.

II. Reply to G. J. Whitrow.

I am grateful to Dr. Whitrow for having called attention to the distinction to be made between the principle of equivalence, which is an assertion about the nature of the gravitational field, and the principle of general covariance, which is a formal requirement to be made of physical theories. They are related to each other, to be sure. If a theory is generally covariant, it will normally incorporate the principle of equivalence. The converse is not true: Newton's theory of gravitation is not covariant, but it does incorporate the principle of equivalence.

A great deal of thought has gone into the most appropriate formulation of the principle of general covariance, and Whitrow's statement reflects a widely shared point of view. I should feel tempted to state the principle not so much as a requirement to cast the laws of nature into covariant form, but rather as an assertion that among the set of curvilinear co-ordinate systems there exists no subset (such as rectilinear co-ordinates) in which the laws of nature take a simpler form. This formulation is close to the 'principle of impotence', which I verbalized in my talk. The obvious weak point in this formulation is the use of the term 'simple'. It is possible to find subsets of co-ordinate systems in which the laws of nature take a form which they do not possess in other co-ordinate systems, but this 'special' form is not 'simple' by our esthetic standards. I have already called attention to the contributions by Kretschmann and Havas. Perhaps I should add one more recent reference, a discussion by J. L. Anderson [1]. This whole subject is both technical and controversial. I doubt that this is the place, or that we have the time, to go into it deeply.

---

[1] J. L. Anderson, 'Relativity principles and the role of coordinates in physics', XV in H. Y. Chiu and W. F. Hoffmann, eds., *Gravitation and Relativity*, Benjamin, New York and Amsterdam, 1964, pp. 175–194.

THE INFLUENCE OF EPISTEMOLOGICAL ANALYSIS ON SCIENTIFIC RESEARCH: 'LENGTH' AND 'TIME' IN THE SPECIAL THEORY OF RELATIVITY

BÉLA JUHOS

University of Vienna

1. *The definition of magnitudes by measuring operations.* We describe and characterize empirical phenomena by magnitudes, whose values are determinable directly or indirectly by measurement. Measuring a magnitude, however, is not limited to one special process, but in accordance with different experimental circumstances different methods of measuring are applied. In such cases empirical science usually speaks of the *same* magnitude being measured by different procedures. The main reason for this assumption is the equality of the results practically attained, when, in order to determine a magnitude describing one and the same phenomenon, different measuring procedures are used. Provided, of course, that the application of different methods is empirically possible. But in epistemology we have to ask whether this is sufficient for maintaining that the *same* magnitude is measured by the different procedures under the mentioned conditions. There is perhaps no case known in which, in measuring empirical states, the application of different methods to determine the value of a magnitude leads to results which practically do not conform. Nevertheless we must not lose sight of the fact that in most cases different operations, which we apply to measure a magnitude, presuppose different theoretical suppositions. So we have to be aware of the possibility that concerning the same magnitude disparate results may be deduced from the diverse theoretical assumptions underlying different measuring operations.

With respect to this possibility I believe Bridgman [1] is right in

---

[1] Cf. P. W. Bridgman, *Reflections of a Physicist*, Philosophical Library, New York, 1956.

asserting that by different methods of measuring in principle different magnitudes are defined. So we have for instance to distinguish, as Bridgman explains, two kinds of lengths according to the totally different operations, by which lengths are measured on the one hand in mechanics, on the other hand in optics. The difference of the theoretical presuppositions in the two cases is surely striking. But Bridgman says that, in spite of the different conceptions of length defined by the different measuring operations, we are practically justified in using for the different magnitudes the same name 'length', as the operations practically do not differ in their results. I think, however, we have to apply logical analysis to the measuring theories last but not least with respect to critical cases where the different suppositions appear in the form of incompatible results.

2. *The analysis of the concept 'length'.* Let us compare the method of measuring lengths with the help of optical signals with the method applied to measure the lengths of electromagnetic waves. In the second case the distribution, breadth and shifting of spectral lines are observed, in order to determine the wave lengths.

In the special theory of relativity 'length' is defined as the distance of the projections of simultaneous positions of the extreme points of an object. By this it is assumed that the projections are to be performed by light rays. From this definition result according to the relativistic metric different lengths of an object relative to systems S and S' if the systems are moved with respect to each other. Let v be the velocity of this translatory motion. The length of an object resting in S may be l_0. Then its length l' relative to S' is, according to the special relativistic metric:

$$(1) \qquad l' = l_0 \sqrt{\left(1 - \frac{v^2}{c^2}\right)}.$$

This means that lengths experience a contraction relative to the moving systems.

Now let us assume that an electromagnetic wave has the length λ_0 relative to S. The direction of the electromagnetic ray may be the x-direction. In the same direction S' is moving in relation to S. Then the length λ' of the wave concerned relative to S' is:

$$(2) \qquad \lambda' = \lambda_0 \sqrt{\left(\frac{1 + (v/c)}{1 - (v/c)}\right)}.$$

This result can be deduced from the relativistic Doppler formula:

$$(3) \qquad \nu' = \nu_0 \sqrt{\left(\frac{1 - (v/c)}{1 + (v/c)}\right)},$$

where ν_0 is the frequency of the electromagnetic ray relative to S and ν' the frequency of the same ray relative to S'. According to formula (1) lengths experience a contraction, and according to formula (2) they experience a lengthening in relation to moving systems. Both effects depend *only* on the relative velocity v. These differing results support the opinion of Bridgman that by different measuring operations different magnitudes are defined. Perhaps one could here reply that the difference between the formulae (1) and (2) does not entitle us to assume two kinds of lengths, because the relativistic definition of the magnitude 'length' can not be applied to electromagnetic wave lengths. A wave is a process during a finite time. So the extreme points of a wave never have simultaneous positions. Therefore projections of simultaneous positions of the extreme points of a wave are not possible. But in this case the problem arises as to what we have to understand by the 'length' of an electromagnetic wave, and by that Bridgman's interpretation of the measuring operations seems justified even more. We leave undecided, whether with respect to the different behaviour of mechanical and electromagnetic lengths a uniting definition for the two magnitudes can be found, or whether a crucial experiment can be designed to test the different effects. We will rather attempt to pursue the logical analysis of the suppositions of the relativistic theory of measurement.

3. *The analysis of the concept 'time'.* Time is measured by periodic motions. We can use for measuring time periodic mechanical motions, e.g. the motions of a pendulum, or periodical electromagnetic motions, e.g. electromagnetic oscillations. S and S' again may be moved to each other with the translatory velocity v. A phenomenon that has the duration t_0 relative to S, will according to the relativistic metric, have the duration

$$(4) \qquad\qquad t' = \frac{t_0}{\sqrt{(1 - (v^2/c^2))}},$$

relative to S'. Now let us choose an electromagnetic ray in the direction x with such a frequency ν_0, that the period $\tau_0 = 1/\nu_0$ of the oscillation shall be:

$$(5) \qquad\qquad \tau_0 = t_0$$

relative to S. Measuring time we can use t_0 or τ_0 as time units. Using t_0 the phenomenon mentioned above has relative to S' the duration t' as given in formula (4). Using τ_0, however, the same phenomenon has relative to S' the duration

$$(6) \qquad\qquad \tau' = \tau_0 \sqrt{\left(\frac{1 + (v/c)}{1 - (v/c)}\right)}.$$

This formula follows immediately from (3), i.e. the relativistic Doppler formula. As $\tau_0 = t_0$ according to (5), we get for the same phenomenon relative to S' different durations even if we use for time measuring mechanical or electromagnetic periodic motions. Again both effects, (4) and (6), depend *only* on the relative velocity v.

Here again we see that from different methods of measuring disparate values may result for the magnitude that is measured.

The further investigation of the epistemological consequences of the deduced differing time effects surely is, I believe, of a certain interest. Next, the objection arises that such time effects also result if we use for time measuring any other wave oscillations instead of electromagnetic waves. The Doppler formula is valid, it could be said, for all kinds of waves and so we would get many numbers of different time duration effects, which are certainly not of importance for time measuring. But this reply omits the peculiar character which electromagnetic waves have in the special theory of relativity. Electromagnetic rays have, contrary to all non-electromagnetic waves, the constant velocity c relative to all

translatory systems. Therefore the time effect derived from the
Doppler formula only for electromagnetic waves depends solely
on the relative velocity v of the compared systems, while for all
non-electromagnetic waves it depends also on the specific propagation velocity of the waves, which is variable from system to
system. So the time effect formula (6), i.e. the Doppler time effect
for electromagnetic waves, can alone be compared with the relativistic time effect formula (4). In these two formulae only the
differing duration effects are dependent solely upon the relative
velocity v.

Comparing the two formulae we find different dilations of the
duration of a phenomenon relative to a system S' being moved
to the system S. The difference of the dilations is given by the
equation

$$(7) \qquad\qquad \tau' = t'\left(1 + \frac{v}{c}\right),$$

which can be derived from the formulae (4), (5) and (6). As in (7)
only time magnitudes related to the system S' alone appear, we
can write generally for the time magnitudes of any translatory
system:

$$(7\text{a}) \qquad\qquad \tau = t\left(1 + \frac{v}{c}\right).$$

But in this case we have to ask what the velocity v means?
(7) and (7a) do not express a relation of transformation between
the time magnitudes of different systems. They express a relation
between time magnitudes measured in one and the same system.
Then, however, in (7) and (7a) the velocity v can not signify the
relative velocity of two systems. With respect to its problematic
character we will substitute for v the unknown x and get so the
formula

$$(8) \qquad\qquad \tau = t\left(1 + \frac{x}{c}\right).$$

We attempt to find the meaning of the velocity x by the following
consideration. The value for τ we obtain by measuring the duration

of a phenomenon with the help of electromagnetic oscillations, or, let us say, by an electromagnetic clock. The values for t we obtain by measuring the duration of the same phenomenon with the help of periodical mechanic motions, i.e. by a mechanic clock. The formula (8) then says that we have to multiply the mechanical time value t with the dilation factor $(1+x/c)$, in order to get the electromagnetic time value τ. By this alone we recognize that mechanic and electromagnetic clocks resting in the same system have generally disparate movement. Only if the problematic velocity x assumes the value 0 do the measurements of time give always the same values for t and τ. In other words in a system where $x=0$ mechanical and electromagnetic clocks have the same movement.

For all cases where $x\neq0$ the two clocks have disparate movement and to be sure the hands of a mechanic clock move more speedily than those of an electromagnetic clock. For $x=c$ we get $\tau=2t$, i.e. in this case one electromagnetic time unit is in its duration equal to two mechanic time units. As the two clocks rest in the same system they can be read simultaneously. The disparate movement of the clocks then becomes obvious in the increasing distance between the positions of the hands. This discrepancy D is given by $D=\tau-t$. From (8) we get

$$(9) \qquad\qquad x = \frac{(\tau-t)\,c}{t} = \frac{Dc}{t}.$$

The value of the expression on the right-hand side can be determined by observation (by measuring). Thus the velocity x has to be ascribed to a system in accordance with the disparate movement of the electromagnetic and mechanical clocks resting in this system. Let us call the velocity x the 'virtual 'velocity of a system. x is 0 if and only if $D=\tau-t=0$. In this case there is no difference in the movement of the two kinds of clocks of a system and we have so to ascribe to this system the velocity $x=0$. For all cases where $D\neq0$ we have to ascribe a virtual velocity >0 to the systems concerned.

In the model investigated by us x has the character of a uniform velocity in a straight line (i.e. of a translatory velocity). That means that the quotient $(\tau - t)c/t$ must take in a system invariably the same value for all values of τ and t, which are read simultaneously from the positions of the hands of the two kinds of clocks. If the quotient $(\tau - t)c/t$ assumed different values in various cases by reading the positions of the hands at the same time, then x would denote a variable velocity, i.e. an accelerated virtual movement would have to be ascribed to the system. This possibility we will leave aside here.

4. *The concept of virtual velocity found by epistemological analysis and its influence on physical research.* Now the question arises how the character of the virtual velocity x is compatible with the principle of relativity according to which only relative motions are possible. The virtual velocity x is ascribed to a system S by observing solely the disparate movement of the mechanical and electromagnetic clocks resting in S. x is determined therefore independently from any other system. But it would be rash to conclude that for this reason the virtual velocity x must be an 'absolute' velocity. We have deduced the concept of 'virtual velocity' under supposition of the relativistic metric. All the formulae we have used to infer the virtual velocity of a system are expressions of the special theory of relativity. Even if we observe effectively in a system the deduced disparate movement of the mechanic and electromagnetic clocks, the relativistic metric remains valid in the system concerned according to the suppositions of our investigation. The problem of the virtual velocity therefore must be reconciled with the principles of the theory of relativity in such a way that the relativistic metric remains unaltered. I have investigated such possibilities in several papers [1].

A further question results in connection with the different movements of the mechanical and electromagnetic clocks. Characterizing the physical state of a phenomenon by space and time co-ordinates we have to take into consideration that measuring time under the

---

[1] Cf. B. Juhos 'Die zweidimensionale Zeit', *Archiv für Philosophie* 11 (1962), pp. 3–27, 'L'introduzione di ordini fittizi nei domini relativistici non univoci', *Rivista di Filosofia* 53 (1962), pp. 403–437, 'The characterization of states of translatory motion', *Ratio* 6 (1964), pp. 28–49,

mentioned conditions we get two time values. So we have to characterize a physical state by three spatial and two time co-ordinates. This result suggests the interpretation that time is a two-dimensional schema. I think this conception is more suitable than to assume two kinds of time according to the two different methods of time measurement. The value of the virtual velocity x can thus be understood as a measure of the two-dimensional time metric valid in the system concerned. Of course new problems arise by asking what special mathematical form the metric of the two-dimensional time schema should have, and further how a unifying metric for the five-dimensional spatio-temporal schema should be defined?

These are, however, questions of piecemeal scientific research, and here I have tried only to show, how epistemological analysis of scientific concepts and suppositions can lead to new, perhaps unexpected, scientific problems and thus influence scientific research.

G. J. WHITROW: *On an argument of Professor Juhos.*

I am extremely puzzled by the argument and conclusions of this paper. In particular, I cannot understand equation (7). This has been obtained by combining equations (4), (5) and (6), but I think that the derivation is fallacious because these equations are incompatible. Equation (6) comes from the Doppler effect formula (3). This formula relates the frequency of emission of electromagnetic waves in one system S with the frequency of their reception in the other system S'. It therefore relates the actual measures by S and S', respectively, of *two different intervals* of *time*, one occurring at S and the other at S'. On the other hand, equation (4) relates the measure of a time interval on the clock carried by S with the value theoretically assigned to this same time interval by S'. Consequently, in equation (4) we are concerned with the different values attributed by S and S' to the same interval of time occurring at S. It follows that equation (7) cannot arise, because it is deduced from formulae that are incompatible. Consequently, all the conclusions drawn from (7) have no foundation. In particular, there is no reason for introducing the complicated idea of a two-dimensional time.

M. BUNGE: *The nonoperational nature of theoretical concepts.*

The specific problems dealt with in this paper arise from the operationalist thesis 'To define is to measure'. If this claim is disavowed those problems dissolve. Now the very conclusions of the paper show that measurement fails to supply unambiguous definitions of physical magnitudes. Since special relativity does employ a single concept of relative time, the operational analysis is self-defeating. The function of measurement is not to define physical magnitudes but to estimate some of their numerical values. The physical magnitudes themselves are either introduced as primitive concepts or are defined in terms of primitives – never in terms of laboratory operations. Take for instance the concept of physical length, i.e. the concept of length as interpreted in physics. As Carnap showed long ago, the numerical value l of the length of a body b, reckoned in a given scale-cum-unit system s, is a function L of b and s, i.e. $L_\theta(b, s) = l$. The *general theoretical concept* of physical length is obtained by taking all possible ordered couples (b, s), i.e. by forming the Cartesian product $B \times S$ of the set B of bodies and the set S of scale-cum-unit systems, the function L_θ maps the set $B \times S$ of body-scale pairs into the subset R^+ of nonnegative reals, i.e. $L_\theta: B \times S \rightarrow R^+$. This is an analysis, not a definition of the physical length concept. Nothing is said in it about measurement; there is a single general concept of length in nonrelativistic theoretical physics. (The extension to relativity is straightforward by taking the domain of L_θ to be $B \times S \times K$, where K stands for the set of reference frames.) It is only the empirical estimates of length values that depend on the measurement technique: if t is such a technique, for every triple (b, s, t) a single real value interval $i = (l - \varepsilon, l + \varepsilon)$ is obtained, where ε designates the measurement error associated with the interval and the technique. In general, then, the *experimental concept* of physical length is the function $L_\varepsilon: B \times S \times T \rightarrow I$, with T the set of all conceivable length measurement techniques and $I \subset R^+$. Both functions, L_θ and L_ε, satisfy the axioms for length given in topology. And every one of them subsumes an infinity of special length concepts. Now in relativity theory the length concept is not defined but is adopted as a primitive. Something similar is the case with the time concept: it is a primitive in every known physical theory – which does not prevent one from analysing it. Thus in special relativity we can regard the relative time as the numerical value of a function T that sends every triple (event, event, reference frame) to a point on the real line, i.e. $T: E \times E \times K \rightarrow R$, where E designates the set of all possible point events and K the set of all physical reference frames. Just as in the case of length we can distinguish a lot of experimental times, as many as time reckoning techniques: but none of these will occur in physical theory. In particular, special relativity employs a single time concept, as can clearly be seen by axiomatizing the theory (see my forthcoming *Foundations of Physics*). This explains why the theory has not been affected by the recent revolutions in time measurement techniques.

B. JUHOS: *Reply.*

According to Dr. Whitrow the equations (6) and (4) in my paper are incompatible, the derivation of formula (7) from (6) and (4) being therefore inadmissible. But I think that Whitrow's interpretation of the formulae (6) and (4) is erroneous. Equation (6) relates according to him 'the actual measures by S and S' respectively, of *two different intervals* of *time*, one occuring at S and the other at S''. On the other hand, again according to Whitrow, 'in equation (4) we are concerned with the different values attributed by S and S' to the same interval of time occuring at S'. If these interpretations were correct equation (6) would relate the duration values (periods) of two different waves, one occuring at S and the other at S'. But I think this is an untenable interpretation of (6). For it would mean that the Doppler effect formula (3) would also relate the frequency values of two different waves, which is, I think, a fundamentally erroneous interpretation of the Doppler effect. According to my interpretation, equations (3) and (6) relate frequency values and period values characterizing *one and the same wave* relative to S and S'. From this point of view (6) and (4) are not incompatible. Equation (4) likewise relates time-values, which characterize the duration of *one and the same phenomenon* relative to S and S' respectively. I believe therefore that my derivation of (7) from (4), (5), and (6) is justified.

Professor Bunge's argument is not, I think, against my derivation, but against the interpretation of my results. Physical magnitudes, Bunge asserts, are not defined by measurement, but 'are either introduced as primitive concepts or are defined in terms of primitives – never in terms of laboratory operations'. At the end of my paper I stressed that the problem of how we are to define a physical concept in a suitable manner is a problem for piecemeal physical research. One method of defining a physical concept is described by Bunge. Applied to the results of my paper, this method of definition would make it necessary to explain why the duration of a phenomenon is characterized by different time values according to the Lorentz and the Doppler formulae, and the measuring operations which correspond to them. The meaning of the concept of time would remain unaltered by such an explanation. This is, of course, a possible way to use physical concepts independent of measuring operations. Whether this method is suitable in the case concerned is open to discussion. But Bunge is mistaken if he means that magnitudes *never* are defined 'in terms of laboratory operations'. The relativistic time magnitudes for instance, are to a large extent defined, in opposition to the absolute time magnitudes of classical physics, in terms of the relativistic time measuring operations. So I would not exclude the possibility of defining the concept of time in terms of the results which we get by combining the Lorentz and Doppler equations and the corresponding measuring operations. But I would repeat that the method explained by Professor Bunge is equally possible, that it does not contradict my derivations at all, and that piecemeal physical research has to decide which method of definition of the magnitudes concerned is the most suitable one.

INFORMATION PROCESSING AND CHOICE BEHAVIOR [1]

PATRICK SUPPES

Stanford University

1. *Introduction.* Because the discussions at these meetings have been more philosophical than scientific, at least with respect to problems in the social sciences, I have reorganized and reoriented my paper to try to give a more philosophical discussion of current mathematical work in the social sciences. I originally planned to try to give some sort of survey, albeit rather superficial, of the current state of things in several of the social sciences, and emphasize why I thought the work in economics and psychology was at a greater depth and had achieved more fundamental results than in the other social sciences. What I now choose to do is to concentrate on a single topic. It represents, I would claim, an important direction of work since World War II and an important set of new ideas for the social sciences as a whole. Any such general claim about a wide variety of sciences is naturally subject to criticism, but I think there would be much agreement about its importance. In discussing information processing and choice behavior, I shall concentrate on the work in economics and psychology which falls under this general heading.

There is a classical distinction in the social sciences that I shall use, although under close scrutiny it can be challenged. This is the distinction between normative and descriptive theory.

2. *Normative theory.* The normative theory of choice behavior has a very old history in economics; it certainly does not begin with economics since World War II. The roots of the theory go back

[1] The research on which this paper is based has been supported by the U.S. Office of Education under Contract 3–10–009 with Stanford University and by the Carnegie Corporation of New York.

to Adam Smith and it was developed in a fairly continuous way in the latter half of the eighteenth century and throughout the nineteenth century. After a certain amount of confusion as to how the theory should be formulated, it was recognized by Pareto [1] at about the beginning of this century that the classical ideas of individual choice behavior in economic contexts could be represented by merely ordinal choice. To take a simple example, suppose a person is choosing between bread and beer, or more realistically between x amount of bread, y amount of beer, and x' amount of bread and y' amount of beer. The classical representation of this situation in terms of a demand curve would show bread on the abscissa, say, and beer on the ordinant; the demand curve would have for any reasonable person a shape something like that shown in fig. 1. The formalization of economic behavior in terms of these

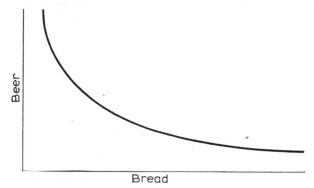

Fig. 1.   Demand curve for bread and beer.

simple ideas of preferring one bundle of goods to another and satisfying some obvious properties as expressed in the curve of fig. 1, which is convex toward the origin, has been well formalized in the classical theory of demand. In many respects this theory is a very finished piece of work as expounded, for example, in Wold and Jureen [2]. By the time of World War II the ordinal theory

[1]   V. Pareto, *Manuale di economia politica, con una introduzione sulla scienze sociale*, Società Editrice Libraria, Milan, Italy, 1906.

[2]   H. Wold and L. Jureen, *Demand Analysis, a Study in Econometrics*, John Wiley and Sons, New York, 1953.

of choice had very substantial developments in welfare economics, but I shall not pursue matters in that direction but rather restrict myself to the fundamental theory of choice.

From a conceptual standpoint the important limiting characteristic of the classical ordinal theory is the requirement that a person know with certainty the consequences of his choice. The first new step was the analysis on many fronts of choice behavior in situations of uncertainty. Two distinguished investigators prior to World War II of this kind of analysis were Ramsey and De Finetti [1], but it is still true that the general recognition of the importance of decisions or choices taken in situations of uncertainty and of the inadequacy of ordinal preference theory comes after World War II. To illustrate the fundamental ideas, suppose a man is thinking about going to a football game, and he is uncertain whether it is going to rain. He has some reasons for thinking it will rain and some reasons for thinking it will not rain. What it is natural here to label as states of the weather are ordinarily called states of nature, and for simplicity we have dichotomized the possible states of nature into just two: *rain* or *no rain*. With even more justification, it is natural to dichotomize the decisions the individual may take: (d_1) go to the game or (d_2) not go to the game. Moreover, we may easily represent in qualitative terms the consequences of the two decisions, depending on the two states of nature. If he goes to the game and it doesn't rain the consequence is something good, but if he goes and it rains then the consequences

		d_1 go	d_2 not go
s	rain	bad	neutral
$1-s$	no rain	good	neutral

Fig. 2.

---

[1] F. P. Ramsey, Truth and probability, in F. P. Ramsey, *The Foundations of Mathematics and Other Logical Essays*, Harcourt and Brace, New York, 1931, pp. 156–198; B. de Finetti, 'La prévision: ses lois logiques, ses sources subjectives', *Ann. Inst. Poincaré* 7 (1937), pp. 1–68. English translation in H. E. Kyburg Jr. and H. E. Smokler, eds., *Studies in Subjective Probability*, John Wiley and Sons, New York, 1964, pp. 93–158.

are bad. If he does not go we may simply describe the consequences for the present purposes as being neutral. The situation may be represented as shown in fig. 2. Now we may assume that the individual prefers the good consequences to the neutral consequences, and the neutral consequences to the bad consequences, but it is also perfectly clear that even in this simple example a merely ordinal knowledge of preference is not sufficient to determine what decision it is reasonable to take. In order for the ordinal theory to be applicable, it is necessary to know the state of nature with certainty, but in this example and in many others, the individual can only attach a certain probability to each state.

The proposal of Ramsey, which in certain respects goes back at least to Bernoulli [1], is that a rational person must behave as if he had a utility function on the outcomes or consequences, and a probability function on the states of nature, and then select the decision that maximizes expected utility with respect to his subjective probability function on the states of nature. Thus in the present simple example if the individual assigns a probability s to raining and $1-s$ to not raining, the utility c_1 to the good consequences, the utility c_2 to the neutral and the utility c_3 to the bad consequences, as these phrases are used to refer to the situation described in fig. 2, then the expectations of decisions d_1 and d_2 are:

$$E(d_1) = sc_3 + (1-s)c_1,$$
$$E(d_2) = sc_2 + (1-s)c_2 = c_2.$$

The rule of behavior proposed by Ramsey and originating with Bernoulli represents a specific new idea in the history of discussions of rational behavior. That new idea is that the decision maker should maximize his expected utility. Thus in our simple example he should select that one of the two decisions which has the greater expected utility. This concept of maximizing expected utility is very closely related to the Bayesian ideas that have been talked about in many of the sessions on inductive logic at this colloquium,

---

[1]   D. Bernoulli, Specimen theoriae novae de mensura sortis, *Comentarii academiae scientiarum imperiales petropolitanae*, v, 1738, pp. 175–192. (Transl. by L. Sommer in *Econometrica* **22** (1954), pp. 23–36.)

and this framework of ideas has been investigated in both economics and related parts of statistics.

The Bayesians are clearly imperialistic and would in many contexts maintain that the rule of maximizing expected utility should be held to without exception. But there is one context in which a very good counter-case can be made and also in which a second, absolutely fundamental new concept with respect to rationality has been introduced. The context is game theory. I shall not attempt to describe any of the results in detail, but I think they can be sketched in terms of their conceptual impact on philosophy rather simply. It was the contribution of von Neumann to define and analyze what are to be regarded as optimal strategies in purely competitive games between two players. The famous minimax theorem of von Neumann shows that stability of behavior results between two intelligent opponents when each is selecting a minimax strategy [1].

The simplest interesting example perhaps is matching pennies; the minimax strategy for matching pennies is to pick heads with probability half and tails with probability half, and then of course the expected outcome for both players is zero.

The fundamentally new concept here, and one that I am sure will not be easily swallowed by many philosophers, is that the concept of *randomness* of choice is directly and intimately tied to the concept of rationality. It is contrary certainly to the main thrust of historical discussions in philosophy of prudent or rational behavior to come out with a recommendation that one should ignore much of what one knows about the situation – individual predilections, past history and intuitive insights into the nature of the universe – and should, if one is up against a clever, intelligent opponent, simply randomize in terms of a minimax strategy. The applications of this recommendation at a normative level go in several directions, but from a philosophical standpoint, what I would like to emphasize is this new step of tying the concept of randomness to the concept of rationality. Explicit probability

---

[1] J. von Neumann and O. Morgenstern, *Theory of Games and Economic Behavior*, Princeton University Press, Princeton N.J., 1944, 1947, 1953.

concepts occur surprisingly late in the history of thought. For example, in the vast technical literature of Greek astronomy there seems to be no systematic consideration in explicit form of the theory of error, a ready-made situation if ever there was one, for the introduction of probability and the concept of random error. The depth and perfection of Greek mathematics compared with the beginnings seventeen hundred years later of the probability calculus is surprising; very elementary probability questions were the subject of heated and prolonged discussions at a very late date. There seem to be inherently difficult and subtle things about the concept of randomness, which perhaps account for the lateness of its introduction.

Without doubt an important aspect of the difficulty of the concept of randomness is the strongly entrenched belief that every event must have a determinate cause. Insofar as this belief is dominant the concept of randomness can at best be assigned a derivative position, for if every event must have a determinate cause there can be no objective randomness in nature. And, so this line of thought goes, since there is no genuine randomness in nature, the concept of randomness can have no fundamental philosophical importance. To move from consideration of the external world to errors or ignorance on the part of a human observer or a measuring instrument manipulated by someone is itself a highly sophisticated step, and this seems to have been required before the concept of randomness could come to the surface as an important scientific concept – not, certainly, in violation of the principle of determinate causality, but as, roughly speaking, a measure of subjective ignorance. Laplace puts the matter very succinctly in the opening lines of ch. 2 of his famous *Philosophical Essay on Probabilities*, 1951, first published in 1812.

'All events, even those which on account of their insignificance do not seem to follow the great laws of nature, are a result of it just as necessarily as the revolutions of the sun. In ignorance of the ties which unite such events to the entire system of the universe, they have been made to depend upon final causes or upon hazard, according as they occur and are re-

peated with regularity, or appear without regard to order; but
these imaginary causes have gradually receded with the
widening bounds of knowledge and disappear entirely before
sound philosophy, which sees in them only the expression of
our ignorance of the true causes.

'Present events are connected with preceding ones by a tie
based upon the evident principle that a thing cannot occur
without a cause which produces it.'

It is another long step from Laplace to von Neumann, from randomness as an expression of ignorance to randomness as an expression
of rationality.

3. *Descriptive theory.* Although it is possible to cite certain studies
in economics and sociology, the main investigations of the descriptive theory of information processing and choice behavior
have certainly been in psychology. Again, there are various links
to be established to what went on before World War II; perhaps
the primary predecessor is the general literature on psychometric
scales, but the main results of that literature are not of central
importance to what I want to say today.

In the discussion of descriptive theory I shall be concerned to
look at increasingly detailed and complicated levels of analysis.
These levels of analysis will relate to some of the problems of
categoricity and incompleteness that have been mentioned in discussions of other topics at this colloquium, including the foundations
of mathematics. The animadversions of many people about the
inadequacy of mathematical work in the social sciences to express
the full complexity of human behavior have in many cases rested
on a misunderstanding of what can be expected of the work as
yet done. It is in no sense categorical; it does not offer a categorical
structural model of human thought and human activity. The thrust
of the models is to be highly noncategorical, to catch certain aspects
of behavior, and to hope, in catching those aspects, to have got
hold of something that can in itself be studied and analyzed without
understanding the full mechanisms. This is a procedure that one
can claim is very similar to that followed in the history of physics.

Perhaps the first and most elementary level of analysis is at the level of simple choice behavior in selecting one of two alternatives presented. One of the first points to be observed in the psychological literature is that the normative theory already described for such situations is entirely too algebraic in character. Once an individual has applied, consciously or not, his utility function and subjective probability function to compute expectations of the decisions among which he may choose, then according to this algebraic theory he should, with probability one, pick the decision with the highest expected value. The psychological criticism of this model is that there are too many situations in which the preference or choice of individuals will vary. From a philosophical standpoint it is always possible to argue that the same situation is never presented twice, there is always a new element that accounts for a change, and therefore the individual always satisfies the algebraic model. However, for scientific purposes it is much more fruitful to identify the circumstances as being of the same character and to ask what is the probability that alternative or object i will be selected over alternative or object j. The first kind of model I would like to mention is one due to Duncan Luce [1] and others. It has been termed a *response-strength model*. For simplicity of discussion, let us suppose we have 10 objects which might be 10 kinds of food and we want to look at the choices of an individual when presented with pairs of these objects. In general we will be looking at 45 parameters that describe the probability of choosing i over j. The only general constraint is that $p_{ij} + p_{ji} = 1$. (Here p_{ij} is the probability that i will be chosen over j.) The natural first question is to ask what kind of model will lead to a reasonable reduction of the number of parameters to be considered. The response-strength model postulates that for each object or alternative i there is response strength v_i, and the probability of choosing i over j is expressed by the following equation in terms of these response strengths

(1)
$$p_{ij} = \frac{v_i}{v_i + v_j}.$$

---

[1] R. D. Luce, *Individual Choice Behavior: A Theoretical Analysis*, John Wiley and Sons, New York, 1959.

It is obvious that this simple response-strength model reduces the number of parameters from 45 to 10. With this reduction we have something of manageable proportions and at the same time a model that has sufficient theoretical implications to be tested against experimental data. I shall not try to review the relevant experimental literature [1].

Perhaps the most serious limitation of the response-strength model is that it is static in character. It does not include in its conceptualization any process that permits the individual's utility function or the individual's response strength to change on the basis of experience.

The next move is to consider models of behavior in which we postulate mechanisms of adaptation or learning by means of which the behavior will be affected over time depending upon the kind of environment in which the organism is placed. This takes us to learning models that are designed to handle this kind of situation. The simplest sort I shall mention here is the *linear model* [2]. The individual is presented with choices to be made, let us say from a finite set – we might as well restrict it to a set of two responses for the present purpose, and let p_n be the probability of making response 1 on trial n, and $1 - p_n$ the probability of making response 2. The model will be more meaningful if we consider it against the background of a characteristic experiment on choice behavior. The subject is facing a board on which two lights are placed and his task, he is told, is to predict, on each trial, which light will flash. Now I think we all recognize, if we put it in a philosophical context, the relation of this kind of experiment to some fairly simple problems of induction. I hasten to add, already

[1] For a discussion of this and a good many of the other models to be mentioned below, see R. D. Luce and P. Suppes, 'Preference, utility and subjective probability', in R. D. Luce, R. Bush and E. Galanter, eds., *Handbook of Mathematical Psychology*, III, John Wiley and Sons, New York, 1965, pp. 249–410.

[2] R. R. Bush and F. Mosteller, *Stochastic Models for Learning*, John Wiley and Sons, New York, 1955; W. K. Estes and P. Suppes, 'A linear model for a continuum of responses', in R. R. Bush and W. K. Estes, eds., *Studies in Mathematical Learning Theory*, ch. 8, Stanford University Press, Stanford, Cal., 1959, pp. 137–179.

in this situation we can generate problems of induction considerably more complex than any model of induction yet proposed in inductive logic can handle. So even though this is a seemingly simple experimental situation, its conceptual analysis is not so simple. A schema of the experimental apparatus is shown in fig. 3. The

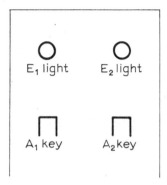

Fig. 3.   Schema of experimental apparatus.

lights that flash are labeled E_1 and E_2, and are ordinarily called the reinforcing events. The keys used by the subject to respond are labeled A_1 and A_2. It should be obvious that the subject makes the A_1 response to predict the E_1 event, i.e., the flashing of the light on the left. The linear model postulates a linear function for p_{n+1} in terms of p_n if E_1 occurs, and a related linear function if E_2 occurs, with the first function being such that $p_{n+1} > p_n$ if $p_n \neq 1$ and the second such that $p_{n+1} < p_n$ if $p_n \neq 0$ – whence the appropriateness of the term *reinforcing event* for E_1 and E_2. The occurrence of E_1 reinforces response A_1 and the occurrence of E_2 reinforces response A_2. The linear model is defined by the equations defining the two linear functions already qualitatively described. These two functions are determined by a single learning parameter θ that must be estimated from the experimental data.

$$p_{n+1} = \begin{cases} (1-\theta)\,p_n + \theta & \text{if } E_1 \text{ occurs} \\ (1-\theta)\,p_n & \text{if } E_2 \text{ occurs.} \end{cases}$$

Obviously this model depends on a highly simple – in fact I should say for many situations a highly simple-minded – adaptive mechanism. The linear model turns out to be satisfactory for certain kinds of situations, and, in view of its simplicity, I am sure it is no surprise that it is also not difficult to find experimental situations in which it is not satisfactory. I am not concerned here and certainly do not have the time to review the situations in which it works and those in which it does not work [1].

What I would like to emphasize is the relation of this kind of model to the theory of induction. The inductive problem, I take it, is to predict from trial to trial the occurrence of an E_1 or E_2 event, and the predictions should be based on the outcomes of the previous trials. The first point is that if the sequence is finite, then even from the standpoint of the most powerful tools available, the imposition and justification of the optimum way to proceed is by no means a trivial task, in fact a very complicated one that is not fully and satisfactorily solved. If we conceptualize the situation as going on to infinity, for many situations it seems obvious that the linear model is wrong from a normative or optimizing standpoint, and secondly, what the appropriate solution should be. But remember, when I say this, it is too easy to think of describing the discrepancy between this kind of model and recommended inductive behavior in terms of sitting outside the experimental situation and having in hand the experimenter's verbal description of precisely what has happened and what will happen on subsequent trials, the *schedule* as it is called of the reinforcing events. If I place a competent inductive philosopher or a competent statistician in the experimental environment it should be apparent without demonstration that it is very easy to generate sequences that will be extremely difficult for him to handle in terms of optimizing his predictions. The reason I think is apparent. If we leave the situation open, the degree of complexity and the types of schedule to be considered are unbounded in

---

[1] For a summary of experimental data for the linear model, see, W. K Estes, 'Probability learning', in A. W. Melton, ed. *Categories of Human Learning* (*Proceedings of the Michigan–ONR conference on human learning*), Academic Press, New York, 1964, pp. 89–128; and Luce and Suppes, op. cit,

number. It is not only possible to criticize inductive theories of behavior – the kind of inductive logic that has been much discussed in this colloquium – which do not even begin to touch this problem, the problem of making an inductive inference in a stochastic process, but it can also be a problem to tax the best statistical tools available.

My point is that the study of the actual behavior of organisms in this kind of environment is not as conceptually trivial, even from the standpoint of induction, as might be supposed, and one of the kinds of things that can be studied of some interest from a mathematical standpoint is the following. With respect to a schedule S of reinforcing events we may ask if a model M is Bayesian or at least asymptotically Bayesian. If it is asymptotically Bayesian, then as the number of trials goes to infinity the model will select a Bayesian optimum strategy. As you might expect, many learning models are not asymptotically Bayesian for some schedules, but the point of interest from the standpoint of induction is that the analysis of the situation in which one model is Bayesian and another model is not, is rather enlightening regarding the kind of information processing that is required in order to be Bayesian. Let me give an example. If we have a binomial distribution so that E_1 occurs with probability π on every trial and E_2 with probability $1-\pi$, with exactly one of the two events occurring on each trial independent of what the subject does (simple noncontingent schedule), then the linear model is not Bayesian. To be Bayesian would require that $\lim_{n \to \infty} p_n = 1$ if $\pi > \frac{1}{2}$ and $\lim_{n \to \infty} p_n = 0$ if $\pi < \frac{1}{2}$, but in fact for the linear model

$$\lim_{n \to \infty} \frac{1}{n} \sum_{m=1}^{n} p_m = \pi.$$

A model introduced by Luce [1], the so-called *beta model* that grows out of the discussion of response strengths, is Bayesian for the noncontingent schedule and appropriate choice of parameters. The one-parameter beta model, like the linear model, is defined

---

[1] R. D. Luce, op. cit.

by two equations

$$p_{n+1} = \begin{cases} \dfrac{p_n}{p_n + \beta(1-p_n)} & \text{if } E_1 \text{ occurs} \\[3mm] \dfrac{p_n}{p_n + (1/\beta)(1-p_n)} & \text{if } E_2 \text{ occurs,} \end{cases}$$

with $0 < \beta < 1$. (These two equations are derived from using equation (1) to relate p_n to response strengths and by postulating linear transformations on the response strengths to reflect the effects of the reinforcing events E_1 and E_2.) The argument to show that with probability 1, $p_\infty = 1$ if and only if $\pi > \frac{1}{2}$ is straightforward.

The most important fact about the beta model is that the operators β and $1/\beta$ commute. In particular, if in the first n trials there are m E_1 events and thus $n-m$ E_2 events, it is easy to show that

$$p_{n+1} = \frac{p_1}{p_1 + \beta^{2m-n}(1-p_1)}.$$

We want to show that $\beta^{2m-n} \to 0$ with probability one as $n \to \infty$, and thus $p_n \to 1$. First we may define the random variable X_n recursively by

$$X_{n+1} = \begin{cases} X_n + \log \beta & \text{with prob } \pi \\ X_n - \log \beta & \text{with prob } 1-\pi, \end{cases}$$

which defines a simple random walk. By the strong law of large numbers, with probability one as $n \to \infty$

$$X_n \to \infty \qquad \text{if } \pi > \tfrac{1}{2}$$
$$X_n \to -\infty \quad \text{if } \pi < \tfrac{1}{2},$$

and since $X_n = (2m-n)\log \beta$

$$\beta^{2m-n} \to 0 \quad \text{if } \pi > \tfrac{1}{2}$$
$$\beta^{2m-n} \to \infty \quad \text{if } \pi < \tfrac{1}{2},$$

whence

$$p_n \to 1 \text{ if } \pi > \tfrac{1}{2}$$
$$p_n \to 0 \text{ if } \pi < \tfrac{1}{2},$$

as desired.

On the other hand, if we now move to the next most simple schedule, namely, the simple contingent schedule in which the probability of an E_1 response given A_1 is equal to π_1 and the probability of E_2 given A_2 is equal to π_2, then the beta model also is no longer Bayesian (this follows from Theorem 5 of Lamperti and Suppes [1]). Indeed, under fairly general restrictions on the amount of information that is carried no commuting-operator model is asymptotically Bayesian for simple contingent schedules. One can begin to get a rather sensitive idea, by the consideration of various schedules, of the kind of models that lead to inductively optimal behavior and the kind that do not. In many respects the degree of complexity to be found in learning models of the sort discussed already exceeds that of inductive logic, which has yet been scarcely developed for temporally ordered processes.

In terms of information processing the most relevant part of psychology is the theory of concept formation. It is apparent that learning models of the sort already discussed do not provide a mechanism that will begin to explain or to account for the learning of a concept by an organism, and the next level of complexity in models of behavior is to move to the postulation of underlying mechanisms that will provide a framework for the analysis of the learning process. I shall first consider models of stimulus-sampling theory, which in its standard formulation does not provide sufficiently complex mechanisms to explain concept formation, but does constitute a large step beyond the linear and beta models in providing a schema of how relatively simple learning takes place. The basic ideas of the theory derive from an important and fundamental paper of Estes [2]. The axiomatic formulation given here follows that of Suppes and Atkinson [3]. The axioms will be formulated verbally, but it is clear how to convert them into a formulation that is mathematically rigorous. The axioms depend upon

[1] J. Lamperti and P. Suppes, 'Some asymptotic properties of Luce's beta learning model', *Psychometrika* **25** (1960), pp. 233–241.

[2] W. K. Estes, 'Toward a statistical theory of learning', *Psychol. Rev.* **57** (1950), pp. 94–107.

[3] P. Suppes and R. C. Atkinson, *Markov Learning Models for Multiperson Interactions*, Stanford University Press, Stanford, Cal., 1960.

five basic concepts of association and reinforcement psychology. These are the three categories of stimulus, response and reinforcement, and the two processes of stimulus sampling and stimulus conditioning. The formulation of the theory depends upon conceiving the sequence of events that takes place on a trial as being essentially of the following sort. A set of stimuli is presented to the subject. From this set he samples a single stimulus or stimulus pattern, as it is often termed. On the basis of the conditioning of the sampled stimulus a response is made. After the response is made a reinforcing event occurs and depending upon the nature of the reinforcing event the conditioning of the sampled stimulus is changed or kept the same. The reconditioning of the sampled stimulus places the subject in a new state of conditioning and he is now ready to begin another trial. The occurrences of the various events described, as is made clear in the formulation of the axioms, are governed by probability laws. The axioms as formulated are meant to apply to a finite set of stimuli, a finite set of responses and a finite set of reinforcing events, with a natural 1–1 correspondence obtaining between responses and reinforcing events of the sort described above in discussing paradigm experiments for the linear and beta models. The axioms are divided into three groups with the first group dealing with the conditioning of sampled stimuli, the second group with the sampling of stimuli, and the third with responses.

Conditioning Axioms

C1.   On every trial each stimulus element is conditioned to exactly one response.

C2.   If a stimulus element is sampled on a trial, it becomes conditioned with probability c to the response (if any) that is reinforced on that trial; if it is already conditioned to that response, it remains so.

C3.   If no reinforcement occurs on a trial, there is no change in conditioning on that trial.

C4.   Stimulus elements that are not sampled on a given trial do not change their conditioning on that trial.

C5.   The probability c that a sampled stimulus element will be conditioned to a reinforced response is independent of the trial number and the preceding pattern of events.

Sampling Axioms

S1.   Exactly one stimulus element is sampled on each trial.

S2.   Given the set of stimulus elements available for sampling on a trial, the probability of sampling a given element is independent of the trial number and the preceding pattern of events, and is the same for all available elements.

Response Axiom

R1.   On any trial that response is made to which the sampled stimulus element is conditioned.

It is important to note that in this formulation of stimulus-sampling theory the processing of information is formulated in terms of the conditioning of stimuli and not in terms of more explicit cognitive processes. This language of sampling and conditioning of stimuli would seem to stand in rather sharp contrast to the Bayesian ideas of information processing that were discussed earlier as part of normative theory. However, as we shall see later, this contrast is not as sharp as it seems. Another important remark about these axioms is that although they provide a mechanism for the processing of information in terms of the sampling and conditioning of stimuli, they have restricted applicability to complex information processing because no structure is imposed on the set of stimuli. Without some devices for imposing structure on the set of stimuli, or constructing structure by considering sets of sets of stimuli and so forth, as is done in axiomatic set theory in constructing classical mathematical objects, there is little hope of dealing with problems of complex concept formation.

The mathematical tool for applying stimulus-sampling theory to the noncontingent and simple contingent schedules discussed earlier is the theory of finite state Markov chains. It is straightforward to derive from the axioms that for all the relatively simple rein-

forcement schedules the functions that describe the possible states
of conditioning of the stimulus elements constitute a finite state
Markov chain. The finiteness results from the fact that we have
assumed that there is only a finite set of stimuli and a finite set
of responses and therefore, a finite number of possible states of
conditioning. To illustrate how the theory works out in detail,
let us suppose that the set S of stimuli contains only two elements
s_1 and s_2. We may represent the states of conditioning in the two-
response case by the subset of S conditioned to response A_1. We
then have four states of conditioning corresponding to the four
subsets of the two-element set $\{s_1, s_2\}$. It is easy to derive from
the axioms stated above the following transition matrix for the
two-element model and the simple noncontingent reinforcement
schedule.

	0	$\{s_1\}$	$\{s_2\}$	$\{s_1, s_2\}$
0	$1-c\pi$	$c\pi/2$	$c\pi/2$	0
$\{s_1\}$	$c(1-\pi)/2$	$1-c/2$	0	$c\pi/2$
$\{s_2\}$	$c(1-\pi)/2$	0	$1-c/2$	$c\pi/2$
$\{s_1, s_2\}$	0	$c(1-\pi)/2$	$c(1-\pi)/2$	$1-c(1-\pi)$

From the elementary theory of Markov chains it is also straightforward to show that the Cesaro mean asymptotic limit of p_n is
the same as for the linear model, that is, π.

The next step up in complexity is to models of behavior that
are adequate for analysis of concept formation. For many reasons
it is appropriate to claim that the most complex act of information
processing is that of forming a new concept, and it is therefore
not surprising that an understanding of how organisms form
concepts seems to be a difficult and subtle affair of an as yet
undeveloped theory. There has recently been a certain amount
of controversy about which aspects of concept formation represent
innate structures and which structures are learned. My response
to this is rather like that of a starving man offered a choice between
chicken and steak. It scarcely matters which choice is made at
the moment. The fundamental and important thing for the present
is to be able to conceive and define structures that are adequate

to account for the concepts that are formed, regardless of whether these structures turn out to be innate or acquired.

A natural course at this point would be to survey recent work in psychology on concept formation and evaluate the extent to which it is providing the sort of structures needed. Because of the paucity of deep-running theory I prefer to move in a more philosophical direction and comment on the relation of the search for an adequate theory of concept formation to the aims and achievements of constructivists working in a philosophical rather than a psychological or scientific tradition. (In mentioning philosophical constructivists I naturally think mainly of Russell, Whitehead, Carnap and Goodman.) It is natural to ask what if any are the fundamental differences between a psychological and a philosophical theory of concept formation.

Generally speaking, philosophers are wont to emphasize the differences and play down the similarities between philosophical and psychological approaches to concept formation. Part of this tendency perhaps arises from a desire not to become entangled with the complexities, the uncertainties, the open-endedness, the conceptually vague character of much traditional psychological research on concept formation, but there is also a deeper view supporting the separation. It seems to be believed that a satisfactory philosophical theory of concept formation can be worked out more or less independently of related scientific work in psychology. There are many reasons to be skeptical of this view. Of primary importance in my mind is the fact that a satisfactory theory must take account of the special nature, the powers and limitations of human beings. It is philosophically interesting to analyze what can be said about the manner of knowing of an omniscient God, or of a Turing machine, or of an idealized human with perfect memory and remarkable powers of perception, but such analysis, even if satisfactory in its own right, does not fill the need for a theory of human knowing.

It is precisely the task of psychology to lay bare the necessary and sufficient conditions of human learning and concept formation. To imagine a philosophical theory of concept formation which was hailed as a triumph but had no relevance for psychology and no sharply defined relations to psychological theory seems to me as difficult as to imagine what it would be like to have two distinct theories of the real numbers, one philosophical and the other mathematical.

If human characteristics are not imposed, foreign and uninteresting solutions to all sorts of concept formation problems are easily found. Suppose, to take one example, we want a theory of how to find or form the grammar of some natural language. If we grant that an adequate grammar can almost certainly be written in less than a million words, we can solve the problem in theory and in a completely finitistic way by simply enumerating all possible strings of one million words. There are only a finite number of such strings because there are only a finite number of different words in standard English – or, if someone wants to argue this point, we can restrict the words occurring in the strings to those occurring in the *Unabridged Oxford Dictionary*. Yet this solution is totally uninteresting for reasons that are too obvious to mention. Admittedly my example is simple-minded and artificial, but still it is good enough to establish the point that philosophical constructivists' approaches to concept formation lose interest if they stray far from the facts we know about human capacities and limitations.

I would agree that philosophical theories of concept formation need not be identical in every respect with psychological theories of the same phenomena, just because the two sorts of theories can be addressed to somewhat different aspects of the same phenomena. For instance, a psychological theory will be concerned with learning rates and the parsimonious introduction of learning parameters – like the parameter of conditioning mentioned above in the discussion of stimulus-sampling theory. Such considerations, important for fundamental psychological theory and practical applications as well, are not likely to be of much concern to even the most constructivist-minded philosophers.

Indeed, one of the most important aspects of the relation between adequate philosophical and scientific theories of the same phenomena is that a satisfactory philosophical theory can often be much less categorical and detailed than the corresponding scientific theory. For example, for philosophical discussions of the nature of matter in the seventeenth and eighteenth centuries Descartes and Boscovich provide two conceptually clear alternatives, with Descartes emphasizing the plenum and contact forces, and Boscovich the emptiness of space and forces acting at a distance [1], but neither Descartes nor Boscovich offered a physical theory of matter that was correct in detail or of much help in the development of quantitative physics. To take another sort of example, the theory of perception begun in Goodman [2] does not even begin to account for the barest fraction of what we know about visual perception; as a psychological theory it is primitive and vastly incomplete in character.

But I do not want to overemphasize this difference. Descartes' *Principia* is also philosophically mushy in several parts, and Goodman's book only begins the treatment of the philosophically interesting problems of perception and concept formation. Unlike what some Oxford philosophers seem to believe, philosophical and psychological theories cannot be of radically different sorts, with each discipline blithely free to go its own way in seeking a satisfactory theory. How can this claim best be substantiated? One argument is to point to the lack of such pairs of theories, one scientific and the other philosophical in other domains of experience. Philosophers who have attempted to construct theories about the physical world which were primarily independent of actual scientific experimentation and detailed observable fact seem uniformly to have come to grief. Descartes has already been mentioned. Among major philosophers a still better example is Kant. The generalities of the *Critique of Pure Reason* can be argued every which way – as the fantastic secondary literature on Kant attests –, but the *Metaphysical Foundations of Natural Science*, with all its *a priori* detail about kinematics and dynamics, cannot be so easily twisted to fit any new scientific development. Its beautifully clear wrongheadedness is a fitting monument to philosophers who desire to

---

[1] P. Suppes, 'Descartes and the problem of action at a distance', *Journal of the History of Ideas* 21 (1954), pp. 146–152.

[2] N. Goodman, *The Structure of Appearance*, Harvard University Press, Cambridge, Mass, 1951.

construct theories of real phenomena without analyzing any empirical data. Chemists and physicists don't theorize in exactly the same way, although there is much overlap in what they do. Certainly it would seem strange to say they were doing entirely different sorts of science totally independent of each other. And the same it seems to me is true of philosophers and physicists, or philosophers and psychologists.

I have written these last few paragraphs as if it were always the case that philosophers were dependent on scientists, but not the other way around. In the present state of affairs psychologists interested in concept formation can learn a good deal from constructivist philosophers like Carnap and Goodman, and probably one of the reasons Carnap and Goodman often describe what they are doing as if it could be independent of psychology is the lack of substantial systematic psychological theories about concept formation or perception. And in fact Goodman's work has had some impact in psychology [1].

But now the situation is rapidly changing and it is my own prediction that in the immediate future the most interesting constructive work will be done outside of philosophy by mathematically trained psychologists and by mathematicians, statisticians and engineers concerned with pattern recognition, the construction of machines that can learn and perceive, and related problems in artificial intelligence. The man entrusted to build a machine that can perceive a cup on a table and pick it up has got to have some sort of highly constructive, nearly categorical theory of perception and concept formation. As an evaluation of the depth of theory either in philosophy or psychology, we may ask what does either discipline have to offer such a man, and the answer, I am afraid, is still pretty starkly negative.

But I do not want to end on this pessimistic note. I think we are at a turning point in the history of these matters. The underbrush has been cleared by hardworking constructive-minded myth choppers in both philosophy and psychology. A convergence of

---

[1] See E. Galanter, 'An axiomatic and experimental study of sensory order and measure', *Psychol. Rev.* **63** (1956), pp. 16–28.

effort on the most difficult cognitive problems, those of perception and concept formation, has been building up at least since 1960, and we could well be on the edge of some genuinely spectacular results. Many scientists working on these problems feel we are getting very close to hitting on the one or two fundamental ideas needed to move rapidly ahead. If so, the theory of information processing and concept formation might even give quantum mechanics and molecular biology a run for their money for the title of most important scientific development of the twentieth century. Certainly the short run impact of the technology of computers has already been far greater than was generally anticipated. Even the most widely acclaimed results in molecular biology are best regarded as fundamental discoveries about the genetic code for information processing. Title-winner or not, there is no doubt that information processing and choice behavior are typical major themes of twentieth century science. I just wish I could have given them deeper and more thorough coverage at this colloquium.

J. C. HARSANYI: *Bayesian theory and randomization – resolution of a paradox.*

I would like to comment on a problem connected with the concept of randomness. Professor Suppes has pointed out that most laymen would be shocked by a suggestion that they should use randomized strategies. But statisticians, I take it, would be even more shocked by a suggestion that they should *not* use randomized strategies, such as random sampling.

Yet, paradoxically, this is precisely the conclusion one reaches on the basis of the Bayesian theory – even though the latter is in my opinion (and I believe Suppes takes a similar view) a highly convincing theory of rational behavior for individual, i.e., non-game-theoretical, choice situations. Indeed, it is a well-known mathematical theorem that under the Bayesian approach it never pays to use a randomized strategy.

Let me briefly indicate why this is so. Suppose a given individual has to choose between two alternatives having the utility values u and v, with $u > v$. Then any probability mixture of these two alternatives will have some intermediate utility value w, where $u > w > v$. Hence the randomized strategy yielding such a utility w will always be inferior to the pure strategy yielding the utility u. On the other hand, if both alternatives yield the same utility $u = v$ then any probability mixture of the two will also yield this same utility. Hence in this case the use of a randomized strategy will not do any harm but will not do any good, either. Thus randomization is always pointless and is in most cases actually harmful.

Now clearly we cannot fight against a mathematical theorem. But I think we can overcome the paradox if we carefully consider the reasons why statisticians use random sampling (or what we call stratified random sampling), e.g. in public opinion polls. The basic reason is that nonrandom selection methods are likely to introduce a *bias* in their sample, i.e., a systematic tendency to have various currents of opinion overrepresented or underrepresented in their sample as compared with the relative importance of these currents of opinion in the whole population. In other words, the purpose of random sampling is to avoid selection criteria which may be positively or negatively correlated with the opinion variables we are interested in.

Thus the underlying hypothesis is that selection based on some table of random numbers is less likely to introduce such unexpected systematic correlations than would be selection based on some nonrandom criteria, such as taking the first one hundred names from an alphabetic list (which may favor people of particular ethnic backgrounds), or taking every tenth house in a given street (which may, e.g., favor corner houses, whose inhabitants may have nontypical social characteristics). This hypothesis is really a hypothesis about the likely form that sociological correlations will take, and more generally about the likely form of the laws of nature in various fields. The use of random numbers as such is less important than is the use of numbers free of any obvious and simple mathematical regularities. For instance, to use the digits of the number π may do just as well as to use true random numbers, but to use numbers forming a simple arithmetic or geometric progression may be rather risky.

Of course, under the Bayesian model, any hypothesis that a given statistician entertains about the likely form of lawlike regularities in nature or in society represents a partial description of his own *prior subjective probability distribution*. Thus a Bayesian philosopher of science must seek the justification of random sampling, not in its random nature as such, but rather in people's assessment of certain prior probabilities. He must seek the justification in the fact that statisticians and other scientists tend to assign *low* prior probabilities to the existence of lawlike regularities of very complex and highly unusual form – while assigning much *higher* prior probabilities to the existence of relatively simple lawlike regularities similar in their general form to already known and well-established laws of nature in that particular area.

L. KISH: *Randomization in sample design.*

Should your sample always be random or never? Neither. To be consistent with their respective current principles, it seems that classical (objectivist) statisticians should always randomize, but that those of the Bayesian (personalist) persuasion must never do so. The theories are often preached in these extreme forms, and some people practice what they preach. However, my friends are wiser: whether objectivist or personalist, they both arrive readily at the same designs as I do for actual samples. Nevertheless we abhor wide chasms between theories and practice, and we want to bridge them.

Suppose first that we need to select one or two units (cities, schools, or hospitals) to represent a population; most of us would prefer careful personal choice rather than random selection. This preference would often extend to the choice of 4 or 6 units. The powerful arguments against randomized strategies can readily cover these situations of selection also.

But suppose now that we agree to divide a population into 100 strata and to make two selections from each; this design is basic in survey sampling. This new field is even better suited than its venerable parent, experimental design for exploring some basic questions about randomization. Should we select those pairs with randomization or with careful personal judgment? Most of us would prefer random selection within strata. I emphasize the paradox that for any single stratum we should, as above, prefer personal choice. The analogy with strategies appears different when applied to the union of 200 separate strategies. Generally the preference would also extend to subsets of 50 or 20 strata.

We need a theory in which these opposite decisions about randomization are consequences of the same principles. The difference in decisions is due chiefly to balancing possible biases of personal selection against random selection errors. The latter loom large for selecting only 2 units, but small for 200. Consider also the cost of 200 careful personal selections; also the public character, objectivity, communicability of random selection. These considerations of bias, random error, cost, and communicability are not extraneous; they occupy central roles in statistics. A satisfactory statistical philosophy must eventually embrace them to bridge the gap from theory to practice.

Personal selections tend to be biased because they are not independent from the experimental (or survey) variables. Unfortunately the relationships are too elusive to be placed under control. Furthermore, the lack of independence not only biases the principal results, but also interferes with a valid assessment of measurement errors, as Fisher argues in *The Design of Experiments*. The literature of diverse sciences is replete with examples of effect of selection biases; with cases where assumptions about natural randomization of the universe failed badly and openly. Only after these failures are revealed within a particular field, do its scientists feel obliged to undertake the extra effort of formal randomization.

As Professor Suppes points out, millenia were needed to reconcile science to the inevitability of error. But after reluctantly abandoning an errorless uniformity, the scientist first imagines a new kind of uniformity: the uniformity of random variation. In place of a determinate universe, he would substitute a universe that is simply, uniformly random, like a well-mixed urn, or a table of random numbers. Unfortunately, natural irregularity does not generally possess that uniformity of simple random variation. Rather the distribution of irregularity is often characterized by 'lumpiness': by local, irregular, and elusive clustering of characteristics. Randomization is strategy against such lumpiness (as I argue in *Survey Sampling*, sec. 1.7).

Random sampling then is an economical way of obtaining large samples whose correspondence to the populations can be readily accepted with high confidence. Stating clearly its proper functions poses challenging problems for the philosophy of science, for statistical inference, and especially for Bayesian theory.

P. SUPPES: *Reply.*

There do not seem to be any major differences between Harsanyi, Kish and me about randomization, but I feel there are still a good many things to be said, and I would like to say some of them here.

Both Harsanyi and Kish have emphasized that randomization provides a method of achieving objective results, which in the present context may be characterized as interperson agreement. I think another closely related aspect of randomization is just as important. Likelihoods of observations under various possible hypotheses may be *calculated* under the simplification introduced by randomization. This simplicity of calculation can be important even for the single observer. Put this way, randomization is a powerful procedure of simplification – a procedure for eliminating unwieldy complexities. A simple artificial example will illustrate the point. Suppose I am sampling balls from an urn and I know that either 10 of the 30 balls are white and the remainder black, or 20 per cent of the balls are white. I am permitted to draw three balls with replacement. Each time I replace a ball I consider it wise to shake the urn or use some other *physical* procedure to make sure the drawn ball is now well mixed in. The complexities of calculating the likelihoods are thus notably reduced.

The second related point I want to note is that randomization usually involves some physical act, and is not just an intellectual change of viewpoint. Either the act of randomization or its consequences in making a selection, perhaps both, have physical consequences. What Harsanyi says in the last paragraph of his remarks is relevant and important in this connection. It is a natural, additional Bayesian question to ask how these physical acts of randomization are to be interpreted. As Harsanyi points out, the physical procedures of randomization must be ones that tend to assign low prior probabilities to the existence of unusual lawlike regularities. But it seems to me that the other side of the coin requires an equal emphasis. The physical procedures of randomization commonly used are accepted because they embody principles of symmetry that have very *high* probabilities of being controlling, and it is these principles of symmetry that make calculations of likelihoods practically possible, whether it be a case of a game of chance or a survey sample.

The explicit formulation of relevant principles of symmetry for a significant range of cases of random sampling would be a useful step toward developing a deeper constructive theory of randomization. Surely in most cases common acceptance of certain applicable principles of symmetry is the basis for interperson agreement about likelihoods.

INDIVIDUALISTIC AND FUNCTIONALISTIC EXPLANATIONS IN THE LIGHT OF GAME THEORY: THE EXAMPLE OF SOCIAL STATUS [1]

JOHN C. HARSANYI

University of California, Berkeley

1. There are at present two major theoretical approaches in use in the social sciences. One is based on the assumption that people's behavior in society can be largely explained as a more or less *rational pursuit* of various personal objectives and interests: for the sake of brevity we shall call this the *rationalistic approach*. The other is the *functionalistic approach* based on the assumption that social institutions and various forms of social behavior can be explained in terms of their *social functions*, that is, in terms of the social needs they serve and in terms of the contributions they make to the survival of the society and to the maintenance of its existing institutional framework. The rationalistic approach is completely dominant in economics, and is quite important also in political science, in the analysis of international relations, and in the theory of social organizations. The functionalistic approach, connected with the names of Bronislaw Malinowski, A. R. Radcliffe–Brown, Robert K. Merton, and Talcott Parsons, is today the dominant theoretical approach in anthropology and in sociology.

In terms of Sir Karl Popper's terminology, the rationalistic approach represents an individualistic methodology while the functionalistic approach represents a form of collectivism. This is so because the rationalistic approach explains people's behavior in terms of their personal objectives, as well as the strategies and the information personally available to them. In contrast, the functionalistic approach explains social behavior in terms of the functional needs of society as a whole.

---

[1] This research has been supported by grant No. GS–722 of the National Science Foundation, administered through the Center for Research in Management Science, University of California, Berkeley.

Indeed, functionalism is the only form of methodological collectivism with any significance in the present-day social-science literature. The cruder forms of collectivism, once fashionable in the nineteenth century – such as the theory that society is one large organism or that social behavior is governed by some sort of group mind – are now virtually extinct. This fact makes it rather surprising how much effort in philosophical journals is still being devoted to refuting these long-abandoned cruder forms of collectivism, as compared with the very little effort spent on critical evaluations of contemporary functionalism, which is still very active and alive.

In my own view, functionalism has the very wide currency it actually has, mainly because up to very recently no satisfactory individualistic explanations of social behavior were available in areas outside the traditional boundaries of economics (and indeed outside the area of perfect competition, traditionally the core concept of economic theory). In this paper I propose to show – both in general terms and on the specific example of social status – how the advent of game theory, and some other recent theoretical developments, have changed this situation, making it possible to analyze non-economic social behavior in individualistic terms, in terms of some suitable concept of rational choice.

2.   For lack of space I shall only briefly summarize what I believe to be the main shortcomings of the functionalistic approach.

(1)   By concentrating on the social functions that various social institutions supposedly serve, and by assuming that every existing social institution does serve some useful function, the functionalistic approach tends to overstate the efficiency of existing social institutions in serving social needs, and to neglect the inefficiencies and the possible outright detrimental social effects of these institutions.

(2)   Like nineteenth century economics (which however few economists would take seriously today), functionalism tends to overstate the harmony of interests among different social groups, and to play down the important conflicts of interest existing in every society with the possible exception of the simplest primitive peoples.

(3)   Since social changes are due largely to dissatisfaction with existing social institutions and to conflicts of interest between different social groups – and since functionalism tends to minimize the importance of these factors – it has an unduly conservative bias. It can be at best a theory of static social equilibrium and cannot provide a theory of dynamic social change.

(4)   But even as a static equilibrium theory, functionalism is highly unsatisfactory. If functionalistic explanations are to have any explanatory value then it is not enough simply to *assume* that social institutions arise in response to actual social needs. Rather, one also has to be in a position to point out the specific *social mechanism* (or mechanisms) by which these social needs supposedly give rise to institutions satisfying these social needs – and functionalism plainly fails to do this.

Functionalists have been mislead by inappropriate biological analogies. In biology, it is permissible to explain the existence of various organic structures in terms of their functional usefulness. But this is so only because it is known that random mutations together with natural selection do provide a mechanism fully accounting for the observed correspondence between organic structure and biological function. In contrast, given the relatively short time span of human history, natural selection among different societies cannot possibly produce any close correspondence between social institutions and social needs. Moreover, careful observation of existing social institutions in various societies discloses considerable functional inefficiencies and directly disproves the assumption of any close correspondence between social needs and the existing institutional framework. Indeed, the constant pressure for social reforms we find in many societies would be hard to understand if the existing social institutions were already meeting the functional needs of these societies in an efficient manner.

We shall consider a few more specific objections to functionalism in section 7 below, when we come to discussing the functionalistic theory of social status relationships.

3.   The concept of rational behavior used in economics, and also in decision theory and game theory, is essentially a generalization,

as well as a more rigorous reformulation, of the concept of rational behavior used at the common sense level. In common sense discourse, the term 'rational behavior' usually means the use of the appropriate means for achieving *given* ends. For instance, if a person wants to get from San Francisco to London in one day then it will be rational for him to go by jet, and it will be irrational for him to go by boat – because a jet is able to cover the distance in one day while a boat is not.

Already at the common sense level, this concept of rational behavior is a very powerful explanatory principle, because it often enables us to explain a large number of complex facts about people's behavior, in terms of a few simple assumptions about their goals or objectives. Thus the simple assumption that a person wants to get from San Francisco to London may explain a long sequence of complicated actions he has undertaken.

However, classical economic theory has made an important step forward over this common sense concept of rationality, by introducing a broader concept of rational behavior which not only allows the analysis of a person's choices between different *means* to a given end, but also allows analysis of his choices between different *ends* as such, in terms of his preferences, that is, in terms of the relative importance he attaches to alternative ends. Economic theory also shows that if a given person's choice behavior satisfies certain consistency and continuity requirements then his choices can be represented as involving maximization of a well defined mathematical function, called his *utility function*.

Yet, classical economic theory is largely restricted to the analysis of choice behavior under *certainty*, where the person concerned knows with complete assurance the consequences of any action he may choose. It has remained for modern decision theory to develop a more general concept of rational behavior which also covers rational choice under *risk* and *uncertainty*. Modern decision theory shows that if a person's choice behavior in the face of risk and uncertainty satisfies certain consistency requirements (stronger ones than needed in the case of certainty) then his choices can be represented as involving maximization of the *mathematical expectation* of his utility function.

However, this concept of rational behavior is still essentially restricted to rational choice by an isolated individual, and does not cover rational behavior in a social setting – at least not in situations involving strategical interdependence between two or more rational individuals.

Rational behavior in the latter type of situations comes under game theory. Yet, even modern game theory in its original form as developed by von Neumann and Morgenstern [1] failed to give a unique answer to the question of how to define rational behavior in various game situations. More particularly, von Neumann and Morgenstern's approach did yield a unique solution for two-person zero-sum games, but in general failed to yield unique solutions for two-person non-zero-sum and for n-person games – both of which are much more important than are two-person zero-sum games in social-science applications.

Only in recent years has the present writer succeeded in developing a new approach to game theory which does yield determinate solutions for *all* classes of games, and thereby provides a rational-behavior concept rich enough to serve as a basis for a general individualistic theory of social behavior [2].

4. Let me explain why these recent advances in game theory have been in my view an essential precondition for a general theory of social behavior based on some concept of rational choice. This is so because such a theory has to provide an analytical framework for predicting the behavior of rational individuals if

---

[1] John von Neumann and Oskar Morgenstern, *Theory of Games and Economic Behavior*, Princeton University Press, Princeton, 1944.

[2] John C. Harsanyi, 'A general theory of rational behavior in game situations', *Econometrica* 34 (July 1966), pp. 613–634. For a non-mathematical exposition, see John C. Harsanyi, 'Bargaining and conflict situations in the light of a new approach to game theory', *American Economic Review* 55 (May 1965), pp. 447–457. See also John F. Nash, 'The bargaining problem', *Econometrica* 18 (1950), pp. 155–162; 'Two-person cooperative games', *Econometrica* 21 (1953), pp. 128–140; and Lloyd S. Shapley, 'A value for n-person games', in H. W. Kuhn and A. W. Tucker, eds., *Contributions to the Theory of Games*, II, Princeton University Press, Princeton, 1953; pp. 307–317.

their utility functions, their strategical possibilities, and the information available to them, are given. (This is true not only if this theory is to be used for prediction in a literal sense, but also if it is to be used for explanation of people's behavior after the event, since in a formal sense explanation can also be regarded as a form of prediction – viz. retrospective prediction.) Yet, in order to make such predictions, we need a concept of rational behavior sufficiently specific to tell us what a rational individual would do in that particular situation. This is necessary because, appearances to the contrary, common sense alone does *not* give us a clear and consistent answer to the question of what a rational individual would do in various social situations involving cooperation or conflict between two or more individuals.

For example, many social scientists have assumed, without much further thought, that if two individuals or social groups have divergent interests on some social issues, this will automatically give rise to a conflict between them – at least if both sides pursue their own interests in a vigorous manner. For instance, Karl Marx's theory of class conflict is based on the assumption that the interests of the working class are in opposition to the interests of the capitalist class on many important social issues, and that this very fact *implies* that the interests of the working class will be best served by an uncompromising struggle against the capitalist class. I shall try to show that this argument is fallacious. I shall call it the '*conflict-of-interest fallacy*'.

Other social scientists will rightly argue that in any conflict situation there is always a peaceful solution preferable to *both* parties over the conflict situation itself. This is so because if the two parties can reach a peaceful agreement they will save the costs of a conflict and will be able to divide up this saving so as to make both of them better off. (In technical terms, in a non-zero-sum game a conflict always represents a non-Pareto-optimal situation.) This reasoning seems to imply that if both parties act rationally then no conflict can arise between them at all. As we shall see, this argument is closer to the truth than the opposite (which we have called 'conflict-of-interest fallacy') – but in this unqualified form it is equally false.

The whole problem can be clarified only in game-theoretical terms, by means of such distinctions as that between cooperative and non-cooperative games; or between games where the players do know, or do not know, each other's payoff functions; or between games where the players have positive, or have negative, risk preferences.

To start with the first distinction, consider a so-called 'prisoner's dilemma game':

	B_1	B_2
A_1	(10, 10)	$(-10,$ 11)
A_2	(11, -10)	(1, 1)

Here we must distinguish between the case where agreements between the players are enforceable and are absolutely binding, and the case where this is not true. In the former case we speak of a *cooperative* game, in the latter of a *non-cooperative* game. If the game is played as a cooperative game then the two players will agree to use strategies A_1 and B_1, which will yield a payoff of 10 units to each player. But if the game is played as a non-cooperative game then such agreement would have no binding force. Hence player A will know that if he used his cooperative strategy A_1 his opponent would still use his non-cooperative strategy B_2, and conversely. Hence both players will come to use their non-cooperative strategies A_2 and B_2 and will obtain a payoff of 1 unit only, in spite of the fact that both could obtain 10 units if both of them used their cooperative strategies A_1 and B_1.

In other words, though both players would benefit if they cooperated, they will not actually do so because they mutually *distrust* each other (in the sense that each player would expect his opponent to use a non-cooperative strategy even if the first player himself used a cooperative strategy). But this failure to cooperate need not represent irrational behavior on the part of the players – because they may have perfectly good reasons to distrust each other. (Many discussions of the cold war seem to be based on the completely unwarranted tacit assumption that mutual distrust – i.e., the expectation that the other side would not abide by agreements if it could profit by violating them – cannot be the result of rational judgment and of a realistic assessment of the situation [1].)

Next, take the distinction between cases where the players do know, or do not know, each other's true payoff functions. Suppose that A wants to buy a house from B, and that B mistakenly believes the house to be worth $30 000 to A, though in actual fact it is worth only $20 000 to him. As a result B may insist that A should pay, say, $26 000 for the house (which would be still $4 000 below what in B's opinion the house is worth to him). But since this price would actually exceed the value of the house to A by $6 000, the two parties will be unable to complete the transaction, even though at a lower price (say, $18 000) perhaps both of them would profit by it.

Finally, take the distinction between games played by players with positive risk preferences and those played by players with negative risk preferences. Players who like risk may engage in a conflict because they prefer some chance of a total victory (even if it is combined with some chance of total defeat) to the certainty of an 'unexciting' compromise solution. On the other hand, players who dislike risk, may sometimes prefer a relatively 'safe' mild conflict to the risks associated with a peaceful agreement of which the actual consequences they find hard to predict. (For instance, in oligopolistic industries the member firms may be unable to agree to refrain from certain forms of competition, e.g., from competitive advertising, because such agreements may have unpredictable long-run consequences for the relative balance of power among the different firms.)

These examples show that game-theoretical analysis is often quite essential for understanding the conditions for social cooperation and for social conflict in various social situations.

Another example showing the need for game-theoretical analysis

---

[1] John C. Harsanyi, 'Mathematical models for the Genesis of war', (A Review Article on L. F. Richardson's work), *World Politics* **14** (1962), pp. 687–699, esp. pp. 696–699.

is provided by bargaining situations. Suppose that a given individual wants to sell his house for at least $30 000 while another individual wants to buy it if he can obtain it for no more than $40 000. In this situation classical economic theory can predict only that the actual price will lie between $30 000 and $40 000, but cannot say anything about the factors determining the price between these two limits. It is again only modern game theory, in this case Nash's theory of two-person bargaining games [1], which enables us to specify the factors determining the outcome. (Nash's theory suggests that the main factors involved are the two parties' attitudes toward risk taking, and the threat strategies available to them.)

5. Let me add that one of the leaders of the now fashionable functionalistic approach, Talcott Parsons, has come quite close to developing an individualistic–rationalistic theory of social behavior, such as advocated here – since his own theory, which he calls the *theory of social action*, is essentially an attempt to generalize the rational-behavior model of classical economic theory so as to make it applicable also in the analysis of non-economic social behavior [2].

Parsons has recognized that the basic task of any general theory of social behavior is to explain social cooperation. (My only disagreement with him on this point lies in the fact that I would attach equal importance also to explaining why social cooperation *fails* or is seriously restricted in many social situations – see sec. 4 above.) Where Parsons went wrong in my opinion was at the point where, following Durkheim, he came to the conclusion that the model of rational behavior in itself cannot explain social cooperation, for which reason he added *social norms* as a further-not-analyzed basic constituent of his theory of social action. This meant giving up any possibility of explaining the existence of these social norms themselves in terms of the personal objectives and interests of the individual members of society.

---

[1]   Nash, 'The bargaining problem' and 'Two-person cooperative games',

[2]   See, e.g. Talcott Parsons, *Working Papers in the Theory of Action*, The Free Press, Glencoe Illinois, 1953.

Thus the only way Parsons could try to explain the existence of social norms was in terms of their social functions, that is, in terms of the social needs these norms supposedly serve. But, as I have argued before, this is no explanation at all unless Parsons can also specify the actual social *mechanisms* through which the functional needs of the society are translated into the appropriate social norms – that is, unless he can specify the personal *incentives* the individual members of the society have to establish and maintain these social norms in accordance with the best interests of the society as a whole. Since Parsons never specifies these social mechanisms, his explanation of social behavior in terms of social norms always leaves these norms themselves completely unexplained.

In my opinion the problem of social cooperation once more requires a solution in game-theoretical terms. It can be shown that in many game situations the players will cooperate with one another even in the absence of any social norms enjoining cooperation simply because

(1) all of them will benefit from mutual cooperation, and because

(2) agreements about mutual cooperation will be self-enforcing. (That is, any player who tried to double-cross the others would automatically suffer heavy penalties.)

In other situations the players may cooperate because they take an unselfish interest in each other's well-being – again quite irrespective of whether there are any social norms requiring cooperation in this particular situation.

In other situations again, cooperation may be admittedly the result of social norms. But the existence of these social norms themselves will admit of explanation in terms of people's personal objectives and interests, including their possible unselfish interests in each other's well-being. For instance, in many social situations the social norms enjoining cooperation between two parties are imposed and enforced by more or less *neutral* third parties who would be personally inconvenienced by a conflict between the first two parties, or who want to prevent a conflict between them out of unselfish interest in the two parties' own well-being (or both).

For instance, public opinion may prevent a strike in a given industry because it would be a nuisance for the general public, or because it is felt that a strike would impose intolerable hardships on the two parties themselves.

Later of course the relevant social norms, and in particular the moral norms of the society, may become internalized by the interested parties themselves, so that violation of these norms will come to arise guilt feelings in them. But in my opinion a careful analysis of moral concepts will show that the moral norms originally do not represent the points of view of the individuals whose rights and duties are regulated by these norms, but rather represent the point of view of a sympathetic but impartial 'neutral' observer whose personal interests are not directly involved and who therefore can afford to take a detached attitude toward the individual interests regulated by these norms [1].

6. As will be apparent from the preceding discussion, in order to explain people's behavior in game-theoretical terms, we have to make specific assumptions about people's actual objectives in various social situations, that is, about the main variables entering into people's utility functions. Classical economic theory could get away with the simple-minded assumption that in most economic situations people are motivated primarily by their economic self-interests. But if we want to explain people's behavior in non-economic situations then we obviously need a more sophisticated theory of human motivation.

On the one hand, people are obviously not always motivated by self-interest at all. Even in economic life they may be more concerned about the economic well-being of their family than about their own; and they may also work for some more general non-egoistic purposes, e.g., for the benefit of some humanitarian cause. Even people who are normally concerned mainly with their personal self-interests are often willing to judge social issues in terms of general social considerations whenever their personal

---

[1] John C. Harsanyi, 'Ethics in terms of hypothetical imperatives', *Mind* 47 (1958), pp. 305–316.

interests are not significantly affected. The great decision-making powers entrusted to judges and administrative officials are based on the assumption that – at least in the absence of a strong 'conflict of interest' between their public duties and their private interests – they will tend to act in accordance with the social interests they are expected to serve. If this assumption were quite unrealistic, society would soon disintegrate.

On the other hand, even if a person is motivated mainly by self-interest, this need not be economic self-interest. It may be rather an interest in participating in some enjoyable physical or intellectual activities, in gaining popularity with a particular social group, in achieving higher social status, etc.

Of course we must be wary of introducing too many independent motivational variables. If we make our motivational assumptions complicated enough then we can always explain every conceivable form of social behavior in terms of these assumptions, which means that we are actually explaining nothing. To account for the complexity of real-life social behavior we obviously need a more complex motivational theory than that of classical economics. But we must use the least complex motivational assumptions, and the smallest number of basic motivational variables, that can account for the social behavior we have to explain.

7. Let me now illustrate the difference between the functionalistic and the game-theoretical explanations of social behavior, on the specific example of social-status behavior.

Apart from economic gain, social status is probably the most important motivating force of social behavior. It seems to me that any general analytical theory of social behavior will have to use the striving for social status (for achieving higher social status or at least for maintaining one's existing status) as one of its major explanatory variables. This makes it particularly important to obtain a better theoretical understanding of the nature of social status itself. We need a theory explaining why social groups *grant* higher status to some of their members, and also why these members themselves *seek* higher social status within the group.

Among sociologists at present the most widely accepted theory of social status is the functionalistic theory proposed by Davis and Moore [1]. They argue that differences in social status exist in every known society because these differences serve a very important social function. Together with higher income and other privileges, higher social status serves as an *incentive* for the occupants of important social positions so that they first accept the responsibilities associated with these positions and then perform the duties attached to them in an efficient manner.

This theory is obviously subject to all the objections we have raised in general against functionalistic explanations. In particular, it does not explain the personal incentives the other individuals of the society have to grant high social status to a given individual occupying an important social position and performing important services for the society.

Our own theory of social status overcomes this difficulty by assuming that, whenever a given person is being granted higher social status in a social group, the initiative is always taken by individuals who attach great importance to his services for personal reasons (whether selfish or unselfish), and who therefore have a personal interest in making his association with the group as pleasant as possible so as to secure his services on a continual basis. (For instance, I will tend to treat a visiting great musician with deference if I attach great importance to his music and therefore, e.g., want to give him an incentive to repeated visits to our town.) Other members of the group, who have less appreciation for his services, may also be persuaded to recognize his higher social status and to give him deferential treatment – but this will occur only as a result of social pressure from those individuals who do have a high personal appreciation for his activities. Thus the mere fact that a person performs important services for society as a whole will not explain another individual's deferential behavior toward him – unless this individual has a personal interest in his services, or is under pressure from other individuals having a personal interest in his services.

Hence social status is a *power relationship*. High social status

---

[1] Kingsley Davis and Wilbert E. Moore, 'Some principles of stratification', *American Sociological Review* **10** (1945), pp. 242–249.

is based on the fact that the other members of a given social group are personally dependent on a particular individual for the services he is performing for them. Moreover, social status is a *reciprocal* power relationship. When a person performs valuable services for the other members of the group he will very often himself also receive valuable services from them. In such cases his social status within the group will be determined by the relative importance of the services rendered and the services received by him. He will enjoy high social status only if the former are much more important than the latter – that is, if the other members of the group are much more dependent on him for *his* services than he is dependent on them for *theirs*.

Our theory can explain many empirical facts concerning social status relationships that Davis and Moore's functionalistic theory cannot explain. In particular, Davis and Moore have to assume that there is always a very close correspondence between people's social status and the real value of their services from a social point of view. Thus they cannot explain how charlatans, confidence men, demagogues, or even common criminals, can often obtain high social status as a result of their anti-social activities.

Our own theory has no difficulty in explaining these facts. Since under our theory a person's social status depends on the importance other individuals ascribe to his services, a charlatan may achieve high social status because people may mistakenly *think* he can perform important services for them. Moreover, in a criminal gang a person may achieve high status by performing important services for the other members of the gang even if from the point of view of the larger society his services consist in highly undesirable criminal activities. Indeed he may obtain high social status merely as a result of being able to perform important *disservices* for the other members of the gang – since *not* performing a disservice one *could* perform, itself amounts to performing a valuable service for them. For example, a bully may obtain high status in the gang by threatening everybody with violence who does not recognize his high status – even though the only service performed by him for the other members may be his refraining from violence if his high status is accepted by them, etc.

Our theory can be briefly summarized by saying that a person has high social status in a given social group if he is being given V.I.P. treatment by the other members, owing to the very important services or disservices he can perform for them.

8. In formal game-theoretical terms, the social status of a given individual A within a certain social group can be regarded as a result of (usually tacit) bargaining between him and the other members of the group. As is the case in all bargaining situations, the strength of the two sides' bargaining positions will depend on the cost of a conflict to each side – that is, in our case, it will depend on the benefits each side would lose and on the penalties it would incur if the two sides could not reach an agreement on individual A's social status within the group.

The costs of a conflict for individual A would be given by the expression [1]

$$(1) \qquad c^* = r + p + c(P) - c(R),$$

where r is the utility to individual A of the rewards (other than social status itself – e.g., monetary rewards) he is normally receiving from the group, which he would lose in case of a conflict; p is the disutility of the penalties (retaliatory actions) he would suffer from the group; $c(P)$ is the utility cost to A of the penalties (retaliatory actions) he would himself impose on the group in case of a conflict; and $c(R)$ is the utility cost to him of the rewarding activities (services) he would normally perform for the group. (This last quantity has a negative sign because in case of a conflict individual A would *not* perform these activities and so would not incur this cost item.)

Likewise, the cost of a conflict to the other members of the group (on the average per individual member) would be

$$(2) \qquad C^* = R + P + C(p) - C(r),$$

---

[1] Small letters refer to utilities and disutilities (utility costs) to individual A whereas capital letters refer to utilities and disutilities to the other members of the group.

where R is the utility, to the average member of the group, of individual A's services; P is the disutility of A's retaliatory actions (disservices); $C(p)$ is the utility cost of retaliatory actions against A; and $C(r)$ is the utility cost of the rewards normally provided for A (which would not be incurred in case of a conflict).

We can measure A's social status within the group by the amount (or frequency) π of deferential behavior he will receive from the other members of the group. On the basis of Nash's theory of bargaining games, our bargaining model predicts that this quantity will take the value

$$(3) \qquad \pi = \tfrac{1}{2}\left[\frac{C^*}{C(s)} - \frac{c^*}{s}\right],$$

where C^* and c^* are the two sides' conflict costs as defined by equations (1) and (2); s is the utility individual A would derive from the highest possible social status within the group (involving complete deference by the other members); and $C(s)$ is the disutility cost the other members would incur by granting him the highest possible status and treating him with complete deference [1].

9. So far we have analyzed only the factors explaining the willingness of social groups to *grant* high social status to some of their members. Now we shall briefly consider the reasons why people *seek* high social status.

The high social status an individual enjoys in a given social group is an indication of the importance the other members attach to his services and to continued association with him. Thus high social status gives some assurance of *stability* and *security* for the social position he has in the group.

Moreover, high social status usually means that the other members of the group will welcome close social ties with the individual concerned in all sorts of social activities, including private personal sociability. Therefore high social status normally allows an individual a much freer access to desirable social associates and a much

---

[1] For details see John C. Harsanyi, 'A bargaining model for social status in informal groups and formal organizations', *Behavioral Science* **11** (Sept. 1966), pp. 357–369; see also the references there quoted.

freer selection in choosing friends, marriage partners, business contacts, etc. This is probably the most important advantage and the greatest attraction of high social status.

10. To sum up, game theory is an essential tool in understanding social behavior, because a considerable part of social behavior is more or less *rational* behavior, in the sense of representing a fairly consistent pursuit of some reasonably well-defined personal objectives. The game-theoretical approach is necessary because common sense alone would not tell us how a rational individual would behave in social situations involving cooperation or conflict between two or more individuals.

Yet, game-theoretical analysis can be used only if we have a sufficiently specific theory of human motivations specifying the objectives people are actually seeking by engaging in various types of social behavior, i.e., a theory specifying the main variables entering into people's utility functions. We have argued that *social norms* should not be used as basic explanatory variables in analyzing social behavior, but rather should be themselves explained in terms of people's individual objectives and interests.

It has been our contention that game-theoretical analysis, supplemented by appropriate motivational assumptions, will provide a general analytical theory of social behavior, far superior in explanatory power to the now fashionable functionalistic approach.

We have tried to illustrate the use of game-theoretical analysis by outlining a game-theoretical bargaining model for social status, which we have elsewhere already discussed in greater detail [1]. We have also very briefly indicated how this analysis can be supplemented by an analysis of people's motivation in seeking high social status.

---

[1] See the preceding footnote.

L. P. FOLDES: *A note on individualistic explanations.*

I agree broadly with Harsanyi's critique of functionalism, and with his view that the rationalistic and individualistic method used in economics and game theory should be more widely applied in the social sciences. Nevertheless I think it is important that the current enthusiasm for decision and game theory – which I share – should not blind us to the limitations of this method, or lead us to assert dogmatically that it is the only method proper to social science. In particular, I do not believe that, in the present state of knowledge, this approach provides a firm basis for 'a general theory of social behaviour based on some concept of rational choice' [1].

My remarks will be arranged as follows. I shall first discuss the explanation of *individual* behaviour in rationalistic terms, and point out circumstances in which this method is not particularly fruitful. Next, I shall consider whether *social* regularities should invariably be explained in individualistic terms, and suggest some instances to the contrary. Finally, I shall discuss in particular whether the methods of game theory are adequate for sociological explanation, with special reference to social norms, and shall suggest that in this respect also Harsanyi has claimed too much.

1. *The rationalistic explanation of individual behaviour.* In this section, I shall discuss the scope of the rationalistic method of explaining the behaviour of a single individual in a given situation. In particular, I shall criticise the so-called (methodological) principle of rationality, i.e. the doctrine that the social sciences should use only this method of explaining individual behaviour.

According to Harsanyi's definition, 'the rationalistic approach explains people's behavior in terms of their personal objectives,

---

[1]   Harsanyi, p. 309,

as well as the strategies and the information personally available to them' (p. 305). It is common to think of people as having various objectives or aims and choosing among them according to their preferences, but for present purposes it is convenient to follow the usage of economics and regard the concepts of aims and preferences as equivalent. Now clearly the scope of the rationalistic method depends on the meaning assigned to this concept. Rather than discuss alternative formal definitions, I shall indicate the main points by referring to the axiomatic treatment of preferences in economic statics, which is generally regarded as the outstanding example of a rationalistic theory.

Consider an individual in a situation of given type, with definite information as to the range of available actions. Let S denote the set of all actions which can ever become available in situations of this type, and suppose that at any particular trial a subset A is actually available. The individual's preferences are represented by a 'preference relation' R defined between pairs of elements of S, which is assumed to be reflexive, transitive and complete. It is now assumed that, if any subset A is made available, the individual will choose an element of A which is maximal for R, i.e. which is most preferred, (assuming only that A is so chosen that the required element exists) [1].

The assumptions about R may be regarded as expressing properties of coherence and stability in the pattern of preferences. These two concepts are not really distinct, but intuitively one may think of the reflexive, transitive and complete character of R as reflecting a degree of coherence in the pattern of choice, while stability corresponds to the fact that R is independent of the particular

---

[1] See G. Debreu, *Theory of Value*, pp. 7–8. A binary relation R is said to be *reflexive* if xRx for all $x \in S$; it is *transitive* if xRy and yRz imply xRz, for all $x, y, z \in S$; it is *complete* if, for all $x, y, \in S$, either xRy or yRx. A relation with these properties is called a complete preordering. For a preference preordering, the formula xRy is read 'x is not preferred to y' or 'y is preferred or indifferent to x', and the formula 'xRy and yRx' is read 'x and y are indifferent'. Finally, x is a *maximal element* for R on a subset $A \subset S$ if $x \in A$, and if $y \in A$, $y \neq x$, yRx implies xRy; intuitively, if x is most preferred and y is preferred or indifferent to x, then the two must be indifferent.

subset which is available to the actor at a given trial, and also – if the theory is one which envisages repeated trials [1] – from the order in which subsets are presented.

These definitions may be regarded as providing a 'basic' concept of preference in economics, but clearly there is no absolute definition. For a given pattern of observable behaviour, the properties which may be assumed for R will vary with the definition of the set S; for instance, the less finely the alternative actions are classified, the stronger the postulates of consistency which can be imposed [2]. More important, the properties of R which can be assumed will depend on the type of behaviour considered. Thus it is common for many purposes to add postulates which ensure that R may be represented by a continuous numerical (ordinal or cardinal) utility function on S. It would also be possible – though the point is rarely mentioned – to weaken the definition of preferences, for instance by sacrificing completeness or transitivity. Another very weak assumption would be to suppose simply that there is a subset B of S – the 'satisfactory' subset – from which the individual selects one element – or, equivalently, that he maximises the value of a numerical function which takes the value 1 on B and the value 0 elsewhere.

This brief discussion of formal models of choice in economics illustrates several important features of rationalistic explanation. First, there is no concept of aims which is defined by a fixed list of postulates, independently of the type of action considered and of the formulation of the set of available alternatives. As a general

---

[1]   The general formulation includes the case where the elements of S are not single repeatable actions, but alternative mutually exclusive sequences of actions covering the entire period under consideration.

[2]   To give a more precise, if somewhat extreme, example, consider a sequence of n choice experiments in which a set E_i of actions is made available at the ith experiment, and suppose that the chosen behaviour is $e = (e_1, ..., e_n)$, where $e_i \in E_i$, $i = 1, ..., n$. Now we may define the set S either as the union of the E_i or as their product set; in the first case the objects of choice considered in the model are actions in individual experiments, in the second case they are the sequences of n-tuples of actions. Clearly the behaviour e may be intransitive in the first model but not in the second.

definition, one may regard as aims or preferences any principle or procedure for selecting among alternative actions, on the basis of specified information; but this statement is subject to the qualifications which follow. The expression 'principle or procedure' is intended to suggest that the method of selection must possess a certain systematic character, a degree of coherence and stability.

Such a definition of preferences does not depend directly on any concept of subjective aims. This accords with the fact that the formal economic model of choice can be interpreted, if we wish, as a purely behavioural theory, by regarding the 'preference relation' R simply as defining a pattern of potential action, without reference to the subjective processes of reasoning and choice which lead to action [1]. This approach has the advantage that it does not restrict the rationalistic method to action which corresponds to particular, clearly defined states of mind. The method is not confined in principle to action which is conscious, or calculated, or deliberately goal-oriented; and its use does not invariably presuppose that the aims attributed to the actor by the theory are, in some sense, his 'true' subjective aims, or that he can perform the

---

[1]   Some economists have held that the preference relation R as defined in the text cannot be regarded as purely behavioural, because it allows for indifference, which does not correspond to any observable behaviour. This statement is not correct if a behavioural theory is defined as one which postulates regularities of behaviour without reference to subjective processes of choice. Even if it is granted that the theoretical relation of indifference does not correspond to an observable pattern of choice, it need not correspond to anything subjective; it may be regarded as a relation defined only in the formal theory, to ensure certain properties of continuity.

It may be added that, whatever view may be taken of the possibility of *observing* indifference, statements about indifference can certainly be made *testable* if the theory is suitably interpreted. For example, consider the standard case where S is the non-negative orthant of the n-dimensional commodity space and R is representable by a continuous utility function with the usual properties (including non-saturation). The assertion that x and y are indifferent is refuted if (say) we can find a point z which is dominated by x but is chosen over y – there are four symmetrical possibilities. The continuity assumptions ensure that it will indeed be possible to find a suitable point z if x and y are not indifferent. Thus R can be regarded as 'purely behavioural' even in the sense that all statements containing R can be tested by observation.

calculations needed for the theoretical derivation of the maximal element of R.

All this is not to say that economic theory should be regarded as purely behavioural; on the contrary, our conception of the subjective processes of reasoning and choice influences both our willingness to adopt a rationalistic approach – which would hardly be appropriate in the case of, say, nervous reflexes – and our selection of postulates. As soon as our interest extends beyond the mere testing of a given formal model to the criticism and formulation of models, our ideas concerning this subjective background, vague as they may be, must be regarded as an essential part of a rationalistic theory. At the same time, within the limitations thus set, the postulates concerning aims are selected for their explanatory value rather than their 'psychological realism'.

The relationship between rationalistic and behavioural theories can therefore be summarised as follows. On the one hand, the part of a rationalistic theory which is directly testable in relation to a situation of given type can be interpreted as a purely behavioural theory; in this sense, restriction of the scope of a rationalistic theory leads, in the limit, to a behavioural theory. On the other hand, a behavioural theory can be interpreted formally as a rationalistic theory, since the regularity of behaviour which it postulates can be regarded as resulting from some suitably defined aims. But this procedure is subject to two reservations. First, it is objectionable if it makes the theory complicated and perhaps misleading, without adding to its testable content or establishing connections with other theories. Secondly, our theories of the subjective sources of certain actions may lead us to regard rationalistic explanation as inappropriate; having mentioned this point, I shall leave it aside from now on.

My conclusions as to the scope of the rationalistic method, and hence as to the validity of the rationality principle, are implicit in the preceding remarks. The rationalistic method is the more successful, the more diverse the actions which can be explained by a given hypothesis concerning preferences, the simpler the hypothesis, and the greater the degree of stability and coherence which can be assumed. The least favourable case is that of a theory which relates to behaviour of such narrow range, or so incoherent, or so little dependent on stable characteristics of the actor that rationalistic explanation adds little but complexity; in this case at least purely behavioural explanation is appropriate.

As knowledge changes, the scope for the various kinds of rationalistic theories and for pure behaviourism is likely to change; indeed the need to explain different aspects of action by theories of different kinds is itself an important source of problems. In a sense, it is true that fruitful rationalistic theories represent a more advanced stage than behavioural theories, because they have many implications and can therefore attempt the unified explanation of a wide range of actions; but it is to be expected that at any given time there will be problems which can more usefully be attacked in other ways.

The following are offered as possible contemporary examples of such problems – but rather diffidently, because they raise specialised technical questions.

(1) The study of conditioned behaviour, specific to a well-defined range of situations, which follows closely the pattern which has been learnt and depends little on stable characteristics present before the beginning of the process (apart from characteristics common to all individuals). For many purposes, a wide range of social behaviour must be regarded as belonging to this category; it will be further discussed in the next section.

(2) Stochastic learning processes exhibiting regularities of behaviour which are capable of various explanations, some rationalistic and some not [1], which cannot readily be distinguished by experiment.

(3) Behavioural regularities which are thought to be the result of systematic miscalculation, such as the effects of 'money illusion' in economics [2].

---

[1] Cf. H. A. Simon, *Models of Man*, ch. 16.

[2] Supporters of rationalistic methodologies like those of Professors Hayek and L. v. Mises will probably feel that the approach which I have adopted is vague and misses all the important distinctions. There is no sharp distinction between actions which are rational, conscious, deliberate, goal-oriented – the criterion varies – and those which are not; no restriction

2. *Individualistic explanations of social processes.* The view that social processes should invariably be analysed in individualistic terms has been formulated in various ways, some more restrictive than others. A relatively weak – though somewhat ambiguous – requirement is that stated by Professor Popper, who writes that 'all social phenomena, and especially the functioning of all social institutions, should always be understood as resulting from the decisions, actions, attitudes etc. of human individuals, and that we should never be satisfied by an explanation in terms of so-called 'collectives' (states, nations, races, etc.).' He distinguishes this doctrine from the more extreme view of J. S. Mill, which he calls 'psychologism', whose 'mistake . . . is its presumption that this methodological individualism . . . implies the programme of re-

---

of social science, and of the rationalistic method, to action of the first kind; no distinction between social science, which takes human action for granted and studies its social consequences, and psychology, which is concerned with the causes of action. I believe, on the contrary – though I cannot give detailed reasons here – that these distinctions are imprecise and largely irrelevant, and can stand in the way of useful work. Human action cannot be clearly divided into such categories as rational and irrational, conscious and unconscious, deliberate and automatic; on almost any definition, these are not dichotomies but distinctions of degree, which moreover refer to variations in complexes of variables rather than to movements along a single scale. In any case the introduction of such concepts raises difficult psychological questions at the very outset. Passing on to the next point, the restriction of social science to action which is conscious etc. is unduly narrow – again on almost any definition – and in any case the attempt to delimit social science rigidly from other fields of study should be avoided. A given action can be studied from many points of view – physiological, psychological, economic – whose scope is never sharply defined but does shift with changes of knowledge. As an example, the reader may wish to consider how the proposed distinction between psychology and social science would apply to the study of the effects of advertising on consumer behaviour. Admittedly one sympathises with the wish of economists like Hayek and Mises to keep the foundations of our subject clear of psychological questions; but unfortunately, as my earlier discussion indicates, the attempt to exclude all subjective factors leads instead to pure behaviourism, a conclusion which these writers would certainly find unacceptable.

The references are to L. v. Mises, *Human Action*, and F. A. Hayek, 'Scientism and the study of society', *Economica* N.S. **9** (1942) and **10** (1943).

ducing all social phenomena and all social regularities to psychological phenomena and psychological laws' [1]. Popper explicitly takes into account the fact that human action is always influenced by social institutions, and that the institutions themselves cannot generally be explained without reference to other or earlier institutions. Harsanyi's statement of the explanatory variables as 'people's personal objectives and interests, including their possible unselfish interest in each other's well-being' (p. 314) is perhaps rather narrower; he also has special views on the explanation of institutions by means of game theory, which will be discussed in the next section.

I shall start from the view, which accords closely with Harsanyi's approach, that the use of the individualistic method must be justified by its explanatory (predictive) power, and shall leave aside all attempted justifications which invoke special epistemologies of social science [2]. Now this power depends on various conditions,

---

[1]   *The Open Society and its Enemies*, II, 2nd ed., p. 98.

[2]   Both Mises and Hayek advance special arguments for methodological individualism, which it may be of interest to quote briefly. Mises writes, for example: 'That there are nations, states and churches, that there is social cooperation under the division of labour, becomes discernible only in the actions of certain individuals. Nobody ever perceived a nation without perceiving its members . . . It is illusory to believe that it is possible to visualise collective wholes. They are never visible . . . We see a crowd, i.e. a multitude of people' (op. cit. p. 43). On this I shall merely comment, first, that one cannot perceive an individual without perceiving his members, a line of thought which leads to absurd conclusions, and secondly that all science uses terms denoting unobservables.

The following quotations give Hayek's main point: 'The structure of men's minds, the common principle on which they classify external events, provide us with the knowledge of the recurrent elements of which different social structures are built up and in terms of which we can alone describe and explain them.' (op. cit. I, pp. 283–284). '. . . it is the concepts and views held by individuals which are directly known to us and which form the elements from which we must build up, as it were, the more complex phenomena' (p. 286). I would comment that it is far from clear that my knowledge of my own mind, let alone that of another person's, is more direct or more reliable than my knowledge of, say, the price of carrots in the local shop. Also, external events are not always classified on the same principles by different people, particularly if they belong to different socia

which may be satisfied in greater or lesser degree. In particular, it is important that the aims of individuals should be determined largely outside the system under study and should constitute the relatively stable and coherent elements in that system; otherwise it will be more interesting to regard them as determined than as determining factors. In any case, even if a field of study possesses excellent individualistic theories, there will generally be scope in a given state of knowledge for theories of other kinds, which may not be related in any particular way to the individualistic theories. I cannot attempt a general discussion here, but shall give examples of three kinds of theories which do not appear to fit well into the individualistic framework.

(1) Imagine that we are interested in the distribution of property in a rather static society, during a period extending at least over several generations, and suppose that this can be adequately explained by rules of primogeniture, endogamy, etc. [1] If these rules are rigidly enforced in a way which leaves the individual no effective choice (so that the set of available actions is reduced to a single element), then the introduction of personal preferences, though logically unobjectionable, will add nothing of interest to the theory. Alternatively, suppose that the rules are not so rigidly enforced as to eliminate effective choice, but that the preferences inculcated by a lifetime in the society are such that people generally choose to conform. The preferences are now determined endogenously, and to introduce them again adds little to the explanatory value of the theory. In either case the explanation of the distribution of property in terms of the rules seems more significant than an explanation in terms of individual actions. Of course, this conclusion depends on the assumption that the rules may be regarded for the purposes of the discussion as unalterable, or at least unaltered; and a change in the scope of the study to include the reasons for their survival or original adoption might call for a change of method.

---

structures; moreover any common principles are inextricably linked with the structure of language and culture – a conclusion which takes us no closer to Hayek's brand of individualism.

[1] I am indebted to Professor M. Ginsberg for suggesting this example.

(2)   Sharper issues are raised by the important class of regularities which stem from group structure and, in particular, from conscious organisation. It is common in economic and political theory to treat even large organisations as single units, whose behaviour is in many respects comparable to that of individuals, and to explain certain processes in terms of the interaction of these units. This procedure is justified by the high degree of co-ordination achieved in some organisations; indeed it is not difficult to find instances of organisations whose behaviour in certain respects achieves a higher degree of coherence and stability than that displayed by individuals. It is unnecessary here to try to delimit the class of problems which should be treated in this way; the important methodological point is that the considerations which apply are closely analogous to those which determine whether it is appropriate to regard individuals as the basic units in terms of which a given social process is to be explained. Of course, the mechanisms which ensure coherence and stability are different in many respects, and the behavioural postulates which are appropriate must be expected to vary from one kind of organisation or cohesive group to another, and to differ from those which apply to individuals.

These considerations suggest that it may be entirely appropriate in certain cases to use theories in which the actors are groups such as nations, churches or large firms, provided that there is reason to believe that their behaviour will be sufficiently stable and coherent. Moreover, while it is clearly desirable to investigate the social mechanisms which ensure these properties, the use of the theories need no more await a complete understanding of the workings of organisations than the use of individualistic theories of social processes need await a complete account of the psychological mechanisms by which personal action is co-ordinated.

This discussion incidentally clarifies the proper scope for functionalism. The functional method, as I understand it, is essentially the rational method applied to social aggregates, and its value depends on the considerations which have been set out. Some of Harsanyi's criticisms can therefore be regarded as asserting that the method has been applied to aggregates which cannot be expected to behave in a stable or coherent way, or alternatively that the mechanisms which might ensure such behaviour have not been investigated sufficiently to justify the conclusions which have been drawn.

(3) The last group of cases raises problems of a different kind. A wide variety of regularities has been discovered in economic data – cycles in the time series, constancy of distributive shares, functional relationships among aggregative quantities, stable frequency distributions – and these may serve as useful theories even where there are no adequate explanations of the relevant individual behaviour, or where no clear or complete connection has been established. A full discussion of these theories, and of their bearing on methodological individualism, would lead too far afield. I shall merely mention one among many possible examples; it is designed, in particular, to show that an economic theory which is not clearly related to rational individual behaviour need not be 'purely empirical', but can have a theoretical derivation of a different kind, based on probability theory.

The example is Pareto's law of income distribution. If y denotes an individual's annual income and $f(y)$ the relative frequency of that income in a given economy, then the law asserts that $f(y) = Ae^{-cy}$, where A and c are parameters characterising the economy. Originally the law was stated as a purely empirical regularity, but was regarded as interesting because of its agreement with certain observations. Later, it was possible to show that, if y is regarded as a stochastic process with certain transition probabilities for proportional changes, then $f(y)$ is the 'steady state' distribution. This derivation establishes connections with stochastic processes generating other economic variables, and greatly increases the predictions which can be obtained from the theory [1]. It can be regarded, in a sense, as an individualistic derivation; nevertheless, it treats the individuals as entirely passive, as mere particles, and does not establish a connection with the ordinary rationalistic theory of individual decisions concerning the earning of income [2]. Whether

---

[1]   See, for example, B. Mandelbrot, 'Stable Paretian functions and the multiplicative variation of income', *Econometrica*, October 1961.

[2]   It goes without saying that the treatment of given behaviour as a

or not such a connection can be established, the theory is interesting, testable, and useful.

The extent to which methodological individualism as a general rule of method is invalidated by these examples – assuming that they are accepted as instances of useful and interesting work – depends on the version of the doctrine which is considered. I shall merely comment on two general attitudes which may be adopted.

First, it may be argued that, although some of the theories admittedly use methods which are not individualistic, we 'ought not to be satisfied' with them until the connection with rational individual action has been fully established. This statement is too vague to offer any practical guidance; strictly speaking, it merely lays down a supposedly 'ideal' state which in most parts of social science will never be reached, or may be reached and destroyed by further research, (as has happened in important parts of economic theory). More generally, we ought in any case not to be permanently satisfied with our theories, and at any given time most of them give rise to a variety of problems. It is true that the search for connections between social regularities and individual behaviour is a source of important problems, but it is only one of many; for instance, it is also important to establish links among regularities at different levels of aggregation. The search for these connections is not necessarily the most urgent or the most fruitful work at a particular stage; in particular, its value depends largely on the quality of the individualistic theories which are available. It would therefore be incorrect in general to single out as particularly unsatisfactory those theories for which this work is relatively incomplete; and the injunction that we should not be satisfied with theories which are not fully individualistic certainly cannot be regarded as the main special rule of method of the social sciences.

Alternatively, it may be said that all the theories which I have cited as examples are quite capable of an interpretation which is consistent with methodological individualism, in a suitably wide version which admits institutional and statistical explanations. But

random variable need not be incompatible with the treatment of the same behaviour as rational; for example, consider the obvious explanation of the act of raising an umbrella.

on such an interpretation the doctrine would be almost empty; I say almost, not entirely, for two reasons. First, it can still be regarded as insisting that all social theories be cast in an individualistic form; but, as in the case of the rationality principle, this procedure is objectionable where it makes a theory more complicated, and possibly misleading, without adding significantly to its testable content. Secondly, methodological individualism presumably forbids the use of such concepts as collective personality, will, purpose and aims. As Harsanyi points out, this prohibition is largely redundant in relation to modern social science. In any case, to the extent that the questions connected with group minds, wills, etc. concern matters of substance rather than definition [1], they are not to be settled by an arbitrary principle of individualism, but in the usual way according to the testable consequences of hypotheses. If it were possible to define concepts of mind and will with sufficient precision, and if some social phenomena could not be adequately explained without postulating group mind and will, then there would be no objection in principle to such a procedure.

3. *Game theory and social norms.* In this final section I shall comment briefly on Harsanyi's special arguments for using the

---

[1] In this connection, it may be of interest to comment briefly on the following question, which turns out to be largely terminological: if explanations in terms of collectives such as organisations are to be allowed, is it permissible to ascribe aims to these collectives? Now, it is possible to distinguish between two common uses of such terms as 'group aims', namely 'aims which are formulated through a group' and 'aims which are related to group action in the same way as individual aims are related to individual action'. We leave aside the first meaning as unobjectionable, and further dismiss as trivial the case where 'group aims' are simply the aims shared by all members of a group. Turning to the main problem, we recall our definition of individual aims – any principle or procedure, possessing suitable properties of coherence and stability, for choice among alternative courses of action. Now, if we restrict ourselves to principles or procedures which operate to some extent in minds, then we can have group aims only if we postulate group minds. Alternatively, if we regard mind as inessential, then groups can have aims without minds – though on such a view the concept of aims would admittedly be redundant.

particular rationalistic and individualistic methods of game theory to explain practically the whole range of social phenomena, including social norms and even morality. Let me say at once that I consider his claims to be out of all proportion to the proven, and even to the potential, value of game theory.

While it is common ground that many social problems can usefully be analysed by means of game theory, Harsanyi claims excessive universality and definiteness of prediction. It has often been pointed out that even the 'classical' game theory, which follows the approach of von Neumann and Morgenstern, relies on strong assumptions which do not appear to fit most social situations; and despite its great intellectual importance, the range of social phenomena for which it has offered new and correct predictions is strikingly small. As is well known, this theory does not offer unique predictions for most games, other than zero-sum two person games; only if the possibilities for play are particularly restricted is a unique answer obtained. As to the Zeuthen–Nash theory, which Harsanyi has developed as a theory offering 'determinate solutions for all classes of games' (p. 309), it is not generally accepted as a general answer to either the predictive or the normative problem, and there is (so far as I am aware) little empirical evidence in its favour. Despite its theoretical interest, it can at present be regarded as no more than one of a number of alternative suggestions, which may be applicable in some cases. Since these matters have been discussed in the relevant literature, it is unnecessary to go into technical details here [1].

As a first corollary of these remarks, I believe that Harsanyi does not sufficiently recognise that the scope of individualistic explanation is far wider than that of game theory. Secondly, his view that every game has a unique solution leads him to exaggerate the extent to which social co-operation can be explained without reference to social norms, or alternatively the extent to which

---

[1] For a brief critique of Harsanyi's contributions, see R. L. Bishop's remarks in the *American Economic Review*, May 1965, pp. 467–469. General surveys of the literature are given in R. D. Luce and H. Raiffa, *Games and Decisions*, and R. L. Bishop, 'Game-theoretic analyses of bargaining', *Quarterly Journal of Economics*, November 1963.

social norms themselves can be explained in purely rationalistic and individualistic terms. From the standpoint of 'classical' game theory, norms can be regarded as special rules of the social game which reduce the scope for incompatibility of mutual expectations, and hence the range of indeterminacy of the outcome. In fact, this is quite an interesting interpretation of the doctrine, which Harsanyi attributes to Durkheim and Parsons, that 'the model of rational behavior in itself cannot explain social co-operation . . . (without introducing) . . . *social norms* as a further not-analysed basic constituent'. (p. 313) I agree with Harsanyi that social norms call for explanation, and that this explanation need not be functional; but he goes too far when he states that 'the existence of these social norms themselves will admit of explanation in terms of people's personal objectives and interests' (p. 313) – if he means that the explanation can be given entirely in these terms. In general, it is not possible to explain norms without reference to other norms and institutions. If a given norm is regarded as the outcome of a game, other norms will generally figure among the rules; and even then the outcome may not be unique.

Although I am ill qualified to discuss the question of social status, it seems to me that Harsanyi's theory suffers from all the defects of the method which it is intended to illustrate. It is unduly rationalistic, since much status behaviour is conditioned and automatic rather than goal-oriented in any significant sense. The theory does not allow fully for the important part played by tradition in the determination of social status in most societies; even if there were a tendency for social status to adjust according to Harsanyi's principle of the 'balance of power', tradition might ensure that this mechanism operated so slowly that it would be of little help in explaining the relationships at a given time. Finally, Harsanyi talks as though the status structure could be determined from very limited, specific information, apparently without reference to traditions, institutions, etc. I can see no reason to suppose that a single formula can hope to replace detailed study of the circumstances and history of a given society [1].

[1] Apart from these defects, which are directly related to my methodological remarks, there are various other objections to the theory. Social

To conclude: the rationality principle, and the doctrine of methodological individualism, if interpreted restrictively, exclude from social science some valuable methods which are compatible with general criteria of good scientific work; if interpreted broadly, they permit virtually all methods, but are almost empty, apart from insisting that theories be cast in certain forms which in some cases are misleading and unduly cumbersome. The explanation of individual behaviour by rationalistic methods, and the individualistic explanation of social processes, are among the most powerful methods of social science. But the success of these methods depends on certain conditions – such as the coherence, stability and exogenous determination of preferences – and it may well be unrewarding to apply them to a particular problem at a particular stage of research. Wholesale condemnation of alternative methods is certainly out of place. Finally, game theory is more restricted in scope than the individualistic method generally; the view that every game has a unique outcome lacks support; and it is not usually possible to explain a given social norm as the outcome of a game unless other norms are included among the rules, and even then the outcome will not necessarily be unique.

J. C. HARSANYI: *Reply.*

1. I have no disagreement with many of Foldes' general statements about social-science methodology. I certainly share his view that fundamentally the use of the individualistic method in general – and the use of rational-behavior models in particular – 'must be justified by [their] explanatory (predictive) power' [1], rather than by appeals to introspection, etc.

Moreover, both of us seem to agree that, in terms of this funda-

---

status is not clearly defined; it is treated as if it were a well-defined quantity measurable along a single scale; the mechanisms relating conflict to the grant of status, and the connection between status and alternative forms of reward, are not clearly analysed; the fact that high social status frequently *restricts* the choice of associates and profession is ignored; and it is not recognised that status may be as much a source as a consequence of power.

[1] Foldes, p. 329.

mental criterion, rational-behavior models can claim considerable success in economic theory, which is the social science where the use of such models is most prevalent and has the longest history. But apparently Foldes is much less optimistic than I am about the likely value of rational-behavior models in the analysis of social behavior outside of the traditional boundaries of economics.

My own greater optimism is based on two main considerations. One is the very encouraging success of recent attempts to use rational-behavior models or closely related approaches in political science, the study of international relations, the theory of social organizations, as well as general sociology and social psychology [1]. This success is all the more significant in view of the very recent start and the still very modest scale of the work done on rational-behavior models outside of economics.

The other reason for my optimism is the recent breakthrough in game theory, now enabling us for the first time to define determinate solutions for *all* classes of games discussed by classical game theory – including two-person non-zero-sum and n-person games, both cooperative and non-cooperative, which are the game classes most important for social-science applications [2].

Prior to these recent developments in game theory most social situations simply could not be analysed in terms of rational-

---

[1]   I shall restrict myself to a few illustrative references. See, e.g., Anthony Downs, *An Economic Theory of Democracy*, New York, 1957; Duncan Black, *The Theory of Committees and Elections*, Cambridge, 1958; Mancur Olson, Jr., *The Logic of Collective Action*, Cambridge, Mass., 1965; J. G. March and H. A. Simon, *Organizations*, New York, 1958. Cf. also G. C. Homans, *Social Behavior : Its Elementary Forms*, New York, 1961; and J. W. Thibaut and H. H. Kelley, *The Social Psychology of Groups*, New York, 1959. The last two books make no explicit use of formal rational-behavior models, but most of their analysis could be easily and very naturally restated in such terms.

[2]   A relatively non-mathematical description of my results can be found in my paper in the *American Economic Review*, May 1965. For a more rigorous mathematical presentation, see my paper in *Econometrica*, July 1966. (See footnote 2 on p. 309 above). A more detailed discussion and interpretation of my results will be given in my book in progress on 'Rational Behavior and Bargaining Equilibrium in Games and Social Situations'.

behavior models at all, because they involve interaction between two or more individuals or social organizations, with partly divergent and partly convergent interests, and so would have required analysis in terms of some theory of rational behavior in two-person non-zero-sum games or in n-person games. Yet classical game theory has been unable to provide a clear definition of rational behavior in games belonging to either of these two game classes. As a result it has been unable to make definite predictions about the outcomes of such games (even on the assumption that all players will act in a perfectly rational manner), or to provide nontrivial strategy recommendations for the participants. It has been only our own new approach to game theory which has offered the first clear and unambiguous definition of rational behavior for the whole range of relevant game situations [1].

Foldes seems to take the view that the main weakness of von Neumann and Morgenstern's game-theoretical approach has been the fact that 'the range of social phenomena for which it has offered *new* and *correct* predictions is strikingly small' [2]. In my opinion, a much more important weakness of their approach has been the fact that for most social situations it has hardly offered *any* definite predictions at all, not even incorrect ones. The point is not that the predictions of their theory have been refuted by empirical tests. The point is rather that its predictions are seldom specific enough as to admit of meaningful empirical testing. In most cases all we are told is that the outcome of the game will be any one of a very large (usually infinite) number of possible outcomes, and we are given no indication of how this huge set of possibilities is narrowed down in each case to the unique point representing the actual outcome.

2.   Foldes is of course quite right in saying that my new theory of rational behavior in game situations has not yet found wide acceptance, and has not yet been tested empirically on any sig-

---

[1]   Though earlier work by Zeuthen, Nash, and Shapley has already solved this problem for some important special cases. My own results are largely direct generalizations of theirs.

[2]   Foldes, p. 335 (my own italics).

nificant scale. But this can hardly be expected to be otherwise considering that the first preliminary public statement of my theory was made in 1961 (at the Stanford International Congress for Logic, Methodology, and Philosophy of Science), and that a rigorous mathematical description of it was published only in the 1966 *Econometrica* article already referred to, though a dittoed version of this latter paper has been available since 1964.

My theory of rational behavior in game situations is a generalization of what is now often called the 'Bayesian' theory of rational behavior of an isolated individual under uncertainty. Now, the Bayesian approach itself is today still far from general acceptance, even though it goes back at least to Ramsey (1931), and its more modern version due to Savage (1954), has also been available for more than a decade [1]. This slowness in public response to Bayesian ideas has been all the more remarkable since the problem of how to define rational behavior under uncertainty is incomparably simpler than is the problem of how to define rational behavior in game situations – and since it has been known for more than a decade that all non-Bayesian definitions of rationality lead to wholly unacceptable paradoxes [2].

This long time lag in public reaction to theories of this kind is no doubt due to the fact that their acceptance depends not only on the correctness of the mathematical proofs by which their theorems are derived from their axioms (this is relatively easy to check), but rather depends primarily on one's willingness to accept these very axioms (rationality postulates). Whether these axioms themselves are reasonable, and whether they are likely to lead to a useful theory or not, are not questions admitting of rigorous mathematical proofs but rather are susceptible only of heuristic arguments, which by necessity take a much longer time to produce a convergence of expert opinion one way or the other. This time lag is bound to be particularly long if a new theory challenges some

---

[1] F. P. Ramsey, *The Foundations of Mathematics and Other Logical Essays*, ch. VII, London, 1931; and L. J. Savage, *The Foundations of Statistics*, New York, 1954.

[2] See R. Radner and J. Marschak, 'Note on some decision criteria', in R. M. Thrall et al., eds., *Decision Processes*, New York, 1954.

widely shared theoretical positions, in the way my theory challenges the point of view of classical game theory.

Yet this inevitable time lag in gaining wide acceptance is surely not a reason for not stating the merits (or demerits) of any given theory in the meantime in forceful and unambiguous terms. On the contrary, the only way of reducing this time lag is by making this kind of information widely accessible. Both the supporters and the critics of a given theory can perform a very useful service by making its strong points and weak points more generally known. I am less sure of what useful purposes are served by criticisms based almost wholly on the fact that a given theory has not gained immediate general acceptance, especially if not even one substantive argument is put forward against the theory.

Going over to a closely related point, Foldes writes: 'Despite its theoretical interest, it [i.e., my theory] can at present be regarded as no more than one of a number of alternative suggestions...'[1]. If Foldes means to say that for many games a number of alternative solution concepts have been suggested in the literature then he is certainly right. But my theory is the *only* existing theory which defines a unique solution for each particular game on the basis of the same general rationality postulates, so that all these individual solution concepts become special cases of the *same* general theory. For the time being no alternative theory with this property has been suggested.

At the same time, whereas my theory is certainly the *first* theory providing a general definition for rational behavior in game situations, I surely would not claim that it is the *last* word on this subject. One would naturally expect that technical criticism over time will suggest some modifications in my rationality postulates and possibly in some other aspects of my theory.

Moreover, my theory in its present form primarily aims at defining determinate solutions for the game classes introduced by classical game theory. But work is already in progress to extend my theory to various 'non-classical' games, such as games with incomplete information (where the players are ignorant about each

---

[1] Foldes, p. 335.

other's payoff functions and/or some other basic parameters of the game situation), or games with delayed commitment (where the players cannot commit themselves to specific strategies before the first stage of the game has been completed), etc. [1]. As this work will significantly increase the scope of my theory and will extend it to game situations quite dissimilar to those occurring in classical game theory, it is bound to suggest new points of view also in the analysis of 'classical' game situations.

Another line of investigation that is bound to affect our views about the proper use of game-theoretical and other rational-behavior models in the social sciences is work on what Simon calls the problem of 'limited rationality', i.e., rational behavior by a decision maker with limited computational and information-processing ability [2]. Most existing approaches to economics, decision theory, and game theory (including my own theory of rational behavior in game situations) abstract from the computational and other intellectual limitations of human beings. In many cases this seems to be a perfectly legitimate simplifying assumption. But in other cases we probably cannot obtain realistic predictions without using theories taking explicit account of people's limited information-processing capabilities. Fundamentally, only empirical research can tell us which social situations belong to the first category and which to the second.

3. Some of Foldes's critical remarks are based on misunderstandings. Contrary to what he seems to imply, I have never objected to treating organizations as the units of our analysis, for instance, to treating each organization as one single 'player'. (For example, in my paper in the *American Economic Review*, May 1965, p. 447, I have explicitly characterized the players of a game as 'persons or organizations'.) Under my interpretation of the

---

[1] See my paper on 'Games with incomplete information played by 'Bayesian' Players', I–III, Working Papers Nos. 157–159 (February 1966), University of California *Center for Research in Management Science*, Berkeley. To appear in *Management Science* in 1967.

[2] See, e.g., H. A. Simon, 'Theories of decision making in economics and behavioral science', *American Economic Review* 69 (1959), pp. 253–283.

principle of methodological individualism, this approach will be perfectly consistent with the principle so long as there is some evidence that the people acting on behalf of each organization have strong enough emotional identification with it (i.e., assign high enough positive utility to the goals of the organization), or at least have strong enough external incentives to promote the interests of the organization. Treating organizations as units becomes objectionable only if this problem of individual motivations is not being solved in a satisfactory way – or if it is not raised at all because it is not recognized as a problem.

Furthermore, we must always keep in mind that treating an organization as a monolithic unit can never be more than a first approximation. To achieve closer approximation to the real world we must always take explicit account of all major conflicts of interest existing within the organization – which means treating the organization not as one single player but rather as a coalition of several players, each representing a different social group within the organization. (For some purposes we may even have to carry disaggregation down to the individual members of the organization.)

At the same time, I must strongly disagree with Foldes' contention that the principle of methodological individualism becomes an empty statement under such a liberal interpretation [1]. Admittedly, the individualistic principle – or any other methodological principle – has only *heuristic* significance. It cannot justify any categorical conclusions about the nature of the real world, but can tell us only that some empirical hypotheses are *more likely* to be true than others, or that some methods of explanation are more likely to be successful than their alternatives. Thus the individualistic principle tells us that any hypothesis asserting existence of some 'group mind' is extremely *unlikely* to be true. But it could not justify categorical rejection of such a hypothesis if – contrary to all our expectations – there were overwhelming empirical evidence forthcoming in favor of that hypothesis.

Yet, in spite of its purely heuristic nature, the individualistic

---

[1]   Foldes, p. 334.

principle can play a highly useful role under appropriate conditions. It may be very useful information that existence of a group mind is highly unlikely (even though it is not strictly impossible because it seems to involve no logical self-contradiction). For, this has the practical implication that the group-mind hypothesis should be adopted only if the empirical evidence in its favor were truly overwhelming and could not be explained in any other way.

Basically similar statements apply also to less crude forms of collectivistic explanations, such as functionalistic theories. Their intrinsic improbability is not quite as great as that of group-mind theories. But they are sufficiently improbable to suggest that we should give strong preference to alternative explanatory hypotheses if such are available.

It seems to me that any denial of the importance of methodological principles in scientific research, merely because these principles have only heuristic validity, leads to absurd consequences. For instance, one of the basic principles of modern science is the naturalistic principle, which says that we should try to find a natural explanation for any empirical event. It would be absurd to deny that it was a major intellectual advance when the scientific community generally accepted this principle in the seventeenth century. Yet this principle, also, has only heuristic validity. All it tells us is that it is extremely *unlikely* for any empirical event not to have a natural explanation, and that for this reason strong preference should always be given to such explanations. But, once more, the naturalistic principle could not justify categorical rejection of any empirical hypothesis – for example, of a hypothesis asserting the existence of witchcraft – if, contrary to all our expectations, we were faced with overwhelming empirical evidence for such a hypothesis. Yet, short of such truly overwhelming empirical evidence which could not be explained in any other way, the principle does justify rejection of all supernatural explanations.

4. Again, Foldes is mistaken in attributing to me the view that social norms are to be explained *fundamentally* as the outcome of a game (presumably of a bargaining game) among different members of the society. (I take it that in this game every player would try to get the other players to agree to social norms as favorable as possible to his own personal or sectional interests.) In fact, I would find such a theory unacceptable because it would fail to do justice to the importance of altruistic considerations in the explanation of social norms.

In my paper presented at the Colloquium I have only a brief passage on this problem but have a reference to my paper in *Mind* (1958) where my theory of moral norms is stated at length. Even a superficial glance at this paper would have shown Foldes that my actual theory of social norms is quite different from the theory he is attributing to me.

Very briefly, my theory is essentially a quantitative decision-theoretical version of Adam Smith's theory of morality. I propose to define moral value judgments as judgments of preference that we make when we try to judge a social situation, not in terms of our own personal interests, but rather in terms of impartial and impersonal criteria, with equal sympathy for all the individual interests involved. We may also say that making a moral value judgment is tantamount to trying to judge the situation from the point of view of an impartial but fully sympathetic observer.

I have tried to show that this theory of moral value judgments leads to a form of utilitarian ethics, based on a social welfare function representing the arithmetic mean (or the sum) of all individual utilities [1].

This theory is meant to be primarily a *normative* theory of moral value judgments. Used as a *predictive* theory of people's actual moral attitudes it would obviously overstate the impartiality these attitudes are likely to exhibit in the real world. In my opinion, any realistic predictive theory must combine the basic insights of Adam Smith's theory with game-theoretical considerations.

Though moral value judgments by definition always involve some attempt at impartiality, this attempt is very often less than

---

[1] See my 'Cardinal utility in welfare economics and in the theory of risk-taking', *Journal of Political Economy* 61 (1953), pp. 434–435; and my 'Cardinal welfare, individualistic ethics, and interpersonal comparisons of utility', *Journal of Political Economy* 63 (1955), pp. 309–321.

346

completely successful. Hence the moral value judgments of different individuals and different social groups are likely to be biased in favor of their own personal and sectional interests. On the other hand, the official moral code of any given society is likely to represent a compromise among the social values of different social groups. This compromise itself may be explained as a result of tacit bargaining among these social groups, which itself may admit of analysis in terms of a game-theoretical bargaining model.

Thus I would not deny the importance of game-theoretical considerations (balance-of-power considerations) in explaining the moral code of a given society. But I would regard any purely game-theoretical model of morality as being seriously incomplete. If I had to choose, I would certainly prefer Adam Smith's theory of morality to one based on purely game-theoretical considerations.

5. As my paper presented at the Colloquium has been a paper on social-science methodology, rather than on the sociology of social status, it contains only a short summary of my theory of social status, used merely as an example to make a methodological point. But I have included a reference to another paper of mine describing my theory of social status in full detail. Nevertheless Foldes saw fit to comment on my theory merely on the basis of the short summary included in my Colloquium paper [1]. Otherwise it would be hard to explain why he claimed that I had not defined the concept of social status, had not discussed the connection between status and other forms of reward, had ignored the fact that high status might actually restrict a person's choice of associates, etc.

Foldes asserts, without offering any evidence to this effect, that status behavior is 'conditioned and automatic rather than goal-oriented in any significant sense' [2]. This is certainly not the conclusion that sociologists conducting empirical research on status

---

[1] My paper on social status was published in *Behavioral Science*, September 1966, which was not yet available when Foldes was writing his Note. But a dittoed version of the paper has been available on request since 1964.

[2] Foldes, p. 336.

behavior have arrived at. A few months after my paper on social status was written, Professor Peter Blau of Chicago University published his book on *Exchange and Power in Social Life* (New York, 1964). His book is based on extensive field work, focusing primarily on status behavior in bureaucratic organizations. Relying on these empirical observations and on those of other contemporary sociologists, and virtually uninfluenced by formal game theory, he arrives at a theory of social status basically identical to my own. Needless to say, I find it most encouraging that Blau's empirical findings are in such close agreement with my own views, based primarily on pure theoretical considerations. That much about my theory of social status, which, as Foldes puts it, "sufffers from all the defects of the method which it is intended to illustrate" [1].

6. In fairness to Foldes, I feel I must concede at least one point. As my paper has been concerned mainly with demonstrating the advantages of rational-behavior models, and in particular of game-theoretical models, over functionalistic explanations I have not explicitly mentioned the importance of other types of explanatory theories, such as, e.g., stochastic models of income distribution, etc. This must have given the misleading impression that I want to deny their importance and their often considerable explanatory power, which has not been my intention at all.

I am less convinced of the explanatory value of some other non-rationalistic explanatory theories mentioned in Foldes' Note. For instance, such observed empirical regularities as the relative constancy of labor's share in national income can be used, no doubt, to explain some other social facts. But any such explanation will remain highly incomplete so long as these empirical regularities themselves have not been explained in terms of some characteristics of individual behavior. For instance, few economists would deny that a satisfactory explanation of the relative constancy of income shares would be an important advance in our understanding of the economic system.

---

[1] Foldes, p. 336,

I have similar reservations about explaining the distribution of property in terms of the legal rules concerning inheritance. This explanation may be quite valid as far as it goes. But as Foldes himself seems to admit [1], deeper understanding of the distribution of property in various societies can be achieved only by understanding the social forces responsible for *maintenance* and for *modification* of these legal rules governing property relationships. And if we try to understand these social forces then we are very likely to find that they require a largely game-theoretical balanceof-power model for their explanation.

----

[1] Foldes, p. 330.

THE PRESENT STATE OF THEORY IN SOCIOLOGY

R. A. H. ROBSON

University of British Columbia

Before proceeding to look at different theoretical formulations in the field of sociology, I would like to make a few introductory remarks which should form the context in which this paper is to be understood.

First, what is meant by the term 'theory' or what is purported to be theory in my discipline is extremely varied. It is my guess that in the majority of American university sociology departments, lectures and seminars on theory are principally concerned with a history of social ideas which entails a reading, and occasionally some kind of superficial understanding, of the earlier great masters in the field. Other theorists regard what might be called 'social commentary' or the analysis of social phenomena as theory. This kind of analysis is most often descriptive in character, showing similarities and differences between various social institutions and between different kinds of social behaviour. Yet a third meaning given to the term 'theory' is the development of taxonomic systems; the creation of more or less systematic or comprehensive sets of concepts which may be used in 'analyzing' social behaviour, but not in explaining in a 'causal' or 'relational' sense. Finally, there are those who restrict the term 'theory' to apply to a set of inter-related, general propositions which seek to explain empirical uniformities and from which one can deduce further hypotheses for empirical test.

For fairly obvious reasons, I have not referred in this paper to any 'theories' of the first two kinds I have just mentioned. Further, it has been necessary even with respect to the last two types to select only one or two of each class which I thought would give an adequate impression of the present state of theory in sociology.

I should also like to mention, although I think it should be readily apparent, that it is extremely difficult in the space of a few minutes to present a theory so that it is easily comprehensible to persons who are not trained in or familiar with the discipline, as I am sure *some* of you are not. Since my emphasis in this paper is on *methodological* aspects of theories in my discipline, I have included only the minimum amount of substantive material as it seemed to me necessary to appreciate its methodological characteristics.

Finally, I should point out that my treatment of the subject of this paper is based upon what is, I think, a much more critical view of what passes for theory in sociology than most other sociologists have. By giving a frankly critical evaluation of work in my discipline to an audience composed primarily of persons outside the field, I feel somewhat like a member of Her Majesty's Loyal Opposition who criticizes his own government's policies when speaking in public in a foreign country – it just isn't done! Seriously though, since other views will not have equal time as it were, I would like to emphasize that my views about theory are probably *not* shared by the majority of sociologists. As a social psychologist, I am often regarded as being on the periphery of the field of sociology proper; and I am often called, among other derogatory terms, a 'methodologist', which signifies a set of concerns which are quite different from those of the traditional sociological theorist, who would regard the topic of this paper as more appropriate to *his* competence than to *mine*. This view, however, is not as popular as it once was, and more and more theory is being linked with the discussion of research methods and being treated from a methodological point of view rather than as a separate substantive subject.

Since by now, my defensiveness must be clearly showing, I will proceed quickly to the topic with which this paper is concerned. In what follows, I have tried to describe as briefly as possible, four representative theories in sociology, and after each one, to present a short critical evaluation of it.

1. *Talcott Parsons and the 'General Theory of Action'.* Talcott Parsons is without doubt the most well known 'theorist' in American sociology. He has written voluminously and the almost universal

criticism is that his style is so turgid that it is not only extremely difficult to read, but virtually impossible to comprehend in many places. One reviewer summed up popular feeling when he said of Parsons' written work [1]: '. . . Neologisms abound, sentences sometimes appear to be literal translations of a text originally written in German, the style is complex, the use of terms is not always consistent and some passages still defy comprehension after repeated and earnest scrutiny'.

Parsons began his career by critically analyzing the work of the earlier social theorists and, after publishing several essays, he produced an 800-page book entitled 'The Structure of Social Action', 1937 [2], in which he examined in great detail the work of four theorists, Alfred Marshall, Pareto, Durkheim and Max Weber. His thesis in this book was that in spite of the obvious differences between these writers in the way they analyzed different kinds of social behaviour, their views could be seen to 'converge', and Parsons' principal aim was to draw out from each theorist that which he felt contributed something to a *general* social theory which he called 'the voluntaristic theory of action'.

What is this theory? Parsons starts with the utilitarian position in economic theory, with its concepts of 'means', 'ends' and 'conditions'; but for Parsons this individualistic, rationalistic framework had important weaknesses. While it might, he conceded, facilitate the construction of systematic analytical models, these had very limited utility when applied to the real world where even economic activities are never either purely economic or purely rational, but are affected by broadly social and nonrational factors. Although this has been recognized even by economic theorists, the noneconomic or nonrational factors had at best been relegated by them to a residual category, and Parsons felt that they deserved to have much greater importance placed upon them than this in a *general*, as contrasted with an economic, theory of action. In any such theory, insisted Parsons, room must be left for individual

---

[1]   *The Social Theories of Talcott Parsons*, Max Black, ed., Prentice Hall, New Jersey, 1961.

[2]   Parsons, Talcott, *The Structure of Social Action*, Free Press, Glencoe, Ill., 1949.

choice from among alternative means and therefore the notions of mind, consciousness, values and normative standards must be central. In other words, while using the basic rationalist analysis in terms of means, ends and conditions, he insisted that it was necessary to increase the variety of classes of these from the narrowly positivistic type to include the subjective and the social.

Devereux [1] has succinctly summarized Parsons' conclusions in this first major work, which I will further paraphrase:

(1) His objective is to construct a *general* theory in the sense that it is sufficiently comprehensive to explain any and all concrete social behaviour.

(2) Such a theory must be an action theory, which means that the central focus is upon *actors* orienting themselves to *situations*, with reference to various sorts of *goals*, *values* and *normative standards* and behaving accordingly.

(3) Action theory must be based on a voluntaristic postulate, i.e. the choice between alternative courses of action must be partially free.

(4) A voluntaristic theory must treat ideas, ideals, goals and normative standards as causally relevant variables and not as epiphenomena affected by but never wholly determined by the pressures of the nonideal factors.

(5) Sociological theory must take into account the principle of 'emergence', by which is meant that systems emerge which have properties which cannot be inferred from or explained in terms of the operation of their component parts or elements, and these are treated as causally relevant variables in the theory. However, the emergent systems and their properties never become wholly detached from their component parts.

Is this a theory? It is interesting to note that apparently even Parsons was unsure of the answer to this question, because in the space of four pages [2], although he calls it a theory four times, he also variously uses the terms 'a generalized system of theoretical

---

[1]   Devereux, Edward C. Jr., *Parsons' Sociological Theory*, in Max Black, op. cit.

[2]   Parsons, Talcott, op. cit. pp. 720–723.

categories', 'a structure of conceptual elements', 'a theoretical system', and a 'conceptual scheme' to describe his contribution to social theory. Before giving *our* verdict, we will add to the foregoing a summary of his subsequent theoretical formulations. Parsons' elaboration of the 'voluntaristic theory of action' into what he subsequently calls a 'general theory of action [1]' basically amounts to the development of classes of concepts of which the following are the most important:

(1)   He starts with an 'actor' in a 'situation'. An 'actor' has certain energies, abilities, capacities and various other properties. A 'situation' comprises physical objects, cultural objects and social objects.

(2)   Action is the behaviour of an actor in a situation directed towards goals; it has motivational significance.

(3)   Actors' motivations may be classed as 'cognitive', 'cathectic' or 'evaluative'.

(4)   Action is defined as behaviour in which these several aspects of objects are interpreted in terms of shared (cultural) symbols.

(5)   The standards or criteria by which selection is made among the various orientations possible in a situation are called 'values' which have three modes corresponding to the three motivational modes.

With these concepts, social behaviour or action is seen to be analyzed in terms of motivated actors seeking gratifications and oriented to shared values or standards and thus to interact in patterned ways. The total action system is thus seen to comprise three sub-systems: personality, culture and social systems.

These concepts are relevant to the analysis of the elementary social act; additional concepts too numerous to present in detail here are provided for the analysis of interaction between actors. Briefly, Parsons provides further sets of classifications of motivations, value orientations, culture patterns, interests, evaluative action orientations, and of institutions.

It should be clear that that part of Parsons' work which we

---

[1]   Parsons, Talcott, *Toward a General Theory of Social Action*, Harvard University Press, Boston, Mass., 1951.

have presented so far, amounts to a set of concepts which define certain properties of *all* action or interaction; they are the basic elements into which all action or interaction can be divided, and each action system can be broken down into these elements so that there will be something to go into each pigeon hole. The scheme so far does not by itself enable one to discriminate between *different* action systems. It is Parsons' famous five 'pattern variables' that are supposed to do this. These 'dichotomous variables' are said to represent the universal dilemmas of orientation which have to be resolved before action can take place and, since they are analytically independent of one another, by cross-tabulation he arrives at thirty-two logically possible patterns of orientation. But certain problems have arisen in this connection: even Parsons himself has allowed that some of the *logically possible* patterns are probably *empirically impossible*; and when attempts have been made to utilize these variables in empirical research, great difficulty has been experienced, both in establishing the precise meaning of the concepts and in developing operational definitions of them.

Evaluation

First, I would like to emphasize that Parsons is generally regarded as the *foremost* theorist in sociology. Perhaps because of this, or because of the difficulty of clearly understanding what he writes, it was many years after the publication of the two books mentioned previously that sociologists really got to grips with what he was proposing. A draft of his 'working papers in the theory of action' was presented to a special session of the 1950 meetings of the American Sociological Association, but the major evaluation of his work by a group of nine prominent sociologists (who spent two years talking about it) did not occur until eight years later and their conclusions were not published until eleven years later [1]. What were their conclusions? The principal ones were these:

(1) Parsons' general theory is *not* a theory in the sense that it comprises a set of interrelated propositions from which hy-

---

[1] Black, Max, ed., op. cit.

potheses can be deduced for empirical test or which offer an explanation of sets of empirical generalizations.

(2)   Parsons summarizes several very general assumptions concerning man and society; e.g. all human action is directed towards goals; all human response to stimuli has two distinct dimensions – is simultaneously cognitive and cathectic; all human action involves selection between alternative orientations and responses.

(3)   To support his contention that Parsons' terminology was largely jargon rather than designed to give greater precision, one reviewer suggested that these assumptions could be reformulated into the following language with little loss of meaning; 'whenever you do anything, you are trying to get something done'; 'you cannot do anything without thinking and having feelings at the same time'; and 'human life is one long set of choices'.

(4)   His contribution amounts to a 'conceptual framework' or 'frame of reference' which provides a set of concepts which can be used in describing a vast array of social behaviour.

(5)   While the concepts developed by Parsons may eventually be used in hypotheses which are empirically tested and thus found to be useful, Parsons does *not* present such hypotheses in any systematic way and, in any case, most of the concepts present considerable problems for the researcher because of vague definitions and the difficulty of establishing operational definitions.

2.   *The functionalists*. While Parsons' theory is difficult to summarize because of his ponderous style and technical-sounding jargon, functionalist theory is hard to present because it is hard to find. Functionalists there are (even Parsons claims to be one); the postulates for functional analysis have been set down for all to see, and claims have been made concerning the functions served by various social items, but functional *theory* remains a mystery, an unfulfilled promise to me. Robert Merton is generally regarded as chief spokesman for this school of thought and his book entitled 'Social Theory and Social Structure' (1957) [1] the party programme.

---

[1]   Merton, Robert K., *Social Theory and Social Structure*, Free Press, Glencoe, Ill., 1957.

It is significant that although this book runs to over 600 pages, the part entitled 'Sociological theory' consumes only $\frac{1}{6}$ of this, only $\frac{1}{2}$ of which is directly concerned with functional analysis. The remaining $\frac{5}{6}$ of the book deals with what Merton calls 'studies' of various sociological phenomena. And while there are one or two references in this section to 'theory', the theories are narrow in scope, are not related one to another in any systematic way and their relationship to functional analysis is somewhat obscure.

But what *is* functional theory? Apparently it is any theory which uses functional analysis. And what distinguishes functional analysis from other types? According to Merton, 'the central orientation of functionalism (is) the practice of interpreting data by establishing their consequences for larger structures in which they are implicated . . .' [1]. The functionalist methodological model is frankly taken from the biological sciences; basically, their position is that the similarities between the biological organism and society suggest that a similar methodological framework or model to that developed in the biological sciences is likely to be useful in sociology. It should be pointed out that the functionalists in sociology, however, specifically dissociate themselves from the earlier organismic notions of society.

The procedure for functional analysis taken from the biological sciences is given by the following steps [2]:

(1)   The establishment of those functional requirements of an organism which are necessary to its survival or to operate with some degree of effectiveness.

(2)   Concrete and detailed description of the structures and the processes through which these requirements are typically met in 'normal' cases.

(3)   The detection of substitute mechanisms which fulfill functional requirements.

(4)   A detailed account is given of the structure for which the functional requirements hold.

Merton further elaborates this procedure with what he calls 'a

---

[1]   Ibid. pp. 46–47.
[2]   Ibid. p. 49.

paradigm' for functional analysis in sociology, which 'presents the hard core of concept, procedure, and inference in functional a-nalysis' [1]. These are:

(1)   the items to which functions are imputed,

(2)   concepts of subjective dispositions,

(3)   concepts of objective consequences (functions and dys-functions),

(4)   concepts of the unit subserved by the function,

(5)   concepts of functional requirements (needs, prerequisites),

(6)   concepts of the mechanisms through which functions are fulfilled,

(7)   concepts of functional alternatives,

(8)   concepts of structural context,

(9)   concepts of dynamics and change,

(10) problems of validation of functional analysis,

(11) problems of the ideological implications of functional analysis.

Evaluation

Up to this point, we have been given, as it were, a guide to the 'compleat functional theorist'; but we have not been given the substantive theory itself. In the first edition of Merton's book in 1948, his evaluation of the state of functionalist theory *per se* was a pretty discouraging one [2]: 'as one examines the varied array of functional analyses in sociology', said Merton, 'it becomes evident that sociologists . . . do not typically carry through func-tionally intelligible procedures, do not systematically assemble needed types of data, do not employ a common body of concepts, and do not use the same criteria of validity'. However, by the time the 1957 edition was published, Merton had become more optimistic and in an added postcript [3] he indicated what he conceived to be

---

[1]   Ibid. pp. 50–54.

[2]   Ibid. p. 49.

[3]   Ibid. pp. 82–83.

the major 'theoretical contributions to functional analysis in sociology', which included the work of Parsons previously discussed, one paper by Levi of a taxonomic character, and two other substantive papers by sociologists.

On the other hand, within the last year Professor Homans devoted his entire presidential address before the annual convention of the American Sociological Association to a critique of the functionalist position [1] in which he expressed the view that while functionalists in sociology *talk* about functional theory, no one has produced any, in spite of the fact that they have been trying for many years. According to Homans, in those instances where functionalists have established empirical generalizations and then sought to offer a theoretical explanation for them, they have been forced to use explanatory propositions from the fields of social psychology or psychology. But perhaps Homans is prejudiced, for he is a theorist too and has propounded some of his own theories of a social psychological nature to which we shall turn later.

Apart from the fact that functionalist 'theory' appears at the moment to be restricted to the procedures or rules proposed for developing the theory, rather than an actual explanatory theory, it has also been pointed out that there are serious problems involved in some of the notions and procedures of functional analysis. In my judgement, the two most important ones concern the notions of: (1) 'functions' and 'dysfunctions', and (2) 'functional requirements'. Briefly, the objections to the first of these are that the division of the consequences of a particular variable or 'item' into 'functions' and 'dysfunctions' is extremely difficult without making value judgments, and in addition, since a particular variable may have an enormous number of consequences under different conditions, they will be variously 'functional' or 'dysfunctional', depending upon the circumstances. Turning to the notion of 'functional requirements', i.e. 'the requirements which are necessary to the survival of the system or to its continued operation with some degree of effectiveness', the objection here is that it is unclear

---

[1] Homans, George C., 'Bringing men back in', *American Sociological Review* 29 (6 December, 1964), pp. 809–818.

what constitutes 'survival' or 'effective operation' of a social system; is the standard solely that a group continues to have people in it? If it is, then there are relatively few functional requirements. If the standard is higher than this, what is it? Where does one draw the line?

If these two items of the functionalist paradigm are omitted, then what remains of the eleven-point programme is nothing more than the usual set of prescriptions which define general scientific procedures; viz.: the definition of dependent and independent variables, the statement of the relationship between them, and the conditions under which it holds.

3. *George Homans' theory of social behaviour as exchange.* Homans' theoretical contributions are similar to those of Parsons and Merton in the sense that his objective is the same as theirs, namely: to develop a *general* theory; a theory which is applicable to all forms and types of social behaviour. There is also an important difference between them in that, in contrast to Parsons and Merton, Homans actually produced an explanatory theory in the sense that it comprises a set of relational propositions which are more general than the empirical findings they are designed to explain.

Homans' theoretical propositions [1] are adapted from ones already in existence in psychology and economics. He begins by defining and illustrating the basic terms used in the propositions such as 'quantity' and 'values', and then presents five general propositions. These are of the crude form '*x* varies as *y*', and are stated to be conditional upon 'other things being equal'; some of the 'other things' are specifically identified in the system, but not all of them. The five propositions are:

(1) If in the past the occurrence of a particular stimulus-situation has been the occasion on which a man's activity has been rewarded, then the more similar the present stimulus-situation is to the past one, the more likely he is to emit the activity or some similar activity now.

---

[1]   Homans, George C., *Social Behavior: Its Elementary Forms*, Harcourt, Brace and World, New York, 1961.

(2) The more often within a given period of time a man's activity rewards the activity of another, the more often the other will emit the activity.

(3) The more valuable to a man a unit of the activity another gives him, the more often he will emit activity rewarded by the activity of the other.

(4) The more often a man has in the recent past received a rewarding activity from another, the less valuable any further unit of that activity becomes to him. At this point, further concepts are introduced and defined, such as 'cost', 'profit' (both positive and negative), 'relative deprivation', 'distributive justice' and 'investments'.

(5) The more to a man's disadvantage the rule of distributive justice fails of realization, the more likely he is to display the emotional behaviour we call anger. (The term 'the rule of distributive justice' here refers to 'justice in the distribution of rewards and costs between persons').

Following the statement of these propositions, Homans then analyses a large number of empirical research findings in an attempt to show: (a) that many of them can be 'explained' by one or more of his propositions in the sense that they can be subsumed as special instances under his more general propositions, or (b) that his propositions more adequately explain the research findings in the sense that they not only account for the same findings as the explanation offered by the researcher, but they can also explain some of the 'negative' cases, or (c) that additional propositions which follow directly from the original five can be useful in explaining more complex types of behaviour.

Evaluation

The *form* of Homans' theory is more acceptable to me than is Parsons', since it not only includes concepts which are more precisely defined than most of Parsons' are, but it also includes propositions which are attempts to explain or account for specific empirical findings. My criticism is that in its present form it has very limited utility. Most of the propositions involve the notions of 'reward' and 'cost' and are based upon the generalization that behaviour is determined by 'profit' which is the excess of reward over cost; an orientation very similar to the hedonist position that behaviour is based on the attainment of pleasure and the avoidance of pain. The difficulty as I see it lies in the lack of direction which the theory gives for determining which factors enter into the reward–cost calculus in any given situation, and which are rewards and which are costs in what circumstances. To illustrate the point, let me cite some brief examples that Homans himself gives of how his theory can be used to 'explain' a series of empirical research findings. An experiment by Festinger and Thibaut and another by Schachter both had as their central concern the testing of certain hypotheses concerning the behaviour of members of a group towards one of their number who deviated from the group norms. The hypotheses were derived from more general propositions formulated by the researchers, but Homans suggests that *his* theory not only explains all of their findings but that it is also a general theory with far wider applicability than the more specific formulations of the researchers. Some of the empirical facts and Homans' attempts to account for them are as follows [1]:

	Empirical Fact	*Homans' Explanation*
Item 1:	The greater the distance of the deviate from the group norm, the greater the volume of communication directed to them by the other members of the group.	Trying to convert the deviate is seen to be more valuable than preaching to the converted.
Item 2:	Communication with the deviate diminishes through time.	Communication with the deviate becomes less valuable because it is unrewarded, i.e. he is not converted.
Item 3:	Deviates received less social approval than conformers.	Those who disagree with us are less valuable to us and are therefore less likely to be rewarded.

---

[1] Homans, George C., op. cit., p. 108.

Now, at first glance there may appear to be a certain reasonableness in the claim that the kinds of behaviours group members actually exhibited were all more valuable to them than the behaviours they did *not* exhibit. However, a closer examination suggests that, unless what is most valuable or profitable is tautologically defined as what they in fact do, then one could offer equally plausible reasons for suggesting that the *opposite* behaviour from the one they actually exhibited would be the more valuable or profitable. For example, let us take the explanation that trying to convert the deviate is seen to be more valuable than preaching to the converted. It seems to me equally plausible that directing one's conversation to a deviate may be *less* valuable than talking to someone who agrees with you, since communicating to the converted may result in reducing one's doubts about one's own position, while one's uncertainties may be heightened by communicating with the deviate when he attacks one's own views.

To sum up: Homans' five general propositions are consistent with, or subsumable under, the general postulate that behaviour equals reward minus cost. This formulation is sufficiently general that any behaviour can be 'explained' by a translation of it into the reward–cost form. However, in the absence of more detailed specification of how to determine which activities are rewards and which are costs, the translation of research findings into the terms of this formulation amounts to little more than offering tautologies as explanations. Tautologies can be useful, of course, and the reward–cost orientation did stimulate Homans to develop five general propositions, and presumably still others can be developed. However, there seems to be a substantial gap between Homans' very general explanatory propositions and the actual empirical generalizations he attempts to explain; perhaps these gaps will be filled later, but at the moment, in my judgement, they adversely affect the utility of the theory, particularly because it does not adequately facilitate the deduction of empirically testable hypotheses.

4. *Stanley Schachter's theory of deviation, rejection and communication.* The last example of social theory that I shall present in any detail is from the area of social psychology. It is like Homans' in the sense that it contains concepts which are fairly precisely defined and which are included in a set of relational propositions. It differs from Homans' theory in at least two important respects: (a) the types of behaviour or empirical facts which it seeks to explain are much more limited in scope than is the case with Homans' theory; and (b) after the theory was developed, certain specific predictions were deduced from it which were then empirically tested.

Schachter [1] began with a set of three empirical findings from a previous study, viz.:

(1) that within each of many sub-groups of a larger group, there existed homogeneity of attitude with respect to a particular issue, while between all of these groups attitudes were heterogeneous;

(2) that there was a high positive correlation between the cohesiveness (attractiveness) of a social group and the strength of adherence to group standards;

(3) that deviates in a group were rejected by other group members.

Schachter was particularly interested in the rejection of deviates in a group and sought to establish the factors which determine whether a deviate would be rejected and which factors affected the degree of rejection. Rather than formulating various *ad hoc* hypotheses to be empirically tested, he analyzed the phenomenon of rejection and, on the basis of the research findings already mentioned, and on his own hunches, he formulated a set of propositions or a theory from which he could deduce a set of interrelated hypotheses predicting rates of rejection of deviates under different conditions.

The propositions of the theory can be briefly stated as follows:

(1) Within any social group, there are forces which operate towards uniformity of opinion, belief and behaviour.

(2) The sources of such forces are at least two-fold:

---

[1] Schachter, Stanley, 'Deviation, rejection and communication', *Journal of Abnormal and Social Psychology* 46 (1951), pp. 190–207.

(a)   the definition of 'social reality'. This refers to a situation involving an issue with no empirical referent, where one's own opinion is established by the fact that other people hold similar opinions. Thus, forces exist to establish uniformity of opinion and thus create 'reality'.

(b)   group locomotion. In this case, uniformity of attitude may be necessary or desirable for the group to locomote or to proceed, towards its goal.

(3)   The magnitude of the forces towards uniformity that a group can induce on its members varies positively with:

(a)   cohesiveness of the group (definition: 'All field forces acting on a member to remain in the group');

(b)   relevance (which refers to an ordering, in terms of importance to the group, of activities over which the internal power of the group extends).

(4)   The magnitude of the change that a group is able to induce on its members is called 'the internal power of the group'. The internal power of a group with respect to any individual member is equal to the cohesiveness of the group for that member.

(5)   The magnitude of the internal power of the group will vary positively with the relevance of the activities over which the power is exercised.

(6)   The process of inducing change is through the mechanism of communication.

(7)   Uniformity of opinion can thus be achieved by inducing change on deviates through communication, but where this has been attempted and has been unsuccessful, an alternative is to reject the deviate from the group by cutting him off from communication and thus redefining the membership of the group to include only those with uniform opinions.

Schachter uses the above theory to make specific derivations concerning the degree of rejection of a deviate that would be anticipated under various stipulated conditions. The theory states that there are definite pressures to uniformity of behaviour and attitude among members of social groups. Thus, if a difference of opinion exists within a group, forces will arise on members to restore uniformity. These forces will result in a number of corrective tendencies, for example: pressures will develop to change members' opinions which are different from one's own; pressures will arise to change one's own opinion to coincide more closely with those of others in the group; a tendency will develop to decrease one's dependence on deviant members as reference points in establishing the 'reality' of one's own opinion. Under conditions where there is only one deviate and where the remaining group members' opinions are relatively homogenous, the predominant tendencies will be for the rest of the group to: (a) exercise pressures to change the deviate's opinions, and (b) to decrease their dependence on the deviate as a reference point for establishing social reality.

Next, Schachter formulates six assumptions concerning the interrelationships between pressures to change and dependence on the one hand; and cohesiveness, relevance and extent of perceived difference of opinion between the deviate and the rest of the group on the other. These follow from the theoretical propositions already mentioned and can be summarized roughly as follows:

(1)   Pressures to change are positively related to cohesiveness, relevance and extent of perceived difference of opinion.

(2)   Dependence is positively related to cohesiveness and relevance and negatively related to extent of perceived difference of opinion.

However, these propositions deal with the concepts of pressures to change and of dependence, whereas Schachter was interested in formulating hypotheses concerning rejection of the deviate in a group under various conditions. The next step was to relate rejection to these two concepts, and this he did in the following way. He had already postulated (a) that the mechanism by which pressures to change were exerted on group members was 'communication'; and (b) that one way of securing uniformity of opinion in a group was to cut off communication to the deviate; in other words, to psychologically redefine the group so that there was uniformity. Let us assume, Schachter said, that the extent to which pressures to change actually find expression in the group, that is the amount of actual communication, will be determined by the degree to which the members of the group depend upon the group for their definition of social reality. Thus we have the formula:

Pressures to change × dependence = the amount
of actual communication.

But, there remains some amount of pressure to change which does not find expression; which, in other words, is not communicated, and this is 'rejection' which we have already defined as the absence of communication. Thus, we have a second formula:

Rejection = pressures to change × (1 − dependence).

From this point in the development of the theory to the deduction of the specific hypotheses concerning the amount of rejection of the deviate under conditions with varying amounts of cohesiveness, relevance and extent of perceived difference of opinion, is not very far; although it would take more time than I have at my disposal, and almost surely more patience than most of you possess at this point, to elaborate in detail. Very briefly, however, the procedure Schachter followed was to draw theoretical curves defining the relationships between pressures to change and dependence on the one hand and cohesiveness, relevance and extent of perceived difference on the other, to conform in general terms with the verbal statements of the relationships. The theoretical curves were determined, within very broad limits, rather arbitrarily; but because they were somewhat more precise than verbal statements, they enabled him to apply his rejection formula to the theoretical curves in order to determine the relative rates of rejection of the deviate under different conditions with simultaneously different amounts of cohesiveness, relevance and extent of perceived difference of opinion.

Finally, Schachter also derived from this theory sets of hypotheses concerning the effects of the same group of variables on the pattern of communication to the deviate from the rest of the group, both absolutely and through time.

By and large, the various sets of specific predictions based on his theory were borne out in the experimental tests which demonstrated the utility of the theory for purposes of explanation and prediction. The negative findings with respect to some of the fairly detailed predictions are sometimes accounted for by the suggestion of a less than perfect fit between the experimental conditions created and those demanded by the theory, while others lead Schachter to suggest that certain relatively arbitrary values assigned in the model he devised require modification.

Evaluation

It will, I am sure, be fairly evident that I regard theory-building of the type developed by Schachter as more useful in my discipline at the present time than the other attempts I have discussed in this paper. Such theories are initiated by a desire to explain in more general terms a given set of empirical findings. The explanatory theory offered defines terms fairly precisely and their relationships between each other are made clear. The propositions themselves are both closely interrelated and are assumed to be relatively complete in the sense that they are believed to comprise all of the most significant propositions necessary to account for the phenomenon to be explained, in this case the rejection of deviants.

However, by comparison with the attempts at theory-building previously discussed, it is narrow in scope; in other words, the types of behaviour which it attempts to explain are very limited.

5. *Summary and conclusions.* In the short time at my disposal, I have tried to briefly outline some of the major theoretical positions in sociology at the present time; I could not cover all or even the majority of what purports to be theory in my field, but my selection is, I think, quite varied. It includes those which seek to be *general* theories and thus to explain all types of social behaviour as well as those of much more limited range: it includes theories at the 'institutional' or 'macro' level, and at the 'individual' or 'micro' level, and it includes examples of axiomatic or deductive theories as well as one which is basically a taxonomy. All of this goes to show that in sociology, what purports to be 'theory' is a very mixed bag of tricks – and it must be remembered that I have only covered a part of the entire spectrum of theories in my discipline.

With such a variety of different types of theory, one would expect that the discipline would be ringing with the sounds of battle between the various theoretical and methodological camps, but strangely enough this is far from being the case. Apart from the isolated skirmish provoked by Homans recently, that I mentioned earlier, the air is relatively quiet and serene. In fact, the present situation with respect to views about theory may be called the 'Eisenhower' era. You may recall that his speeches outlining the Republicans' electoral platform were composed almost entirely of vague, generalized platitudes; in sum, we learned that he was for motherhood and virtue and against sin. Pronouncements about theory in sociology at the present time tend to be of the same order; we are all for it, we all agree with theory defined as a set of inter-related propositions from which we can deduce certain hypotheses for testing and so on. We all say the right words, but, as you have seen, our individual behaviours based upon them are quite, quite different one from the other. To the extent that this is due to the fact that we mean different things when using the same words, it suggests that we should be more specific and detailed in our notions of what theory is and how it should be developed. This is not a particularly popular observation among theorists in sociology who generally counter that a concern with methodological considerations without reference to substantive issues is unproductive. However, perhaps it is unproductive precisely because the concern in the past has been at too general a level. It is also pointed out that, generally speaking, the physical sciences seem to have developed well enough, even though most physical scientists were not aware of the philosophical and methodological rationale for what they did. But what they did have, I suggest, was a set of procedures established by tradition for undertaking research and for formulating explanatory theories which the social sciences did not have. On the contrary, what impresses me are the false starts of the earlier social scientists in their attempts to scientifically explain social phenomena (many of which have been analyzed by Professor Popper) frequently based on misconceptions of what the physical scientists were doing and what their objectives were. The present traditions of research and theory-building in sociology have, in the course of their establishment, been significantly affected by many of these past mistakes and, in my view, in one form or another still perpetuate them. Some of the confusions which seem to me to be evident in my discipline for example are:

(1)   The place and purpose of concepts and taxonomic systems in theory construction.

(2)   The difference between explanations of concrete events or specific empirical phenomena on the one hand and the construction of general explanatory theories on the other.

(3)   The form of explanatory theories, e.g. is there a difference in kind rather than degree between the explanation of a empirical generalization by formulating a somewhat more general proposition of which the empirical generalization is a particular instance, and an explanatory system which comprises a number of related general propositions? And if there is a difference, what is the relationship between these two types of propositional forms from the point of view of theory construction?

(4)   While almost everyone agrees that empirical research and theory construction go hand in hand, what precisely is the most useful relationship between them? How far can theoretical propositions get from empirical facts, or how far should theoretical formulations progress which are not related to any empirical generalizations or which, while they cover some empirical generalizations, have no apparent relevance to vast amounts of other empirical facts, before the theories become so dissociated from empirical data that it is difficult or impossible to judge their utility?

This is not, of course, an exhaustive list of methodological issues with respect to which opinions in my discipline are either contradictory or unclear, but most of them can be seen to arise in work of the theorists I have examined in this paper, and I hope that they give you some idea of the state of theory construction in sociology at the present time; at least as far as I see it.

I think it was Dr. Lakatos whom I heard characterize the work of philosophers of science as telling scientists what they did and why they did it after they had done it. Perhaps some of you should perform these same functions for sociological theorists before they do the kind of theorizing that they are at present doing. In suggesting this, however, I am not unaware of the fact, particularly after attending the sessions on Tuesday, that philosophers of science themselves appear to be divided on the kind of advice and counsel they would give us!

DISCUSSION

J. C. HARSANYI: *Reward values as explanatory variables in social theories.*

Professor Robson criticizes Homans' theory that people act so as to maximize their 'profit', that is, the excess of 'gain' or 'reward' over the 'costs' of achieving it. He speaks of 'the lack of direction . . . (Homans') theory gives us for determining which factors enter into the reward–cost calculus in any situation, and which are the rewards and which are the costs in what circumstances' (p. 361).

I think this statement is correct but this fact in itself, it seems to to me, is not a decisive objection against Homans' theory. This fact is merely a special case of the general observation that scientific theories often contain adjustable parameters of which the actual values are not predicted by the theory itself but rather must be estimated from the empirical data. As Popper has pointed out, a given theory containing such unspecified parameters may still fully qualify as a scientific theory with a testable empirical content, so long as the number of independent empirical facts it explains is significantly greater than the number of its unspecified parameters. The real question is in my opinion whether Homans' theory satisfies this crucial requirement.

In Homans' theory, just as in experimental psychology (e.g., in learning theory) and in economics, the reward or penalty values (positive or negative utility values) of various outcomes have the nature of such adjustable parameters. For instance, a psychologist usually cannot predict on theoretical grounds what particular kinds of food will have a positive reward value for a given animal species: this must be ascertained by appropriate experiments. But in most cases after a few such experiments he will be able to list the most important kinds of food the animals of a given species like or dislike, and *from then on* he will be in a position to make some **non-trivial** predictions about their behavior. (For example, he may be able to predict that their learning performance will strikingly improve if they are rewarded by a certain type of food for which they have displayed a strong positive preference in his earlier experiments.)

Yet, theories of human behavior are in a more difficult position than theories of animal behavior are, because in the case of human subjects any detailed specification of the reward and penalty values of various possible outcomes to different individuals under different circumstances – that is, any detailed specification of their utility functions – will require estimation of a very large number of psychological parameters.

Luckily, as the example of economic theory shows (as well as the example of some fairly successful recent attempts to use a similar approach in some other social sciences), rational-choice models based on some reward–cost calculus can often explain a wide range of empirical facts about social behavior, by making use only of some very weak and very general assumptions about people's motivations, without any more specific hypotheses about the psychological parameters characterizing the utility functions of various individuals or groups of individuals. For instance, economic theory can explain many important empirical facts about the operation of the economic system, without using stronger psychological hypotheses than the assumption that in certain situations most people are primarily motivated by economic self-interest.

Of course, if we want to explain social behavior outside the economic sphere (and even if we want to explain certain aspects of economic behavior) then we obviously cannot use economic self-interest as our only motivational assumption. But in many cases we can still keep our motivational assumptions very simple, and can avoid any detailed psychological hypotheses about people's utility functions. For instance, it seems to me that we can obtain a theory with very considerable explanatory power without going any further than adding a few additional motivational variables to economic self-interest, such as concern for the economic interests of some people other than oneself (e.g., for the economic interests of one's own family and closest personal friends), and concern for one's own interests in non-economic matters (e.g., for one's social status position and, more generally, one's social acceptance among one's social associates).

To be sure, while such very general motivational assumptions may carry us surprisingly far, they will not carry us all the way. Obviously there will be many important empirical facts about social behavior we shall not be able to explain without making some fairly specific assumptions about people's utility functions; and as soon as we do this we shall have a theory containing a large number of adjustable parameters. As I have argued earlier, *per se* there is no objection to using many parameter theories – except that such theories must always be supported by a sufficient number and variety of empirical observations so as to allow estimation of all these parameters from the empirical data in a convincing manner.

In the case of Homans' theory, many of its empirical predictions depend only on some fairly weak motivational assumptions, and these obviously pose no problem. But other empirical predictions (including the examples Robson criticizes on pp. 17–19) do depend on some rather specific assumptions about the reward values people attach to certain outcomes in the relevant situations. For instance, Homans has to assume (*Social Behavior: Its Elementary Forms*, p. 105) that in the relevant experimental situations people find it more rewarding to convert other people to their own opinions than to talk with people holding opinions similar to their own. In such cases, Homans' explanations would carry full conviction only if we were shown that his assumptions about the reward values of various outcomes are not mere *ad hoc* assumptions invented only for the purpose of explaining the empirical findings in one particular set of experiments. Thus we would like a fair amount of independent empirical evidence to show that in similar situations people do consistently assign reward values to various outcomes in the assumed way. It should not be too difficult to obtain such independent empirical evidence, and in fact Homans does occasionally offer such evidence. But one may feel that he does not always do this to an extent to make his psychological assumptions fully convincing.

Yet, in spite of this objection, in my opinion Homans' theory is a major contribution to analytical theory construction in the social sciences, and represents an immense advance over the so-called functionalistic theories now fashionable in sociology. (As to the latter, I fully agree with Robson's largely negative evaluation on pp. 354–5 and 357–9.) Even if Homans' theory as it stands is open to certain objections, already in its present form it amply demonstrates the great possibilities of rational-choice models in explaining a wide range of social behavior, in terms of a limited number of general theoretical principles cutting across the boundaries of the different social science disciplines.

If there is any conclusion we can draw from the extensive discussions in the philosophy of science in the last half a century, then it is the proposition that no accumulation of mutually unrelated small-scale theories will ever add up to one self-consistent general analytical theory of social behavior. The only way such a theory may conceivably arise is by the efforts of social scientists, like Homans, who make a serious systematic attempt to construct such a theory and thereby bring in clearer relief many of the methodological problems the construction of such a theory poses to us.

R. A. H. ROBSON: *Reply.*

Professor Harsanyi's comments constitute a useful and effective antidote to the generally negative character of my evaluations of the theories discussed in my paper.

His more positive evaluation of Homans' theory is I think, due to his having concentrated on its probable utility *in the future*, while I was more concerned with its *present* explanatory power. Given the latter basis of evaluation, Harsanyi's views about Homans' theory appear to be very similar to mine. We agree that Homans' theory is to be preferred over the functionalist attempts at theory construction; we also agree that *in its present form*, its explanatory power is quite limited and finally, we agree in general terms, on what needs to be done to increase the utility of Homans' theory.

In this latter connection, Harsanyi's judgement that the explanatory power of Homans' theory can be increased by the addition of a few very simple assumptions concerning motivation, without the specification of utility functions, seems reasonable enough; but whether the theory thus elaborated, will satisfy Harsanyi's 'crucial requirement' of scientific theory can only be determined after the dentification of the specific motivational assumptions to be used and the demonstration of their explanatory 'coverage'.

In the absence of this, judgement about the *potential* explanatory power of Homans' theory has to be based on the kind of reasoning employed by Harsanyi and on the results of the discussion about the methodological problems posed by such a theory, to which he refers in his last paragraph; but while this sort of analysis may serve as a rough preliminary guide to the potentiality of such a theory, a more reliable evaluation of its utility requires the actual elaboration of the theory in order that we can determine its explanatory or predictive power. In making this relatively obvious point, I am trying to emphasize the somewhat premature and therefore the very tentative character of Harsanyi's optimistic view of the potential utility of Homans' theory. The uncertainty of the verdict that should be given in this case is, I think, indicated by Harsanyi's own analysis which, while it suggests certain *possibilities* of improving the explanatory power of Homans' theory, does not, and presumably cannot at this juncture, provide an adequate basis for a judgement as to how successful these attempts are likely to be. Further, Harsanyi's optimistic views concerning the likelihood of Homans' simple theoretical model providing explanations for the more complex forms of social behaviour do not seem to be shared by those sociologists who have so far reviewed his work.

I am not suggesting that Harsanyi's judgement is wrong, but rather that at the moment, there is about as much reason to be pessimistic as to be optimistic about the potential explanatory power of Homans' theory. It is this lack of decisiveness about the theory in its present form, together with what both Harsanyi and I see to be the possible ways in which the theory might be improved, which argues for early elaboration of the theory and its test, in order that we can make a firmer judgement about its utility.

In conclusion, let me say that I would have liked to have been able to discuss in detail the methodological problems that would appear to arise when attempting to use Homans' theory to explain more complex forms of social behaviour, and to consider the probable success of alternative solutions to these problems. Similarly, Harsanyi's contention regarding the 'crucial requirement' of theories with unspecified parameters is very interesting and one that merits close examination. However, to do justice to these important and interesting issues would require more space than I am entitled to at this point in the exchange between Professor Harsanyi and myself.

THE NEW IDEALISM –
CAUSE AND MEANING IN THE SOCIAL SCIENCES

ERNEST GELLNER

University of London

Anthropomorphism is not a live issue in the natural sciences. On the whole, the freedom of natural scientists does not need to be protected from people insisting that the picture presented by the results *must* conform to some human image – that it must resemble man, make room for him, underwrite his purposes, be compatible with his self-image, or with some doctrine concerning these matters. There are notorious exceptions to this generalisation, such as for instance the interference with Soviet biologists or even physicists in the interests of supporting an extrapolated version of a social theory: but these are, happily, exceptions. In an important and extended sense, the Copernican revolution is well established: humanity is known not to be at the centre of things; human requirements are not allowed to limit, or even create presumptions in, the sphere of scientific theory. (Moral philosophers are proud of the autonomy of ethics: this is one point on which a large proportion of professional practitioners of the subject are agreed. They do not quite so often note that the autonomy of ethics only followed on the autonomy of science, the exclusion of the argument from morals to fact, *from* 'ought' *to* 'is', of the form 'This must be true, otherwise our life would not make sense', or 'This cannot be true, otherwise our life would make no sense'.)

In social or human studies or sciences, however, the question of anthropomorphism – though not under this name – is by no means dead. The plea for a *humanist* psychology or sociology is frequently heard. The philosophy of mind has recently witnessed a sustained and interesting attack on the view that individuals have 'privileged access', cognitively, to their *own* minds. But there has been no corresponding attack on the view, which might at least superficially seem parallel, that we have, *collectively*, a privileged access, through our shared human concepts, to the understanding of the social life and institutions of humanity. On the contrary: philosophers associated with the school responsible for the attack on the *individual* 'privileged access' view, have at the same time been prominent in putting forward versions of what I call the collective privileged access theory – that we understand social life through human concepts.

The general motive or attraction of anthropomorphism, in any sphere, is fairly obvious. Anthropomorphic doctrines enlist the world on the side of our values or aspirations. If, to take an example with which I am familiar, the deity or supernatural beings arrange floods, droughts, or other disasters in a way such that these sanctions strike perjurors and their lineages, this provides a convenient underpinning for a legal system. A centralised and effective state may have neither the need, nor indeed be willing to tolerate, the handing over of punishment to the supernatural: but where such a centralised law-enforcing agency is absent, and Nature apparently allows itself to be used in so moral a manner, this makes possible trial by collective oath – a very common institution in anarchic or semi-anarchic tribal contexts. The rain does *not* fall on the just and the unjust alike.

Those concerned with defending anthropomorphism, in any sphere, can do so positively or negatively, or perhaps one should say in an offensive or a defensive spirit. A positive anthropomorphism, one that is on the offensive as it were, puts forward a specific doctrine, a doctrine which if true restores a 'meaningful moral order' to the area which it is meant to cover.

A negative or defensive anthropomorphism is not concerned with putting forward a specific positive picture, but merely with demonstrating that theories which necessarily make the world 'meaningless', which inescapably exclude meaningful visions, *cannot* be true. How can this be shown? Most commonly, perhaps, we show that a class of theories is false by establishing that some other theory, incompatible with all the members of that class, is true. But negative or defensive anthropomorphism (by definition) does not put forward any specific theory of its own. It has an alternative way, and one which we may (in accordance with the terminology of its propounders, I think), call epistemological. It argues that the very nature of knowledge, in the sphere in question, is such that no non-anthropomorphic theory can possibly be true. This leaves the field open for anthropomorphic theories, without however at the same time positively singling out any one of them.

The present argument will be concerned with these negative or defensive, epistemologically based anthropomorphisms. It would be an exaggeration to say that positive anthropomorphic theories are absent from the intellectual scene. They do exist, in social theory, on the fringes of medicine, in psychotherapy, and perhaps elsewhere. One of the appeals of psychotherapeutic techniques is, I suspect, precisely that they restore a kind of moral order: people find it more tolerable to believe that the fault is in themselves, than that they have been struck arbitrarily, accidentally, for no purpose whatever. In the joke, the psychiatrist tells the patient: 'The reason you feel inferior is that you *are* inferior. That will be 20 guineas.' In fact, he does not say anything as brutal. He tells the patient that his suffering is the corollary of something else, has its roots within him. The manifest advantage of this is that it makes the suffering manipulable, but the latent, and perhaps more important advantage, one which survives the possible failure to manipulate and remove the misery, is that it makes it meaningful, and at least quasi-deserved. I think we prefer to be guilty, rather than the objects of entirely accidental 'punishment' which, somehow, is *more* humiliating.

In brief, positive, moral-order-preserving anthropomorphic doctrines do exist, even in the field of 'modern' theories, i.e. those formulated in our time and in a contemporary idiom. But within philosophy we find more commonly the negative, defensive versions, which defend a whole class of meaningful visions against a whole class of, as it were, inhuman ones. The 'meaningfulness' defended need not be a crude picture in which sinners are punished and virtue prevails. It is rather a world in which things happen and are understood in human terms, in some sense to be clarified further. These thinkers are not concerned or able to demonstrate that the human world is a *moral* tale, with justice and truth vindicated and some noble purpose attained: but they are concerned to show that it is, at least, a *human* tale. They wish to defend *the anthropomorphic image of man* himself.

This aspiration is by no means self-evidently absurd. The requirement that human activities and institutions should be interpreted in human terms does not have the offensiveness which nowadays immediately attaches to the requirement that *nature* be seen in human terms. *That* requirement offends both our tacit autonomy of nature principle, and our rejection of a-priorism. (These two might be considered in conflict, but anyway, I think we hold them both.) Hence modern anthropomorphism is doubly transformed, it has undergone two shifts: it has shifted its area (from nature to man), and its grounds (from substantive to epistemological). The *in*human interpretations against which the negative, defensive anthropomorphist guards us may be various, but some of their forms are very notorious: materialistic, mechanistic, deterministic, 'external' causal explanations.

Anthropomorphic or idealistic thought (as we may call it with reference to its contrast, and in order to bring out a certain continuity) has undergone another interesting development, in addition to the shift from nature to man and from substantive to epistemological considerations. This development concerns the *terms* in which the contrast with matter, to mechanical causation, etc., is conceived. Roughly: idealism has moved first from stuff to subject, and then from subject to meaning.

Throughout, the requirement is always to establish a *dis*continuity, between the area abandoned to mechanism or what have you, where anthropomorphism is abandoned, and the redoubt area where the human is to be preserved. But the redoubt is conceived differently at the various stages. Descartes' thinking substance is conceived as substance, in the image of extended substance, and somehow parallel to it and co-ordinate with it. Kant has no truck with a substance-self (a paralogism, this), but for him it is the cognising and acting subject who provides a bearer for those crucial human characteristics (freedom, responsibility, validity of thought), for which there is no room in nature.

The recent form of idealism with which I am now concerned

does not attempt to reassure us by telling us that, as cognisers and agents, we may be allowed a kind of inner emigration from nature: it tells us, instead, that meaningful action, as such, is exempt from nature, in the sense that it is not susceptible to the kind of explanation held to be appropriate in nature, with its attendant moral inconveniences. The outstanding and most un-compromising formulation of this view is found in the work of Mr. Peter Winch, notably in '*The Idea of a Social Science*', London, 1958.

This book is, and is intended to be, the working out of the implications of L. Wittgenstein's mature philosophy for the social sciences. It is in fact meant to be more than this, in as far as Winch believes that these implications are not something marginal or tangential to that philosophy, but on the contrary are altogether central to it. (In that I think he is entirely right.) Likewise, he does not consider these implications to be marginal or tangential for the social sciences either: on the contrary, he believes that they reveal the central and most important features of those sciences. Winch's book has certainly made an impact on those concerned with the philosophy of the social sciences.

All this gives it a double interest. The central part of what he has to say about social sciences and hence (whether he intends this or not) about actual societies, seems to me profoundly and signifi-cantly wrong. Hence it has the interest of an influential and well-formulated expression of an (in my view) mistaken theory. But it also has another interest. It constitutes the best, most elegant and forceful, if quite unintended, refutation of Wittgenstein – one far more forceful than any stated by a deliberate critic. If WM is to stand for 'Wittgenstein's mature philosophy', and ISS for the position argued in Winch's book, the situation is roughly as follows:

$$WM \rightarrow ISS \qquad (1)$$

$$\text{but } \underline{ISS \text{ is absurd}} \qquad (2)$$

$$\text{therefore } \overline{WM \text{ is absurd}}.$$

When I say that ISS is absurd, I mean that it stands in blatant and manifest contradiction with obvious and salient features of both human societies and the practices of social scientists.

Mr. Winch does not think that he is going methodology at all, and would deny that he is interfering with the specific methodology of social scientists. He would, on the contrary, maintain that he is merely clarifying what the social sciences in general amount to, something they share at an abstract level, and that this does not affect the specific research strategies which may be adopted locally in this or that subject, or for this or that problem. This image of his own position and its implications seems to me quite mistaken. For one thing, Winch does say harsh things about some, at any rate, methods or aspirations of social scientists, e.g. the use of the comparative method or the pursuit of causal explanations. A theory cannot be all at once a condemnation of some methods, *and* methodologically neutral.

What underlies Winch's wrong assessment of his own position at this point is simply a preconception, an *a priori* philosophic idea that one can clarify what social knowledge is in general without prejudice to its specific tools. But this preconception has no intrinsic authority: it must be judged in the light of whether in fact Winch's position does or does not have methodological implications, and if it does, the preconception must be withdrawn. The preconception must not be invoked as a reason for why the methodological difficulties must be based on a misinterpretation of his position! In fact, methodological implications, negative and positive, do follow. And more than this: not merely a mistaken methodology, but also quite mistaken substantive beliefs about concrete societies, do follow from Winch's position.

If this is so, and if proposition (1), on which he and I agree, be granted, one should have thought that only a critic of Wittgenstein would have gone out of his way to establish that WM entails ISS. But this, interestingly, was not Winch's case. He is anxious to establish (1).

The steps condensed into (1) are, however, of some interest.

Wittgenstein's central doctrine was the account of meaning in terms of use. Meaning was not reference to an entity, be it transempirical (various forms of Platonism), be it a range of actual or

possible sensations (various forms of empiricism): it was, on the
contrary, the employment of an expression in diverse concrete
contexts. These contexts were endlessly diversified, and were parts
of 'forms of life'.

This is the form in which the doctrine first made its impact,
and, as indicated, it was in this form aimed primarily against
rival theories of meaning, notably those contained in either transcen-
dentalism or empiricism. It does not in this form *seem* to have any
particular relevance to the social sciences.

Winch's interest is that he was the first, at any rate from within
the movement, to read the doctrine in the reverse direction and
work out fully its implications. If 'meaning = use', then 'use =
meaning'. Of course, no one actually formulated the first equation
as a formal equation (which would give us the premise for the
second, reverse order reading), and in any case, it is not very clear
what the thing means when formulated in reverse order. Nothing
in the present argument hinges on this: I use this merely as a
kind of expository device, to bring out the underlying pattern of
Winch's argument.

The inference obtained by inverting the order, as it were, reads
roughly as follows when expanded into more intelligible English:
if the meaning of expressions is their employment, then, in turn,
it is of the essence of the employment of expressions (and by an
independent but legitimate extension, of other social behaviour),
that it is meaningful. This gives us a kind of mnemonic device for
understanding the genesis of Winch's position. We can see why,
all at once, he can claim (rightly, in my view), to be following the
Master, and yet find in a hitherto apparently unsociological doctrine, *the* 'Idea of a Social Science'. Where Wittgenstein taught
philosophers not to ask for the meaning but for the use, Winch
advises social scientists not to look for the cause, but for the
meaning. Social behaviour is essentially meaningful: to understand
it is to understand its meaning. It cannot but have meaning: the
fear that understanding might reveal it to be the slave of antecedent
causes (thus being 'explained' by them) turns out to be an error,
and one demonstrably such in *all* cases: one, it appears, arising
from a fundamental error concerning the very nature of social

understanding. This is where the idealism comes in: remove this one error, and we are freed forever, by an omnibus proof, of the bogies of determinism, mechanism and so on.

'One appears to be attempting an impossible task of *a priori* legislation against a purely empirical possibility. What in fact one is showing, however, is that the central concepts which belong to our understanding of social life are incompatible with concepts central to the activity of scientific prediction' (ISS, p. 94).

What, incidentally, *is* it for an action to 'have meaning', or, in as far as this is meant to be a defining characteristic of an 'action', for an event to become an action through possessing meaning? I think it corresponds roughly to what we would, in unselfconscious unsophisticated moments, describe as 'being lived through consciously from the inside, as it were'; but Winch, of course, in accordance with the principles and customs of his movement, does not operate with notions such as 'consciousness', 'inside', etc. Instead, an event acquires meaning through the fact that it is conceptualised by the agent with the help of shared concepts – and for Winch all concepts are necessarily shared [1] – and that the conceptualisation is essential to the very recognition of the event. Example: a man 'gets married' not merely by going through certain motions in church or registry office, but by possessing the concept of what it is to be married. If the concept were lacking, the same physical movements, in the same places, simply could not be classified as 'marriage'. For Winch, it follows from the fact that an event 'has meaning' that it cannot be caused.

The manner in which this position is extracted from Wittgensteinian premises is interesting and throws light both on those premises and on Winch's idealism. One crucial step has already been stressed: it consists of reading backwards the tie up between meaning and social behaviour, and instead of invoking this connection to destroy both platonic and empiricist theories of meaning, using it instead to establish that 'meaningfulness' is an essential attribute of social conduct, *and* that this excludes causal, mechanical explanation. But there are other crucial steps.

---

[1] In a sense, Wittgenstein went beyond Durkheim; for Wittgenstein *all* representations are collective.

Winch himself highlights these crucial Wittgensteinian premises. On page 40 of his book, he quotes from Wittgenstein's *'Philosophical Investigations'*: 'What has to be accepted, the given, is – as one could say – forms of life.' The first wave of Wittgensteinians, including the Master himself, using this perception merely to beat rival theories of language, did not worry much about the fact that 'forms of life' (i.e. societies, cultures) are numerous, diverse, overlapping, and undergo change. Which of them is to be accepted? All of them? Or each of them, on the principle 'When in Rome do as the Romans do?' But what happens when these 'forms' are in conflict, or when one of them is in fundamental inner conflict?

These questions, obvious though they be, did not seem to have been raised in the course of what I called the first wave of the movement. The significance of Winch is that he has pondered on the fact that others (i.e. social scientists) have also taken an interest in 'forms of life', and tried to bring their concern in contact with the invocation of 'forms of life' in philosophy. The oddity of Winch is that he has used this connection not in a *reductio ad absurdum* of Wittgenstein, but in an attempt to set right the social sciences. Because: the multiplicity, conflict (inner and outer), and change, all undergone by 'forms of life', present a crucial, indeed on its own terms insoluble, problem for a philosophy which would treat them as something 'to be accepted', as 'the given'. For the point about forms of life is that they do not always, or even frequently, accept themselves as given, as something to be accepted. On the contrary, they often reject their own past practices as absurd, irrational, etc. Hence the recommendation of acceptance becomes internally incoherent. It has the form – 'Accept whatever X says as true', when, in fact, (a) there is a number of mutually inconsistent sources called X, and (b) some Xs say: 'What I have said in the past is false'. (There are interesting historical precedents for this incoherence. In the seventeenth century conflict between the Papacy and the French Crown, the Papacy in the end ordered its French supporters to accept the authority of the Crown. Hence the acceptance of the authority of the Papacy entailed . . . its rejection. During the Second World War, the leader of the American Communist Party instructed the members to 'embrace capitalism'.

Hence the acceptance of the authority of Moscow entailed its rejection. Similarly, the acceptance of the ultimacy of 'forms of life' has just this paradoxical consequence.)

Both the argument from plurality and the argument from self-rejection or self-criticism is disastrous for the general position. The early Wittgensteinians simply did not think about societies and social change, and *given* this, it is at least in some measure understandable, why they did not notice this decisive weakness in their position. (What is not intelligible is how any man, in the mid-twentieth century, can be oblivious of social diversity or change.) The oddity of Winch is, as stated, that he is aware of both – and in particular of diversity – and still holds on to the initial premisses.

Let us take the problem of plurality first. Like the other problem (of social self-criticism), it imposes a dilemma on anyone holding the initial premises, a dilemma neither of whose horns is acceptable. But Winch is clearly aware of this particular dilemma, and firmly embraces one of the available alternatives. Hence to explain the dilemma is also to explain the genesis of Winch's position.

The initial position is: 'forms of life' are ultimate, they cannot be criticised from some external viewpoint, by some independent standard. There is not such standard. There is no external reality in terms of which forms of life, 'languages', could be judged, for the distinction between that which is real and that which is not only occurs within a language, a form of life [1].

The first dilemma is this: does this acceptance embrace *all* cultures, or only one?

Either answer entails intolerable consequences. Suppose that only one (or, for that matter, a limited set) is 'accepted': it necessarily follows that it must be selected by some principle of selection. This must be stateable and some reasons should be available for preferring it to other principles or selections. There is of course nothing absurd about this position as such (and I happen to believe that something like this is true), but it is in blatant contradiction

---

[1] Cf. the formulation of this position in P. Winch, 'Understanding a primitive society', *American Philosophical Quarterly* (1964).

with that central Wittgensteinian doctrine, taken over by Winch, to the effect that one cannot seek external and general criteria for the validation of linguistic or conceptual custom. If *selection* is to take place, then it follows that some principle is being employed. This means, in turn, that philosophy must return to the place which in my view it should never have left – the attempt to formulate and defend criteria which are more than mere descriptions of *de facto* custom.

Winch firmly commits himself to the other alternative. The trouble with this branch of the fork is quite different from the first: it does not, at least immediately, lead us to the implicit assumption of extra-cultural norms and hence the contradiction of the initial assumption. It leads us to recognise a multiplicity of 'forms of life', each with its own criteria of distinguishing the real from the unreal, and none of them competent to judge the others. Repeatedly, this is the picture Winch sketches and to which he commits himself. In other words, he commits himself to a profound conceptual relativism: contrary to what, for instance, Sir James Frazer and most of us think, scientific language is not him superior to the witchcraft language of (say) the Azande, even when they appear to be explaining the same type of phenomenon. 'Reality is not what gives language sense. What is real and what is unreal shows itself *in* the sense that language has' (italics Winch's.) Later, in the same article [1], the Wittgensteinian premise is made very clear: 'Oracular revelations (among the Azande) are not treated as hypotheses and, *since their sense derives from the way they are treated in their context*, they therefore *are not* hypotheses' (first set of italics mine, the second Winch's.)

Winch does, it is true, reject *individual* relativism (quite consistently with his position – indeed his position strictly requires this): '. . . it is *within* the religious use of language that the conception of God's reality has its place, though, I repeat, this does not mean that it is at the mercy of what anyone cares to say . . .' (italics Winch's.) A use of language, it appears, does convey reality, though not through the agency of 'anyone', i.e. not, presumably,

---

[1] 'Understanding a primitive society', op. cit.

through any one individual. (We shall have very significant trouble
with the question of how many individuals, or under what conditions of differentiation, constitute *a* use of language. A single
atheist – or, to strengthen the case, a single logico-positivist –
denying that the term 'God' has any meaning, makes no difference.
But how about the Soviet Union?)

He also rejects, more obscurely, 'an extreme Protagorean relativism, with all the paradoxes that involves'. No indication is given
how such an 'extreme' kind differs from the kind he actually puts
forward (without claiming the name, though I do not believe he
would repudiate the title 'conceptual relativism'). The paradoxes
certainly are not avoided.

There can be no doubt about this relativism itself. Concerning
the Zande acceptance of witchcraft and the European rejection
of it, Winch says '. . . it is clear . . . that (Evans–Prichard) would
have wished to add . . . the European is right and the Zande wrong.
This addition I regard as illegitimate . . .' [1] In other words, witches
or the processes alleged to occur according to witchcraft belief, are,
like the deity, though not apparently at the mercy of *individual*
belief, at the mercy of a whole style of thought. For the Azande
they exist, as scientific entities exist for us, and no one is entitled
(or rather: no one can meaningfully) judge between the two!

As Winch does not surreptitiously return to some hidden standard
by which to sort out valid language from invalid, but accepts all
languages as valid – by their own lights, and there are for him
no others – we must consider why such relativism is untenable.
It is worth noting that it is intuitively repellent to pretend that
the Zande belief in witchcraft is as valid as our rejection of it,
and that to suppose it such is a philosophical affectation, which
cannot be maintained outside the study. I should not myself urge
this point against a position – at least, not in isolation. But it
ought to worry Winch, who belongs to a tradition in which the
fact that a given belief can be held by the philosopher in the study,
but not in life, is held to be a serious, or crucial, or indeed *the*
crucial, objection to a belief. Such a state of philosophic schizo-

---

[1] 'Understanding a primitive society', op. cit.

phrenia is held to be an indication that the philosopher in question divorces, in his study, some terms which he uses, from their real (and hence authoritative) use in his real life, and is of course incapable of carrying this divorce over into his real life. Had he but remembered the real use, *and* the fact that this is what gives those terms sense, he would not have embraced the schizophrenia-engendering doctrine. There is thus a pragmatic contradiction within Winch's position.

There is another objection which is frequently urged against any kind of relativism, and that is that it leads to a paradox when applied to itself.

This objection is not applicable to Winch, or at any rate not immediately, for he gives us no warrant to apply his relativism to his own argument. He makes an exception, not merely for himself, but for philosophy in general. (Presumably for sociology as well, in view of its near-identity, in his view, with philosophy.) This view involves its own and very considerable difficulties, but it does at any rate exempt Winch from the conventional and facile charge to which relativists are often exposed.

We are arguing that Winch's account of the social sciences is incompatible with certain conspicuous and important features both of the methods of social sciences, and of societies themselves. The latter class of objections – the contradiction between what Winch says and social reality itself – can be made very concrete. Here again there are two subclasses: the contradictions which arise from certain features internal to individual societies, and those which arise from the existence of a multiplicity of societies and their mutual relations.

Let us take the former. Consider certain crucial events/ideas/ forces in Western history, events without which quite obviously no adequate account of Western society can be given: Christianity, the Reformation, the Enlightenment. All these have something in common with each other and with other movements or systems of ideas which could be added to the list: they are inherently, essentially, committed to proselytising and to a kind of exclusiveness. In this they may be wrong, intellectually or morally: but there can be no doubt about the beliefs themselves. These are not, as it were, tribal deities, willing to accommodate tribal deities of neighbouring communities on terms of tolerance and equality. On the contrary, they contain a claim to unique, exclusive and absolute truth.

For Winch, philosophical theories of meaning, and substantive beliefs of concrete societies, are as it were at different levels and do not, cannot, come into conflict. In fact, however, absolutist and exclusive and proselytising faiths do come into conflict with his contextualist theory of meaning and its appendage, the contextualist theory of truth. Take the example of a Reformer. He says, in substance, that the Divine Will is revealed and accessible in a set of Scriptures, and that its meaning is accessible to the individual conscience. If social practice, the ongoing tradition which claims allegiance to those scriptures, the organised church, is in its real activities at variance with the content of the independently knowable Word – well, then those practices, that church are in error and must be reformed.

That, at any rate, is what the Reformer claims. My argument does not require the Reformer to be right: it merely requires Reformers to be an important social phenomenon – and this can hardly be denied. And what is true of Reformers is, *mutatis mutandis*, true of proselytisers of Christianity itself, of believers in Natural Law, of rationalists of various kinds, and of many of the more radical kinds of secular reformers.

An agent of the Counter Reformation, equipped with philosophic prescience, might have replied to our ideal-typical Reformer as follows: but your insistence on the independent meaning of Scripture and its alleged divergence from the actual practices of the Church betray, on your part, an illusion concerning the nature of meaning. If the sacred formulae seem to you in conflict with practice, ought you not to remember that what gives formulae meaning is the real social context in which they occur? It is *your interpretations* of the formulae, and not reality, which is at fault! Thus, an infallibility of the real social context, of e.g. the concrete church, could easily be deduced from a theory of meaning ...

I do not know whether any of the theoreticians of the Counter Reformation employed variants of this argument. But the secularised descendants of the Reformers, the thinkers of the Enlightenment, certainly encountered it from romantic and conservative political theorists. Rationalist rejection of superstition had the same logic, in this respect, as Protestant rejection of idolatry.

In brief: a very important segment of the *subject matter* of the social scientist, (i.e., certain civilizations, broad movements, etc.) holds beliefs which are themselves in contradiction with the principles which, according to Winch, must guide the social scientist. If whole societies believe that what they believed in the past is profoundly absurd, then Winch, who is committed to excluding the possibility of a whole society being wrong in its belief, is caught out, either way: either the pagans were wrong, or the Christians were (*in supposing the pagans to be wrong*); either the pre-Reformation Church was wrong, or the Reformers were, in supporting *it* to be wrong; either those addicted to superstition were wrong, or the rationalists were wrong . . . One way or the other, *someone* must be wrong!

It is instructive to observe Winch's attempts at coping with this question, crucial for his position, and in my view quite insurmountable. He makes a number of attempts:

(1) A shift from a descriptive or analytical position to a normative or prescriptive one. He says, in effect: Yes, there are proselytisers, missionaries, who attempt to interfere in the customs and beliefs of other societies, and remould them in the image of an abstract ideal. But they are *wrong*. They *ought not* to do this [1].

It is difficult to see how this shift to a normative viewpoint can be either justified or squared with the general purpose of Winch's argument. That he should consider this possible at all is connected with his assumption of a philosophical vantage point outside and above all concrete societies and their beliefs. The fact that from this vantage point certain social trends – notably missionaries, proselytisers – should become open to a supposedly neutral, dis-

---

[1] Cf. for instance, a statement of Winch's in a broadcast on the Third Programme, '*Men and things*', of 2nd May 1961: '. . . this is a way of thinking which I wouldn't support at all . . . I am not generally in favour of missionary activities . . .' These are his comments on the universalist claims of some faiths, claims not mindful of cultural boundaries.

passionate condemnation, makes one suspicious of the alleged neutrality of that viewpoint. This Instant Olympus looks rather like a camouflage for one of the concrete beliefs (for a certain romantic traditionalism), and its neutrality is quite spurious.

One could deal with his whole argument here in summary fashion and say that the social sciences are just as concerned with intolerant exclusive beliefs as with tolerant tribal ones, with reformers as much as with traditionalists, with rationalists as much as with believers: a methodology which cannot explain one side of this antithesis, and turns into an ethic, is useless.

But we need not be quite as summary as this. A small dose of normativism might be tolerable even in an analysis or a methodology [1].

Above all, this would be in total harmony with Winch's general Wittgensteinian position.

That position can be summed up as follows: men speak and live their lives and pursue their manifold interests in the context of 'forms of life', cultural/linguistic traditions, and the concepts they employ derive their validity from, and only from, possessing a place in these forms of life. It is not the task of philosophy to interfere with these traditions. But from time to time misguided philosophers (of the old kind) arise, who, under the mistaken and generally tacit belief that concepts are all of some simple kind, and that they can possess a universal and as it were extra-cultural justification, try to judge, and in effect misinterpret, those actually used concepts, in terms of those supposed external norms. It *is* the task of philosophy to neutralise this error, to protect actual traditions from such misguided interference.

Given such a picture, a small amount of normativism does indeed follow: the philosopher is neutral vis-à-vis cultural traditions proper, (and indeed, this is Winch's view), but he is professionally entitled, or obliged, to castigate that small minority of transgres-

---

[1] Hume was guilty of precisely this in his ethics. He gives a certain account of the basis of moral valuation – roughly, in terms of human convenience – and when he comes across *ascetic* values, which contradict this account, instead of modifying the account, he *condemns* the 'monkish virtues'.

sors, e.g. missionaries, who would interfere with other cultures, or their own, in the name of a supposed universal norm, of a kind of validity which is more than the recognition of a place of a concept in a culture.

The trouble is, however, very simple: *these transgressors are not a minority.* They are the majority. They are not deviants. They are the mainstream of at least one important tradition. Missionaries are not foolish and redundant excrescences from e.g. the Christian tradition: they are of its essence. It is not a contingent, but an essential feature of Christianity, that the Gospel should be spread!

In other words, the normativism does not come in a small dose, but is, in effect, overwhelmingly large. Think away the missionaries who spread Christianity over Europe, the Reformers who reformed it, the Rationalists who secularised it – and what is left of the European tradition?

(2)   A second, and equally desperate way out for Winch is to claim that the offensive doctrines – the absolutism, exclusiveness, universalistic claims – whose proscription would, absurdly, exclude most of the European tradition from the European tradition, are not really part of it at all, but 'about it': that, for instance, the belief that some god is the only true god is not part of the belief in him, but a belief *about* the belief – a philosophical accretion, as it were: something which only occurs to the theoretician looking at the belief from the outside, not to the real, practising believer [1].

There may well be tribal religions concerning which something of this kind is true. The believer subscribes to certain ritually consecrated formulae which, interpreted naturally – i.e. on the assumption that the words employed here have the same meaning as they do on other similar occasions – convey certain meaning: for instance, that the deity created the first man X, where X is also known to be the general tribal ancestor, descent from whom

---

[1] In the same broadcast, Winch says: '. . . the idea that these beliefs are universally valid is a view *about* the nature of these beliefs . . .' (Italics mine.) The contrast is, of course, with the *content* of the beliefs. The universalist claims are, according to Winch's view at least at that time, no part of the content of the belief!

defines membership of the tribe and the moral community. Taking this belief literally, it has certain strange consequences: either, that all men are descendants of X, as the first and only created man, and hence that all men are also members of the tribe – which in fact is in contradiction with the practice of treating foreigners as non-members – or, alternatively, that foreigners are non-human. In fact, and in contradiction of the implications of the legend, the actual practice of the tribe recognises foreigners as humans who at the same time are not members of the tribe.

In this case, it could certainly be false to credit the tribe with holding the manifest implication of its proclaimed belief (i.e. that either all humanity can lay rightful claim to its tribal membership, or that some beings normally considered human are not really such.) The context in which the initial belief is asserted is one which does not lead the believers to ask themselves which of the alternative implications they accept. Hence they cannot really be credited with holding either implication [2]. Only an outsider to the usual practice would ask the question. He might, I suppose, be a member of the tribe acting in, as it were, a different capacity, but the question and its answer cannot really be credited to the tribesmen themselves. (But, as we have noted in connection with Winch's device (1), if the questioner is also a member of the tribe, the supposition that the questioning is only done in a kind of external capacity, as an honorary outsider, as it were, becomes quite absurd when the inner questioners become numerous, a real force within the society, or even the majority!)

But whilst the treatment of theoretical questions concerning the belief – concerning, to take the crucial example, its exclusive validity, for instance – can generally be credited to a real or honorary 'outsider' in the case of *some* tribal religions, it becomes

---

[1]   It would however be disastrously wrong to conclude from this that what the members of the tribe do believe, does not have the implications in question at all, and must be interpreted as meaning something quite different, something more innocuous. The world is full of beliefs with unacceptable implications which are ignored for the time being, till the moment comes when ither the implication becomes attractive, or when its unacceptability can be invoked against the initial belief.

quite absurd to do so in the case of the literate, scriptural world religions. Consider the following news item:

Pope Paul's ruling on Eucharist.

... Pope Paul yesterday published an encyclical letter upholding traditional Catholic doctrine on the Eucharist. ... the Pope reasserted ... that the body and blood of Jesus Christ 'are truly and substantially present' in the consecrated bread and wine during Mass. The 6500-word document is believed to be the Pope's reply to a group of West European Catholic theologians who expressed the view that the bread and wine of the Eucharist were purely symbols ...   *(The Observer,* September 12th, 1965)

At a pinch, one might perhaps allow Winch to say that the views of the group of 'West European Catholic Theologians' were 'about', and not 'within', their faith. But Pope Paul's encyclical letter, whilst as a reply to the theologians it must be on the same logical level as their error, is manifestly also an event, a pronouncement, *within* the Faith itself. This merely illustrates something terribly obvious, but something also in blatant contradiction with Winch's position: in the Western tradition (amongst others), a dialogue between the 'beliefs *within*' and the 'theories *about*' religion has become part of religion and belief itself.

Or take another example, crucial for Winch: the exclusiveness of the Muslim deity. The stress on Its exclusiveness, the classification of un-believers, the prescriptions for their treatment, all this is manifestly *part* of the religion itself, not a piece of speculation added on from outside by theoreticians.

(3)   Winch's third device for coping with the fact that cultures themselves indulge in self-correction and self-condemnation is to assert that the corrections themselves *emanate from inside,* from the practice of the tradition itself, and thus do not lead to the paradoxes with which his critic would saddle him [1].

---

[1]   'Do not the criteria appealed to in the criticism of existing institutions equally have a history? And in whose society do they have that history?' Thus Winch, in 'Understanding a primitive society'. The answer he offers to these rhetorical questions is that it *must* be inside the society itself: '... outside that context we could not begin to grasp what was problematical'.

But the paradox cannot be avoided where the self-correction also involves the view that the previous practice was radically irrational – the view, roughly, which the Reformers have of the mediaeval Church, or the Rationalists of the preceding periods of religious faith. The point of Winch's claim that the corrections somehow arise from within the practice is meant to be that each tradition still fails to rise above that collective solipsism, that private enclosure, with which in his view they are all credited.

But the view that the correction and its norms arise from inside is ambiguous and, on either of two possible interpretations, untenable. The two possible interpretations are: (a) that the corrections or their norms arise from within the society, *as opposed to other societies*, and (b) that they arise from within society as such, *as opposed to some extrasocial realm which houses norms of rationality*.

Taking interpretation (a): as a generalisation, this is simply false in the most straightforward, empirical sense. Sometimes, indeed, social change and new standards are endogenous. But, for instance, the diffusion of Christianity in early mediaeval Europe, or the diffusion of industrial-scientific society throughout the world in the modern period, to take two events which have made the world what it is, have, both of them, meant the transformation of societies by ideas and standards which were in no way the fruits of an inner development, but which, on the contrary, arrived from outside.

But let us interpret Winch's point here in the second sense. There is, I suppose, no way of forcing Winch out of that strange collective subjectivism, if he is determined to hold it. Some criteria of rationality seem to me quite independent of any social tradition, but I don't quite see how I could go about establishing this. But here we return to device (2) and the paradox to which Winch finds himself committed: societies themselves, when reforming their previous practices and beliefs, believe themselves to be acting under the guidance of an external, independently valid principle of rationality, and not merely externalising something emanating from their own nature. So – either they were systematically wrong in their earlier, rejected belief, or they are wrong in their new stance and their belief in its absolute justification. Either way, they contradict Winch. His only way out here is to claim that they speak with a different voice when they claim absolute justification, from the healthy voice in which they assert what are, in Winch's account, more basic, first-order beliefs. But this doctrine of the Two Voices and its total inapplicability to the major literate traditions has already been discussed.

Winch's theory can be destroyed either by appealing to the way in which the major and most interesting traditions actually view themselves, as in the above arguments, or equally by appealing to the multiplicity of existing traditions. This second line of attack, however, calls for some elaboration. Winch's theory and attitude would be, for practical purposes, an acceptable one, *in a certain kind of world*. (It would still be, in an ultimate sense, false, in as far as even in a world designed to fit it, our actual world would remain a possibility.) But it is instructive to sketch out such a world. Ironically, it is a world in which there would be no room for Winch. But no matter: let us nevertheless imagine this world, Winch-less but observed and recorded by a for-the-sake-of-the-argument-Winch. What would this world look like?

Imagine a world populated by a set of fairly small tribes, discontinuous enough to have fairly little to do with each other and – here is an important characteristic of this imaginary world – of roughly equal cognitive power. Not one of these small, fairly discontinuous tribes possesses an understanding of its environment which would, numerically or in power, put it at a decisive advantage vis-à-vis the others.

For the sake of the argument we must now imagine at least two philosophers in such a world. One of them is a bad, pre-Wittgensteinian thinker. The other is a kind of proto-Winch. The bad one has succeeded, by luck, accident, or endeavour, in travelling from one of the tribes to another, and his reflections have been stimulated by the differences he has observed. He tries to judge the practices of one tribe by the standards of another; or he tries to attain speculatively some standards independent of either; or he tries to combine premisses drawn from diverse traditions, or to convert members of one tradition to the beliefs of another, etc.

At this point, he encounters the Ur-Winch, who expostulates:

'My dear friend – you are quite misguided. You are doing nothing but mischief by trying to convert tribe A to the rituals and doctrine of tribe B. The doctrines and rituals of tribe B developed in the natural and social context of tribe B, where they make good sense and perform a valuable role. But transplanted into the quite different social context of A, they make no sense at all. There is no one reality and one set of norms, for all tribes: there are different forms of life, and each of them generates, or contains as an essential part of itself, its own way of distinguishing the real from the unreal, the good from the bad. And do not be misled by the fact that the traditions themselves change! They do, under the impact of new norms emanating from their own practice; but it would be a total misunderstanding to infer from this to suppose that they can or should change under the impact of some outer standard.'

In an ultimate and fundamental sense, the Ur-Winch is still mistaken – because, as indicated, even in this hypothetical world, our real world remains a possibility – but for most practical purposes, *in that kind of a world*, he would be right.

But it is a fact of very considerable interest, that our world is quite unlike this imaginary world. The world we do live in is one of countless, overlapping, interacting traditions – so much so that, for sociological purposes, it is extremely difficult to decide which units are to be isolated for purposes of comparison. (This is, notoriously, one of the crucial problems of the 'comparative method'.) Not small, discontinuous, and roughly equal (in size and in cognitive and real power) tribes: but overlapping civilisations of quite unequal cognitive and technical power.

We have seen how the Winchian collective solipsism, derived from the Wittgensteinian treatment of 'forms of life' as ultimate and not susceptible to external validation, is refuted through the fact that some forms of life themselves refuse to treat themselves as ultimate. It is equally refuted by the fact that, in the world as it is, we simply do not have – and have not had for a very, very long time, if indeed we ever did have – those self-contained units, which could be their own standards of intelligibility and reality (and of everything else). What we do have is a set of traditions so complex, so differentiated internally, that we do not know how to delimit our units – indeed any delimitation is largely arbitrary; and these traditions are so sophisticated, so systematically aware of conceptual and moral alternatives, so habituated to interaction, that it is quite meaningless to advise them to turn inwards.

Winch's philosophy illuminates the world we really do live in by sheer contrast; the real contemporary world illuminates Wittgenstein's position by drawing out its crucial implications. These two illuminations are closely connected. It is useful to approach them through considering the strange role of relativism in Winch and Wittgenstein.

For most modern thinkers, relativism is a *problem*: for Winch and Wittgenstein, it is a *solution*. Other thinkers start from the fact of the diversification of belief and morals, and try to find the touchstone of correct belief, etc. This, I think, is the general form of the mainstream of modern Western thought. (For instance: empiricism is, essentially, a theory of the touchstone of truth, or, in later forms, of meaning itself. Materialism is used in a similar way. The various forms of evolutionism claim to have a touchstone which grades degrees of validity, and which is moreover as it were democratically elicited from the specimens to be graded, instead of operating on the material from outside.)

But Wittgenstein and Winch *arrive* at relativism, they don't start out from it, and they arrive at it as a solution to quite another problem, the problem of meaning. Meaning, they say, is not an echo, a reduplication, a structural mirroring of the thing meant, aided perhaps by the struts of a formal framework (*this* was the rejected theory of Wittgenstein's youthful *Tractatus*): it is the possession of a place, a role, in a 'language', a 'form of life', a culture. Wittgenstein arrived at this solution in too exhausted a state to perceive that it raises further enormous problems, given the kinds of complex, interlocking, competing, internally diversified, and rapidly changing cultures which in fact make up our world. Nor did he seem to perceive the terribly obvious truth that *this* problem provides most of philosophy with its content: for had he noticed this, he could not have seen his own particular arrival at a position, which is a solution to him and a problem for almost everyone else, as *the* paradigm of philosophy, or as its euthanasia.

It is both characteristic and profoundly revealing that, despite the enormous importance which the notion of a 'form of life' plays in his philosophy, Wittgenstein in *The Philosophical Investigations* gives *no* example of it. Is *English* a form of life? Or only subcultures within the great world of English-speakers, such as, for instance, that of Cambridge dons, of the Gorbals, of West African patois? Or must we, on the contrary go to some larger *Kulturkreis*? Or would only self-contained tribes do?

As far as Wittgenstein himself is concerned, it is quite manifest from his writings that he did not bother to ask himself this obvious question. He had found a solution to his particular problem, the problem of how words come to have meaning: this solution was in terms of a highly abstract model, i.e. the possession of a role in a 'form of life', and although 'forms of life' were the cornerstone of this model, he felt no need to provide examples of them. In this, he was entirely true to himself. In his youth, he had elaborated a philosophy of meaning in terms of an abstract model in which notions such as that of a 'fact' or 'thing' played crucial parts. No examples at all were given: and the philosophy collapsed when he and others tried to find some examples, failed, and had the grace to ask themselves why they failed. The philosophy was them replaced by a new model, that of 'forms of life'. But once again – no examples! It is deeply ironic that Wittgenstein's general diagnosis of faulty philosophy is the conceptual intoxication with an abstract model, unchecked by comparison with real examples. His diagnosis certainly has at least one correct application.

The importance of Winch lies in the fact that he does try to relate the abstract model which he has inherited, to concrete examples.

If what matters is cultures, and these are the objects of the studies of social scientists, it follows that philosophy and social sciences have the same subject matter, and that the correct method in the one field is also the correct method in the other. From this, he tries – quite mistakenly, in my view – to inform social scientists of the correct method in their field, by deduction from what he considers the correct method in philosophy; whilst the proper procedure is, it seems to me, to argue the other way, and conclude to the mistaken nature of the method in philosophy, from its inapplicability to the concrete objects of the social sciences.

The importance of Winch lies in his attempt to relate the abstract model to reality; his error lies in doing great violence to reality in the process, instead of correcting the model by reference to reality. Some of the features of the real world which are incompatible with the model have already been stressed. One crucial one which remains to be stressed is this: in the world as we know it, cultures are extremely unequal in cognitive power. Some possess concepts and methods which enable them to attain some degree of understanding of their environment, and some possess such an understanding only to a minimal degree. To deny this cognitive inequality is an affectation, which can at most be sustained in the study, but not in real life. (Here is another profound irony of Wittgensteinianism: it fails the philosophic test which it has itself popularised, namely, whether a view can really be held, in the business of living, as opposed to being held merely in the special conditions of a kind of philosopher's licence. This is closely connected with the irony mentioned above: the reason why a view cannot be held outside the context of real life, is of course connected with a failure to look at real instances of the abstract model.) No one, least of all those who are deprived of it, has any doubts about the superior cognitive effectiveness of the 'scientific outlook'.

Similarly, no one really has any doubts about the cognitive inferiority of the pre-scientific outlook. It is in this obverse form that the situation comes to the notice of the anthropologist, of course: he frequently has to report beliefs of the form 'ox equals cucumber', 'wine equals blood', 'witchcraft causes death', etc. Are beliefs of this kind to be described as false and inferior?

Winch, quite consistently with his symmetrical relativism ('symmetrical' in the sense of being egalitarian as between cultures, refusing to judge any of them in terms of another or in terms of a supposedly external norm), rejects this condemnation. In the context of the practices and institutions in which they occur, these assertions – he holds – are *not* absurd. It is the interpretations which find them so which are at fault.

The first thing to note about this is that this 'principle of invariably benevolent interpretation' is in conflict both with the actual practice of social scientists, and with *any* possible practice on their part. In fact, they continue to translate or give account of the belief of distant cultures in terms which often make them plainly absurd. Cucumbers are not oxen, the laying-on of royal hands does not have any therapeutic effects, etc., etc. Why do we not admonish anthropologists, historians, etc., who come back with such reports, for translating so badly (or, perhaps, for translating at all!) as to give us the impression of absurdity? It is supremely noteworthy that Winch himself does not admonish Professor Evans–Prichard, whose account of Azande witchcraft he uses, for misdescribing, or mistranslating, Azande beliefs; he merely criticises him for his tendency to suppose those beliefs false. Yet *if* Evans–Prichard is basically at fault in being tempted to suppose Azande beliefs to be false (as we are all tempted, including, I believe, contemporary Azande), then surely his mistake occurred earlier – in his account of the beliefs, which seems to imply that Azande have faith in the causal connectedness of magical practices and certain consequences.

But, in fact, one cannot avoid these translations, which give the game away and highlight the strangeness of the belief. Many things over and above the belief in a causal connection may be involved – and, indeed, generally are – but that belief is *also* involved. Evans–Prichard's account, which is left unchallenged by Winch, consists in large part of showing how these beliefs survive falsification. This would be redundant and irrelevant, if they were not in fact frequently falsified! The anthropologist's account, far from being committed to respect the truth, in its context, of the belief, as Winch claims, is in fact based on a recognition of its falsehood. Anthropologists do not generally give complex accounts of how a tribe manages to sustain the faith in fire burning, wood floating, etc.: indeed, it would require an anthropological account if the tribe managed to sustain a *denial* of these.

Nor is the anthropologist at liberty simply to seek some other, non-absurd translation. It is part of the role of witchcraft beliefs that it is held possible to *cause* harm in certain ways. Winch's 'principle of universal benevolent interpretation' would exclude, quite *a priori*, important social phenomena such as the social use of absurdity, ambiguity, etc. An absurd formula may, for instance, be used to highlight the solemnity of an occasion. A translation which emptied it of its absurdity, treating it, for instance, simply as the announcement of impending solemnity, would miss the fact that the absurdity is used as a means of conveying that something special is happening, and hence must be present, *as* absurdity.

The example of transsubstantiation is instructive and useful, particularly as it is drawn from the local culture and thus does not call for specialised knowledge for the appreciation of the issues involved. As we have seen, the recognised authority within the religion himself solemnly excludes 'symbolic' interpretations of it, such as the benevolent-anthropological one. Perhaps Winch would not accept the papal ruling, holding it to be an event *within* the 'form of life', and as such not binding on an outside philosophic observer. But surely any adequate account of the Catholic form of life must include a recognition of the fact that, whatever subtleties are present in the interpretation of a Catholic intellectual, to a peasant the doctrine means just what it says, which is highlighted by the fact that, as the papal letter stresses, the simple believer is distressed when encountering the sophisticated interpretations within the fold itself [1]. And let us remember: the point about miracles is that they are *miracles*. They are such not merely to the unsympathetic observer but also, and above all, to the participants.

Let us return to the interesting and illuminating question of relativism. For Wittgenstein, as indicated, it was a solution and not a problem. It was a rather special kind of relativism, with as it were only one term: in the abstract, a general relativism of 'forms of life' was formulated, but in application, only one form of life was considered – that of the academic philosopher himself, and his disciples. (This was the main basis of the appeal of this philosophy: it provided a justification for a 'form of life' which in fact was threatened by the implication of scientific revisions of our world-

---

[1] I have argued the case against the Principle of Universal Sympathy in anthropological interpretation, at greater length in 'Concepts and society', *Proceedings of the Fifth World Congress of Sociology*, Washington, 1962.

view. The philosophy in question provided an omnibus justification
of the old view, and facilitated the discounting of the new implication by calling them 'metaphysical', and maintaining that they
had the same root as quite artificial, genuinely 'metaphysical'
revisions which were re-invented, as straw men, for the purpose.)

Winch has considered other forms of life and the implications
of their existence and investigation (though not the implications
of the fact that they live non-isolated lives and interact intensely
and violently with each other and with our own 'form of life',
however that is to be delimited). Consequently he *does* face relativism as a problem, not merely as a solution. He accepts it. This
acceptance can be usefully considered a kind of solution. It is
– and this is important for the purposes of my argument – a most
symmetrical solution. It does not favour one form of life over
another. It treats them all as equal.

My main contention here is that *no* symmetrical solution of this
problem is acceptable. (The evolutionists had a symmetrical solution, which was the main source of the appeal of their doctrine:
it 'overcame' relativism by seeing various forms of life as members
of one great series, such that later or superior members of the
series incorporated all or most of the merits of earlier members,
whilst adding something more. In this way, all forms of life had
some validity, but there was some over-all yardstick all the same.
This solution is no longer available, if only because forms of life
cannot be arranged into any neat and unique series in this manner.)
Winch's solution is not merely symmetrical, like that of the evolutionists, but also rather static; all forms of life are equal. Even
if they are credited with change, they all go their own ways. The
starting point of one is not the terminus of another, they form
no grand series.

When formulated in a very abstract manner, I doubt whether
the problem of relativism has a solution. In this it may resemble
the problem of solipsism, of which indeed it may be seen as a
special variant, one in which cultural collectivities replace individual islands of consciousness. But if one considers the world as
it really is – something which Winch refrains from doing – we see
that there is a kind of solution.

The philosophical significance of the scientific-industrial 'form of life', whose rapid global diffusion is the main event of our time, is that for all practical purposes it does provide us with a solution of the problem of relativism – though a highly unsymmetrical one. (It is for this reason that no symmetrical solution can be entertained.) The cognitive and technical superiority of one form of life is so manifest, and so loaded with implications for the satisfaction of human wants and needs – and, for better or worse, for power – that it simply cannot be questioned.

If a doctrine conflicts with the acceptance of the superiority of scientific-industrial societies over others, then it really is out. This point must not be misunderstood [1]. The cognitive and technical superiority does not imply or bring with it superiority in any other field. What it does do is to bring along the *possibility* – no more – of a certain material liberation. On any moderately realistic estimate of human nature, as long as the price of decent behaviour was, in effect, total self-sacrifice (which was the case in the conditions of scarcity which characterise pre-industrial society), the prospects of decent behaviour were negligible. But thanks to the cognitive and technical effectiveness of industrial society, the *possibility*, though no more, is now present.

This effectiveness of scientific industrial civilisation and its diffusion are the central facts of our time. It must be accepted, but it does not uniquely determine the other aspects of our existence. The first task of thought is to understand and perceive the limits within which we operate, and the alternatives they offer.

For this reason, any symmetrical solution of the problem of relativism – which automatically ignores the crucial asymmetry of our situation – is erroneous and harmful. If in addition it obstructs social understanding by making sympathetic acceptance an obligation for all interpretation, by excluding the very possibility of

---

[1] I hope it is not necessary to guard against the misunderstanding that what is being claimed is some version of a 'racialist' superiority of the societies in which the scientific-industrial form of life emerged. The form of life depends on the social organisation and ethos of the societies in which it occurs, and is manifestly independent of the 'genetic' composition of the populations involved.

false consciousness, in a quite *a priori* manner, then so much the worse. Wittgensteinianism proper led to a narcissistic and sterile observation of the alleged conceptual customs of one's own 'form of life' – sterile because, in fact, philosophic questions are *not* generated by misunderstandings of the working of concepts. The more thorough and realistic – but not realistic enough – application of this philosophy by Winch leads to a misunderstanding both of the real social situation – of the way real 'forms of life' are related to each other in history and notably in the twentieth century – and of the methods really employed by social scientists.

P. Cohen: *The very idea of a social science.*

The central purpose of Mr. Peter Winch's book, *'The Idea of A Social Science'*, is to argue that social enquiry is not scientific. There is nothing very original either in this or in his attack on positivism, which is held to be responsible for the dreadful idea that sociology can and should be a science. What is curious, however, is that Winch uses some of the very arguments that are sometimes used by defendants of positivism. For example, Winch denies to social scientists the right to use the term 'social causation'; and E. R. Leach recently disavowed any interest in the causes of social and cultural phenomena, explaining that, as a 'vulgar positivist', he was interested only in the way pieces of cultural data fitted together [1]. On the other hand, Professor Claude Levi–Strauss, who has been called an anthropological 'idealist', but who refers to himself as an 'intellectualist', does not disavow an interest in causation! To complicate matters even further, Winch describes himself as a Wittgensteinian and an opponent of sociological positivism, while Leach has acknowledged his debt both to Wittgenstein and to positivism. To make matters very much worse we have only to remember that F. A. Hayek has stated that social science is *only* possible if it rejects the programme of positivism [2] and that Sir Karl Popper, who has argued that there is no basic difference between the methods of natural and social science, has severely criticised positivism [3].

All of this makes it extremely difficult to discuss Winch's views in terms of some particular tradition of the philosophy of (social)

---

[1] Henry Meyers Lecture, delivered in May 1966 at University College, London.

[2] See F. R. Hayek, *The Counter-Revolution of Science*, Free Press, 1952, esp. pp. 44–52, 80–86.

[3] See K. R. Popper, *The Poverty of Historicism*, London, Routledge and Kegan Paul, 1957.

science. In some respects he is in the same tradition as Durkheim, in that he sees social phenomena as existing only insofar as they are mental phenomena as well; but he is opposed to this tradition insofar as he denies that social phenomena can be truly studied by the methods of science, and defines the aim of social enquiry as the interpretation of meaning not as the explanation of cause.

Winch's indebtedness to Wittgenstein is doubtless of some importance to him. Nevertheless, I do not propose to discuss this aspect of his book. My chief reasons are that I am not competent to do so and that I am interested in the methodology of social science rather than in linguistic philosophy, which I do not understand [1]. This does not, I think, disqualify me from making these comments: my understanding of Winch's methodological arguments is, at least, not inferior to his understanding of sociology.

Winch's methodological arguments [2] can be summarised as follows:

(1) Social phenomena exist only insofar as they are ideational and have meaning for those who engage in social conduct; therefore, they can not be treated in the same way as the objects of the natural world.

(2) The explanation of social conduct consists in the elucidation of motive and meaning; these do not exist other than as part of conduct and can not therefore be called the causes of social conduct: therefore, the aim of social enquiry is understanding, not scientific explanation, and operates with a notion of 'logical relation' not with that of 'causation'.

(3) It is of the essence of social conduct that it involves the making of decisions; but it is in the nature of decisions that they

---

[1] Furthermore, this aspect of Winch's argument is fully discussed and thoroughly criticised by Ernest Gellner in his article 'The new idealism' in this volume. The merits of linguistic philosophy are critically and exhaustively examined in a book by the same author: see E. A. Gellner, *Words and Things*, London, 1959.

[2] Winch denies that his book is methodological and insists that he is only doing philosophy. However, the reader can judge for himself whether or not he does make pronouncements concerning what is possible and what is not possible in social enquiry. See Peter Winch, *The Idea of a Social Science*, Routledge and Kegan Paul, 1958, esp. pp. 45–136.

cannot be known or understood until they have been made – the mind can always be changed; therefore, insofar as social situations are always affected by the decisions of those who participate in them, they must remain unpredictable and, therefore, not amenable to scientific enquiry.

(4) Although social scientists can make statistical statements asserting the likelihood that certain types of conduct will occur or recur, they cannot expect statistics to provide them with a key to science; for a statistic is meaningless unless interpreted, and interpretation involves recourse to statements about motive and meaning; and these belong not to science but to philosophy.

(5) The methods of social enquiry are identical with those of philosophy – at least with those of Wittgenstein's mature philosophy – and have little in common with those of science.

The difficulty in criticising Winch's arguments is that one can find oneself in partial agreement with each assertion yet opposed to the radical conclusions which seem to follow from them.

My own discussion of Winch will consist in elaborating five counter-arguments which are as follows:

(1) social phenomena are ideational; but it does not follow from this that all social conduct is affected by any kind of idea; nor does it follow that all social phenomena are ideational to the same extent.

(2) The explanation of social conduct consists not only in the elucidation of meaning but also, necessarily, in the analysis of causal connexions.

(3) Decision-making, and other aspects of social conduct, rule out determinism, but do not entirely rule out causation.

(4) Statistics do, of course, have to be interpreted; but the interpretations can often be subjected to statistical tests themselves.

(5) The social sciences may owe a great deal to philosophy; and sociology, in particular, may be inseparable from it; but much of sociology has not only benefited from the method of science but could benefit from a great deal more of it.

1. *Social phenomena are ideational.* The notion that social phenomena are ideational – that they do not exist except insofar as

they are in the minds of men – is shared by a great variety of social scientists and philosophers who might otherwise consider themselves in very different philosophical and ideological camps. For Durkheim, the foundation of social life is the 'collective consciousness'. For Weber, social institutions are simply highly predictable forms of social interaction which have obtained the 'seal' of legitimacy; and social interaction consists in the ordering of mutual patterns of conduct which are guided by mutual expectations. Even for Pareto – whom Winch accuses of positivism and, therefore, of behaviourism – the *fons et origo* of all social phenomena does not lie in the instincts but in the 'residues', which are partly ideational [1]. Hayek asserts very strongly that social phenomena can exist only insofar as men have ideas about them. He argues that one must distinguish between those social phenomena which are really only natural phenomena of society, such as birth rates and death rates, and those which are true moral phenomena, such as suicide rates and crime rates. For one can speak of 'birth' and 'death' without implying motive or meaning to those who are born and die, while one cannot speak of 'suicide' or 'crime' without imputing a motive to the agent and a moral reaction to others. He even suggests that these two types of phenomena should be investigated by different types of scientific enquiry [2].

One of the conclusions that is often drawn from this is that social life is changed by ideas, or that social change can be prevented by ideas. But while it is true that social life can be changed by new ideas – particularly, but not only, by scientific ideas, which transform techniques of production – and that these ideas are not *determined* by the conditions of society, it is also true to say that social life can resist the influence of ideas, or that it can change in ways which are quite different from those envisaged by these

---

[1] Pareto gives sexual asceticism as an example of a 'residue', while he gives sexuality as an example of a drive or instinct. Clearly asceticism is ideational, while sexuality may not be. See Vilfredo Pareto, *Sociological Writings*, (Selected by S. E. Finer, translated by D. Mirfin), London, 1966, p. 237.

[2] See F. R. Hayek, *Individualism and Economic Order*, London, 1949, esp. pp. 57–76.

particular ideas. Yet, if social life is itself ideational, what is it that resists the influence of ideas, or that changes independently of ideas?

The difficulty, it seems, lies in the double use of the term 'ideas' in this context. In the first place, there are ideas which are *inherent* in social structure itself, and of which the members of society may not, themselves, be conscious. It is in this sense that one says that a market mechanism can only be said to operate if men share certain ideas about the role of money, the nature of prices, etc. It is in this same sense that anthropologists insist that kinship categories are conventional ideas, not 'natural' discriminations. The second sense in which the term is used concerns men's ideas *about* their society. Even in the simplest societies men have ideas about their social structure and culture and these ideas are often an idealized version of them. In more complex societies men have not only favourable ideas about their system, but often very unfavourable ones.

Now it is indisputable that men are freer to change their ideas *about* society than they are to change those *within* society. There are a number of reasons for this. First, ideas *within* social structure are often not fully conscious ones. Second, they exist as systems, and are mutually reinforcing: the ideas which fathers have about children reinforce those which children have about fathers; and the ideas which fathers have about themselves as both fathers and foremen reinforce one another. Third, the systems of mutual expectations which men have about one another's conduct provide some 'pay-off' for them; and unless circumstances change, or men see that there are advantages in changing their expectations, they may not become fully aware of what their expectations are, let alone change them.

All of the foregoing discussion rests on the assumption that all social phenomena are equally ideational. But they surely are not. Such factors as the size of social groups and human populations and the physical environment in which their social activities are carried on are surely of major importance in explaining the characteristics of societies and of social conduct. This is not to dispute that there may be an important ideational element in group size: for a group or social collectivity exists only insofar as there is some recognition of group membership. However, once this is 'given' the factor of size or number exerts an independent influence. For example there is a limit to the size of a primitive society which can cohere without centralised authority. The factor of physical environment is of course an obvious one. And what is important about it is that it is very often the man-made physical environment which exerts such a great influence on social life. One has only to think of the pattern of urban settlement to recognise this. These factors exert an influence which is partly independent of any ideas which people may have about them.

One can go even further than this and say that it is not only the physical environment, both natural and man-made, which constitutes non-ideational factors in society but that social structure itself may have a constraining influence on the conduct of men which is largely independent of ideas. For example, if one class or sector of society controls the means of coercing another class, the obedience of the latter is governed as much, if not more, by fear or apathy than by expectations of mutual rights and duties. It could be objected that a system based on coercion and fear is no less ideational than one based on moral obligation: for the dominant party expects compliance from peon or slave, and gets it, because the powerless party expects death, starvation or some other penalty or disadvantage in the event of disobedience or rebellion. It is of course true that such a system is, in that sense, ideational. But the analysis of such coercive systems hardly involves much *investigation* of ideas as such. The enquiry is concerned far more with the actual structure of coercion.

It is no coincidence that those sociologists, like Marx and Pareto, who have emphasised the coercive aspect of social structure, have also underemphasised the ideational element in it. But they did not ignore it. Marx frequently pointed out that the 'relations of production', which dominated social life, included the rules and laws concerning the ownership and control of property. There is almost as much danger in overemphasising the ideational content of social relations as in ignoring it; for this may lead one to underestimate the element of coercion in society, particularly in certain types of society.

This is not to deny in the least that ideas about society may have important consequences for social change: in fact, the very idea that society can only be changed by first changing the 're- lations of production' may itself have considerable effects, largely because it is not universally true. If it were universally true, then the idea as such would have little or no effect in inducing men to adopt a policy emphasising the primacy of economic change. But it is as well to remember that the degree to which ideas about society affect its development is itself dependent upon the structure of society itself.

2. *Motive, cause, understanding and explanation.* If one wishes to explain human conduct, whether social or not, one is forced to do so in terms of means, ends and the ideas which men have con- cerning the efficacy of certain means, the moral appropriateness of using them, and the desirability of certain ends in relation to some others. This does not mean that one assumes that in all or most types of human conduct men consciously and deliberately visualise their ends, estimate their relative significance, assess the means, consider the moral implications of using some and not others, and so on. It is not that men usually conduct themselves in this way, but that their conduct can only be explained in this way. Even conduct which is habitual can only be explained in this way; for it is a fact that men do not behave blindly in accordance with habit when there are advantages in, or possibilities of, doing otherwise. The assumption behind all this is that human conduct is not simply reflexive but meaningful. But conduct can not usually be understood by an *a priori* attribution of meaning: if we see a man kneeling down we do not simply assume that he is praying, for he might be exercising his limbs; to attribute one motive rather than another – that is, to elucidate the meaning of his conduct – one must relate it to its context and to the terms in which the man himself describes it.

All of this leads Winch to the conclusion that since motive can only be inferred from conduct and context, and since conduct can only be explained in terms of motive and meaning, the form of the explanation cannot be causal; for, to analyse causal connexions is to identify distinct and separate sets of events and to show that one set is dependent upon the occurrence of the other. Since it is the task of social enquiry to explain human conduct the method must be that of exhibiting the logical relation between the assumptions of conduct and conduct itself. This is what makes social enquiry quite different from science. For science is concerned with causation not with implication.

Of course, human individuals are different from physical objects in that their behaviour is affected not simply by 'objective' conditions but also by their assumptions about them. So that any social science explanation must involve some statement about the 'inner logic' of the objects of enquiry, while natural science explanation need not. But it does not follow from this that there is no causal explanation in sociology. For even if a man's *motive* cannot be called the cause of his behaviour the conditions which elicit this motive can; for they may be produced quite independently of, and external to, the individual himself.

The combination of these two aspects of explanation is well demonstrated in the following example. Let us say we wish to explain an arms race; we do so by saying that each of two (or more) parties expects to be attacked by another if the other should find itself in a superior position of arms; therefore each seeks to obtain a position of at least equal strength with the other and does so by aiming to build up its military power to a point beyond that of its opponent, so as to allow it some margin of advantage; this in effect means that each will continue to build up its arms until their mutual hostility is reduced by a change in the pattern of international power or by an outbreak of war. This very simple model also helps to explain how wars occur in such situations: for each party is tempted to use what it believes to be a position of superiority to prevent a further strengthening in its opponent's position. Thus, even if no party wishes either to expend greater resources on arms or to engage in warfare, it may be induced to do both by the pattern of relations between it and another power. Leaving aside for the moment the fact that this is an oversimple model of explanation and assuming only that it is not far wrong for certain cases, one can immediately see that that is an explanation both in terms of implication as well as in terms of cause. For the model shows not only how the conduct of each party follows from its assumptions about the other, but also how the conduct of each influences the assumptions of the other. This mutual influence is a causal process in any sense of the word.

Much of the trouble with Winch's argument is that he is thinking about the conduct of a single individual whose motives, assumptions and meanings are *given*. It does not occur to him that the social sciences are largely concerned to explain how social interaction produces consequences which are intended by no one, how men's motives, meanings and ideas are fashioned and elicited, and how different features of social life affect one another, coexist and change.

It is not that social scientists insist on using the term 'cause' but that they cannot avoid doing so. Consider the following example. Let us say one observes that sometimes an increase in the consumption of a commodity is accompanied by a fall in its price, while at other times an increase in consumption is accompanied by a rise in price. How does one make sense of this seeming anomaly? Does one do so by denying the existence of causation and upholding the view that social phenomena are capricious? Quite the contrary: one makes sense of this by showing that where price fall is the cause, the effect is a rise in consumption, and that where a rise in consumption is the cause, the effect is a rise in price.

There are, of course, many social correlations or seeming correlations that are governed less by causal connexion than by logical implication; and these cases may mislead one to think that causation is illusory; but a careful examination of them shows that the idea of causation is indispensable. The two following examples, though very different in some respects, demonstrate this quite clearly. If one asserts that profit is maximised at the point at which marginal revenue equals marginal cost, one is not making a causal statement even though one may appear to be. For one is simply saying that if one does one thing one is, by definition, also doing another; to say this is to elucidate the meaning of 'profit maximisation'; the statement cannot be empirically refuted. However, if one states that profit maximisation is less likely to occur where there is a greater divorce between ownership and management, one is making an empirically testable statement which asserts a causal connexion between one factor and another. In principle, one can manipulate the degree of divorce between management and ownership and observe what effect this has on profit maximisation.

The second example comes not from economics but from social anthropology. In a patrilineal society the existence of a rule of matrilateral cross-cousin marriage, to which everyone adheres, will compel each man to marry into the same lineage as his father did, and will establish a tie between each lineage and two others, such that particular patterns of wife-giving and wife-taking are unique to each lineage. This statement is a tautology: the so-called structural implications of matrilateral cross-cousin marriage derive from the meaning of terms like marriage, cross-cousin, lineage, etc. If, however, one asserts that this pattern of marriage serves to maintain a system of hierarchical relations between lineages, or that it serves to increase the overall cohesion of society as against some other society, then one *is* making a causal statement which can be empirically tested and refuted. In principle one can manipulate the marriage rules of a society and observe whether this does have the effect of destroying the hierarchy of lineages or of reducing the cohesion of the society.

To all of this Winch might reply that the idea of causation refers to sets of events, (such that the occurrence of some is necessary or sufficient for the occurrence of others) and that events can only be said to occur at a time and place which can be precisely determined; since social events – such as an increase in consumption, a rise in prices, a state of military preparation – cannot be isolated and easily located, they cannot be said to be events at all.

One would have to agree that the use of the term 'causation' does not have as precise a reference in the social world as it does in the natural world. But if one is to use such strict criteria one wonders what is to be offered in place of 'causation'; for the idea of logical relation or implication is clearly not good enough, as has been shown. In fact one begins to wonder how social policy would be possible without some idea of causation. Or is the idea of social policy also illusory?

Whether they admit it or not social scientists and historians

– the latter for much longer – have always some idea of causation. According to Winch the meaning of a term is to be inferred from the context of its usage, and an idea of the proper usage from the meaning. Either the usage of the term 'cause' (by social scientists) is an exception to this rule or else social scientists really mean 'implication' when they use the term 'cause'. I think that I have shown that the latter is not true.

Imagine that social scientists, convinced that they were really doing philosophy, were to offer themselves on the academic market for teaching posts in philosophy; further, imagine that this would have the effect of reducing the market value of philosophers and so of bringing about a reaction amongst philosophers to exclude both Wittgensteinians and social scientists from their professions and from teaching posts in their departments. Would such a chain of events, one wonders – if one can be permitted to call it a chain of events – convince Mr. Winch of the existence of social causation? Or would he explain the whole thing simply by showing how different people use the terms philosophy, social science and Wittgenstein? He must realise that it makes a difference.

3. *Decision-making and determinism.* If Winch were to be confronted with all of the previous arguments he would still resort to one last one, which is usually considered a trump card. It is the argument which asserts that the pattern of social life and, more particularly, changes in the pattern of social life, are affected by men's decisions, and that decisions are not really explicable in causal terms. The reason for this is that a decision cannot be known until it has occurred; it cannot be predicted because it is not determined; it is not determined because the mind can be changed even after a decision appears to have been reached, and before an action occurs; and this is true even of acts which conform to a rule; for although the rule may state what the action should be, it does not state that it itself will be adhered to; and even if one rule states that another should be adhered to, the governing rule also can be broken; and so on, *ad infinitum.* Let us say one is trying to predict the decision of a man who states his intention of buying one's house: even if one knows that this is the type of

house he wants and that he can afford to pay the price one wants, and that he has stated his willingness to do so, one cannot possibly know that he will; for he might change his tastes after seeing the house; he might react to the manner in which one has bargained with him, and so on. No matter how much one were to increase one's information about the intending buyer, one could not know that he had not anticipated these steps and reacted accordingly. For in predicting a human decision it is not the inability to accumulate information which is so problematic; it is the ability to know how much information is required and whether one has it.

If Winch is right in asserting that an individual decision cannot be predicted, then he would appear to be also right in asserting that the decisions of a large number of individuals cannot be predicted; for to predict the decisions of many men appears to require the prediction of how each one will reach a decision and, further, how the decision of one will affect that of another. But this line of argument is quite mistaken. The prediction of individual conduct – which is not always impossible, anyway – involves a knowledge of the idiosyncratic features of an individual mind and of an individual situation; however, in predicting social conduct, one can assume that individual idiosyncracies are randomly distributed, so that there is a high probability that men who share certain cultural assumptions and who find themselves in certain common situations, are likely to act in roughly the same way; one can often also assume that these assumptions will not change radically in the short run and that the nature of the situations in which men act will also remain, in some respects, much the same.

The making of such *conditional* predictions, as Sir Karl Popper has shown [1], in no way assumes that the social world is fully determined. For determinism implies not just that there are causal chains of events in the social world, but that any particular event is the result of a single causal chain or that the convergence of different causal chains is itself governed by a single causal nexus. The idea of causation itself, and of conditional predictability, makes no such deterministic assumptions. Of course this means that

---

[1] *The Poverty of Historicism*, pp. 126–128.

even if one's causal theories are assumed to be true, one cannot be sure that one's predictions will be successful, because one cannot rule out the possibility that one's limiting conditions will hold. Nor can one avoid this problem by trying to predict whether the limiting conditions will hold or not; for this will involve a further conditional prediction, with a further set of limiting conditions, whose occurrence must, in turn, be predicted, and so on, *ad infinitum*. This does mean that there is a substantive difference between the predictions of sociology and those of *some* natural sciences in which the number of conditional influences can be limited by experimental insulation. It also means that there is some substantive difference between sociological predictions and those of any natural science because of the far greater difficulty of assessing the relative importance of various factors in social causation. It does not mean that social phenomena are quite unpredictable; predictability does not imply determinism.

Of course, it could be argued that nothing in the world is really predictable, insofar as the universe is not known to be fully determined: for any single causal chain should be shown to result from the convergence of other causal chains, and so on *ad infinitum*. But it is worth considering whether human society and culture would be at all possible if the assumption of predictability of the natural and social world were to be entirely suspended.

4. *Statistical interpretation.* Not all sociological statements are explicitly statistical; but most would be improved if they could be put in statistical form. The reason is that no sociological generalisation is meant to 'cover' every possible case; sociological hypotheses can be tested only by showing that they 'cover' every population within which the distribution of 'disturbing' factors is thought to be random.

There are many objections that have been and could be made against the use of statistical measures and other procedures of quantification in sociology. The most important of these are: that many social phenomena can not be adequately weighed and their **degrees** of influence compared; that with many social measures one cannot assume 'equal intervals' and zero points; and that with many social populations the concept of a 'normal distribution' does not apply. But Winch's objection to the use of statistics as a final arbiter in the choice of sociological 'interpretations' is quite different and not at all technical. His argument is that statistics have to be interpreted, and that the interpretation of social statistics involves not a discussion of the external relations between phenomena but an elucidation of 'internal' meaning.

Of course, neither statistics nor, indeed, any other facts ever 'speak for themselves'. Statistical evidence, whether in the natural or in the social sciences, only has meaning if it has any bearing on a particular hypothesis, which may be general or particular. Insofar as sociological hypotheses also refer to meaningful conduct, it can be said that sociological statistics must be meaningful in this particular sense. But Winch wishes to go further than this; he is arguing against Sir Karl Popper's view that sociological hypotheses are tested in the same way as the hypotheses of natural sciences. Popper's view is that an 'intuitive understanding' of social phenomena can only suggest hypotheses and that these must be tested 'objectively', and that such tests are the final arbiter of acceptability [1]. Winch's view is that quoting of evidence simply raises new problems of meaning. His characterisation of Popper's view is correct; but Popper himself also suggests that sociological hypotheses can also be tested by 'internal' evidence – that is, by asking whether they are plausible in terms of the 'logic of social situations' – and this may suggest that Popper's view is not entirely opposed to that of Winch. Furthermore, it might be added that some sociologists also incline to the view that statistical evidence never has 'the last word' in a scientific discussion. It seems to me that there is some confusion in these arguments. On the whole, I agree with Popper's view in this matter; but I think that even it needs further clarification.

Every sociological hypothesis must comply with three requirements before gaining acceptability: it must explain the facts; it must be independently testable; and it must be plausible. The first and second requirements are common to all science and need

---

[1]   Ibid. p. 138.

no further elaboration. *But the third is peculiar to the social sciences for natural science hypotheses may well be implausible in terms of existing assumptions; it demands that any sociological hypothesis be explicable itself – in principle, if not in detail – in terms of some theory or theories of social action and interaction.*

This does not mean that plausibility is sufficient for the acceptance of a sociological hypothesis; for it often happens that several hypotheses explain the same facts and that all are plausible; one can only choose between them, in the final instance, by seeing how they stand up to independent tests. If the facts to be explained happen to be statistical, then the alternative interpretations of statistics should themselves be subjected to further tests which could be, in principle, if not in fact, statistical. The arguments can be best illustrated by a simple example.

Let us say one discovers, in a particular population, that there is a statistical correlation between political orientation and age: for example, the figures may show that those under a certain age are more likely to be radical than those over it. The first thing to do with such a figure is to test for 'statistical significance': that is, to ascertain whether the correlation can be simply explained in terms of a chance distribution; and a high degree of 'significance' will constitute a refutation of the 'null' hypothesis. The next step is to ask whether radicalism is determined by age or age by radicalism, or whether both are determined by something else; since the last two interpretations are either absurd or implausible they are rejected. The next step is to find out whether the connexion between age and political inclination is stronger for some sections of the population than for others, and why the connexion should exist. If it turns out that the connexion is stronger for one section than for another or that it hardly exists for some sections, this would suggest that age alone is not the determining factor, but that it must be accompanied by certain others; and if it can also be shown that the correlation is reversed for some sections, then this would suggest looking more closely at the particular factors which characterise the difference between the sections. So far, all the steps taken to interpret the statistical evidence have been checked by more statistical manipulation. It is now time to attempt an explanation of the connection between the two 'factors'. A number of competing explanations can be put forward: (1) young people are more deprived than old people; (2) young people are more rebellious against social norms than older people because of the manner in which they are treated; (3) young people are more rebellious because they are emotionally more disturbed; (4) young people sense an opposition between themselves and older people; (5) the society requires radicalism from younger people in order to sustain the opposition between age-groups, which in turn helps to define the status of the young in relation to the older; and so on. Hypothesis (5) will be rejected; it does not comply with the requirement of plausibility, for it attributes overall goals to the society itself. It can be made more plausible by being formulated in the following way: if young people are initially more radical than older people, then this will promote opposition between age-groups; this in turn will serve to define the relationship between age-groups as one of opposition; and this will strengthen the radicalism of the young. But even in this form the hypothesis will be difficult to test and is unsatisfactory as an explanation.

Having eliminated (5) one is still left with a number of hypotheses to choose from – *at least* four; and they are all equally plausible and consistent with most of the known facts. The only way of deciding between them is to seek more evidence; for example, one could compare the two age-groups for signs of deprivation and one could compare the less deprived with the more deprived in each age-group, to see whether there was any correlated variation in political opinion; one could compare different groups of young people who are treated differently to see whether they show differing degrees of radicalism; and so on. In addition to this, one could compare the radicalism of cohesive groups with that of isolated individuals, to test whether mutual reinforcement was a factor to be considered or not. It is quite clear that although other criteria are applied in selecting between hypotheses, the final arbiter is that of evidence; or, better still, the final arbiter is the use of evidence to attempt refutations of hypotheses. This is the method of science.

5.   The main purpose of these comments has been to show that sociology cannot manage without the notion of causation or without the logic of science. That it cannot also manage without the elucidation of meaningful conduct is not denied. In his enthusiasm to liken the method of sociology to that of philosophy Winch has emphasised one aspect of sociological enquiry, which is most evident in social anthropology. For it is true that a major task of social anthropology is to translate the ideas of other cultures into those which one can understand in one's own. These are ideas in social structure as well as those about it and about the universe. But this is not the only task, nor indeed the most important. For one wants to understand other cultures in order to explain why human societies and cultures are what they are, how some forms of human conduct affect others, how conduct affects expectations and how these, in turn, affect conduct.

It is probably true that although sociology is no longer a colony of the philosophical empire, it is still, in part, dependent upon it [1]. In its new state of partial independence its spokesmen are bound to be brash and to profess beliefs in absurd ideologies which assert an independence which is not complete, and perhaps never will be. But sociologists will be wise to decline a neo-colonial status under the protection of linguistic philosophy. They can surely do better for themselves.

J. W. N. WATKINS: *Anthropomorphism in social science.*

The problem Gellner set out from could be put like this. Let us agree that the study of nature should not be anthropomorphic and that the study of man can hardly avoid being anthropomorphic. Then what about the study of *society* – to which side should it incline? Gellner went on to assail Winch's Wittgenstein-inspired idea of an essentially anthropomorphic social science. To *this* kind

---

[1]   For a recent example of how sociology can profitably make use of philosophy, and vice versa, see E. Gellner, *Thought and Change*, Weidenfeld and Nicolson, London, 1964.

of anthropomorphism I too am opposed; and I shall reinforce Gellner's objections with an objection of my own. But these objections leave open the possibility that social science should be 'anthropomorphic' in some other sense; and I shall go on to suggest that explanatory social science ought, ultimately, to be humanistic and individualistic, though not naively so.

I take it that Wittgenstein's conception of language dissolves the individual/society dichotomy: language-using human beings are social (game-playing) beings at the outset. Moreover (and this is Gellner's point about Winch's reversal of the implication), each of the various social games individuals engage in can be understood with the help of concepts endogenous to it and familiar to the players, and without the help of alien, theoretical concepts. Human beings are *social* beings and social activities are *human* activities.

Gellner dwells upon the *relativist* implications which he discerns in this idea of the manner in which a social science should 'explain' social activities, or render them intelligible. (The absence of external concepts is taken to imply the absence of external criteria, which is taken to imply that each form of social life must be understood and judged in the light of its own implicit categories and criteria.) I judge his commentary to be so devastating as to render otiose any further criticism along *these* lines. But something remains to be said about a different implication of this idea of a social science: namely, that it would reduce social science to *explanatory impotence* when confronted by the very phenomena for which explanations are most urgently needed.

It is typically when some important aspect of social life is going badly wrong, (or at least when it is known to be *liable* to go wrong) that there is an extra-academic desire for sociological explanation. Consider a society being swept by some political or economic scourge which: (a) hits large numbers of people painfully, perhaps lethally; (b) is quite unprecedented, at least within the afflicted society; (c) seems to get increasingly out of control. (Whether or not any historical phenomena have *completely* satisfied this specification, some of the more notorious twentieth century phenomena have certainly *approximated* it all too well: the 1914–18 slaughter, the post-War inflation in Germany, the Great Depression, the

Russian purges – in each case the *scale*, at least, was unprecedented; and while some of these phenomena were triggered off politically, they all came to seem, for a time, to have acquired an uncontrollable momentum of their own.)

A social scourge of the kind indicated is likely, in addition to inflicting much direct suffering and damage, to engender a kind of desperate *bewilderment*. That these things are happening is bad enough; that nobody seems to know why they are happening and how much worse they will get and where it will all end – this makes it worse still. In such a situation, people who have never heard of social or political or economic science start craving for a bit of social or political or economic understanding [1].

Such explanation-seekers would get a dusty answer from a social science as conceived by Winch. Such a social science might cope well enough with some regularized and smoothly functioning social institution or practice; but to ask it to cope with any sort of social *breakdown* would be like asking a cricket correspondent to explain *in the language of cricket* why the spectators at a match started pelting the players with beer bottles. Even to *describe* the breakdown of a social practice is likely to call for concepts outside the language of the practice; and to explain it is almost sure to do so. The same applies to attempts to explain those aforementioned big, bad, and seemingly meaningless and uncontrollable, social malaises.

But are not such phenomena, which are so alien to the aims of all or nearly all those caught up in them, irreconcilable not only

---

[1] (1) For me, a particularly poignant scene in Remarque's *All Quiet on the Western Front* occurs in ch. 9. The German tommies have been inspected by the Kaiser himself; one of them asks whether there would have been a war if the Kaiser had said 'No'. This starts a discussion about what the war is *for*. It is a fumbling and naive discussion, but the main problem emerges clearly: Why is the war being fought when '*no one in particular wants it*'?

(2) In the last chapter of *Russian Purge and the Extraction of Confession*, by F. Beck and W. Godin, the pseudonymous authors write: 'There was no question that excited the prisoners so much as ... Why? What for?' The authors go on to present *seventeen* 'theories put forward by the examining magistrates and prisoners themselves. During our imprisonment we tirelessly discussed these theories...' (pp. 182–183).

with Winch's anthropomorphism but with *any* anthropocentric or humanistic or individualistic explanation? Are we not bound to invoke impersonal forces, whether infra-human or supra-human, commensurate with these mass-effects, if we wish to explain them?

No; for it may be possible to show how such an alien mass-effect can be unknowingly engendered, without extra-human help, by the interactions of many individuals, each acting roughly according to the logic of his own situation [1]. (Explanations of this character are, of course, already available for the mass-unemployment of the 1930's.) The provision of such an explanation tends, so to speak, to humanize a seemingly inhuman phenomenon. Of course, the suffering directly caused by such a phenomenon is not lessened merely by coming to understand something of its human origination. But such an understanding should at least mitigate the sense of being the helpless captive of giant forces. Moreover, an individualistic explanation may indicate ways in which people's situations might be deliberately and systematically changed, whether by politico-legal intervention or in some other way, so that their actions no longer have the same unwanted, unintended, crazy and inhuman-seeming results.

E. GELLNER: *Reply.*

I find myself in very substantial agreement with both the general position and the specific arguments put forward by Cohen and Watkins. Consequently no very detailed additional comments are really called for.

Still, there is one point at which I am not too sure of my agreement with Watkins. It is perhaps ungracious for me to bite the hand which was raised in my support, for Watkins' argument is, as he states, put up to reinforce my own. My apology for this ungracious conduct is two-fold. First, the issue which may divide us seems to me intrinsically interesting, and well worth clarifying, irrespective of whether Watkins or I are right on this point. The

---

[1]   See K. R. Popper, *The Poverty of Historicism*, London 1957, pp. 147f.

interest of the issue is greater than the obligation of reciprocity, if such an obligation be admitted in scholarly matters at all. Secondly, I am not at all clear in my own mind what the correct answer is on this point, and find myself pulled in contrary directions in different contexts. Hence my observations are less in the nature of a polemic, than a fairly impartial exploration of an inner doubt.

To begin with, some comments on Watkins' summary of my own position. This does not seem to me entirely correct, and misleading in a way relevant to the issue I wish to raise. Watkins says (summing up my position): 'Let us agree that the study of nature should not be anthropomorphic and that the study of man can hardly avoid being anthropomorphic. Then what about the study of *society* – to which side should it incline?'

It is *not* obvious to me that 'the study of man can hardly avoid being anthropomorphic'. The fact that, tautologically, the subject matter of the 'study of man' is indeed *man*, does not seem to me to entail that the *explanatory* concepts invoked must also be, in some sense further to be defined, *human*. The position of, let us say, behaviourists, to the effect that certain very human concepts ('conciousness') must be excluded, whether true or false, does not seem to me self-evidently absurd. There is one fairly straightforward sense in which the study of man can be 'non-human' in form: if it consists of causal explanations of human behaviour, in which the antecedents are events outside the range of ordinary human experience, and only accessible to the scientists with special equipment (for instance, microscopes).

Interestingly enough, on an earlier occasion Watkins himself held such a position [1], allowing *psychology* to be possibly non-human in this sense, though not sociology. At that point, he seemed to consider the asymmetry between sociology and psychology to be the very reverse of what, by implication, he considers it to be in the present note.

In practice, however, my own doubts about the applicability of human explanations of human conduct are not inspired by a

---

[1] Cf. J. W. N. Watkins, 'Ideal types and historical explanation', *The British Journal for the Philosophy of Science*, **2**, 9, (1952).

preoccupation with neurological or similar explanations. For the purposes of my present concern, there is no asymmetry between psychology and sociology. Neither, I suspect, is bound to be anthropomorphic; and sociology does not occupy some middle position, liable to incline either to the non-anthropomorphism of science or the anthropomorphism of psychology. From the viewpoint of my present concern, psychology and sociology stand or fall together.

My concern can be stated very simply. Our life is lived in terms of ideas drawn from the common stock of the society in which we find ourselves, or rather, from the over-lapping number of societies in which we are involved. For a variety of obvious reasons, we cannot avoid using those ideas. For one thing, we have to use *some* ideas. For another, whilst we might possibly introduce some innovations at one or two points, it is beyond the powers of any individual to re-fashion the lot.

These ideas which we take over have theories built into them and often presuppose a good deal about the nature of the world. These ideas and presuppositions can be false, and I believe they frequently are false or vacuous. (They may nevertheless be viable.) *Yoh-hee-hoh* contains little information about the social organization of the Volga boatmen. Many conceptual accompaniments of activities contain no more.

It seems to me an interesting feature of modern life that a certain awareness of this is extremely pervasive. People both act on 'commonsense notions', and are at the same time aware that these 'commonsense notions' are cognitively inadequate and second rate. This is reflected in a number of well-known characteristics of modern life: the invocation of the expert when important decisions are taken, the expectation that the expert's language shall be specialised and unintelligible, the prestige of any unintelligibility when it suggests expertise, the artificial manufacture of such unintelligibility for the purpose of acquiring such prestige, the invention of ideologies whose appeal hinges on a claim that their concepts, underlying assumptions, and so on, are cognitively superior to those of commonsense. The fact that many such claims are spurious in no way undermines the plausibility of the underlying feeling, to the effect that life takes place at two quite distinct levels: those of the concepts of daily life, which we cannot but use but which are grossly inadequate if not positively misleading, and another set of concepts which are accessible, at most, to some genuine experts, but which are cognitively adequate.

The ideological relevance of Winch is of course that he tries to reassure himself and others that this feeling is mistaken. Watkins' argument against Winch is meant to show that Winch may be right in those cases when all is well with some ongoing activity, but that it may become inapplicable, or requires great refinement, when that activity undergoes a cataclysm. In terms of his example, the concepts of cricket can be invoked to explain a cricket game which is proceeding satisfactorily, but not a situation in which the spectators pelt the umpire with beer bottles. My own doubts about the invocation of concepts internal to the activity itself extend *equally* to both situations, to stability and cataclysm.

It may be worthwhile to digress for a moment on the question of just what it is that makes concepts 'human' or 'non-human'. One can be a relativist or an absolutist about this. A relativistic position would be: concepts become 'human' simply through familiarity. Psycho-analytic or cybernetic concepts began by being 'non-human' when they were unfamiliar, explaining familiar concepts in terms of quite unfamiliar notions, but now that those concepts have become popularised and many people commonly use them to describe their own or others' behaviour, they have become 'human'. That is all there is to it. The distinction does not amount to much. Alternatively, one can treat the distinction as permanent and absolute. For instance, one can consider concepts such as 'purpose', 'consciousness' or 'responsibility' to be inherently and permanently human, whilst considering the concepts connected with causal determination as inherently inhuman. If moreover the two sets of concepts are mutually incompatible, and if one set of them is cognitively powerful and inherent either in the results or in the methods of science, whilst the other is a precondition of value, choice and responsibility, we are lead to a very familiar philosophic problem.

Winch attempts to provide an omnibus validation and justifi-

cation of the human concepts. It is instructive to compare him
on this point with Kant. The difference is that Winch thinks that
his aim can be achieved easily, that it is fairly obvious and that
there is a straightforward mistake on the other side. Kant thought
that it was terribly difficult, that the human concepts could only
be saved at the cost of utmost philosophic exertion and of making
the most difficult assumptions, which assumptions, though justified
by this one important purpose, would otherwise not be justifiable.
Winch thinks they are easily justified in themselves, irrespective
of need. Secondly, Winch thinks he can save *all* human concepts,
whatever they be, whereas Kant thought he could only save a
very small number, the minimal and ultimate prerequisites of
value, freedom and responsibility.

My own reaction to this endeavour is the following: much as
one might wish to save our humanity from the corrosive effect
of scientific or sociological explanation, I doubt whether we can
do it in this way, either wholesale or selectively.

If we attempt to do it wholesale, we tend to finish up in a self-
contradictory position: by trying to save *all* our notions, we at
the same time, and self-contradictorily, condemn those of our
common notions which themselves condemn the others. (We
condemn that strong and important element in our shared consciousness which *accepts* the inadequacy of commonsense.) But I
also doubt whether we can do it selectively, whether we can insulate
and guarantee a re-doubt of both crucial and unimpugnable human
notions.

This brings me back to my tentative disagreement with Watkins.
If I understand his position correctly, he is a selective humanist,
as opposed to the Winchian omnibus variety. His selective humanity, however, is different from Kant's. It does not select a
minimal set of notions on the basis of their being the absolute
prerequisites of responsibility etc. The basis for a selection is to be
found in methodology, not in ethics (at least, not directly). The
sociological explanation must be reintegrated into the model associated with the suggestive slogan of the 'logic of the situation'.
This does not give us (at least immediately) responsibility and
freedom, but it does give us *aim* and *belief* as the essential and

irreducible elements of the human situation. An explanation in terms of the 'logic of the situation' is an explanation which shows us, given certain aims, given a certain environment, and given certain beliefs about that environment, how the behaviour which is to be explained naturally follows. If all sociological explanation ultimately has this form, it follows that we shall never need, for sociological reasons, to revise at least one variant of the 'human' view of human life, namely one which sees it as the resultant of the interplay of *purpose* with both environment and *belief* about environment.

The consideration which, at this point, tends to swing me over to Watkins' viewpoint is that indeed, the most satisfying kind of explanation in the social sciences is one which shows, given fairly crude and simple and recognised human aims, how these get canalised by existing circumstances into the social situation which requires explanation. The considerations, on the other hand, which sway me in the other direction are two-fold:

(1) Is it the aims and beliefs *as conceived by the participants* which matter?

(2) If it be granted, as I think it is, that there is a kind of regress here, that the explanation of one social situation invokes the assumption of a further *social* context in which the agents were operating, should the stress be on the ever *un*completed nature of this regress or on the fact that we are impelled to undertake it? Only the latter alternative favours Watkins' position.

Roughly: the general characteristics of societies, their culture and their language, which enable their members to conceptualise aims and beliefs about environments, and which consequently are presupposed by special explanations, are not perhaps correctly represented by the beliefs of those members themselves.

This is a big theme, and clearly cannot be dealt with here. But if this suspicion is correct, then the human interpretation of human beings cannot be vindicated in Watkins' selective manner, any more than in Winch's totally unselective one. Moreover, it is not the case that stable and customary situations are more open to 'inner' explanations than cataclysmic ones. It is true that in stable customary ones, customary notions are more easily accepted by participants (by definition, in effect), but this in no way indicates that those notions are veridical. On the contrary: harmony and consensus may provide opportunities for indulgence in wild ideological fantasy, or vacuity. Who will bother to check the ideologists, when all is going well?

ANTI-DUALIST OUTLOOK AND SOCIAL ENQUIRY

J. O. WISDOM

University of London

The interactionist theory of the relation between mind and body, usually called dualism, enjoys a particularly striking non-status in the general outlook of the time. There are two groups of people who might be concerned with it: philosophers and doctors. Among philosophers there is a widespread tendency to regard it as the most untenable theory of all, and to dismiss it without discussion. Among doctors the growing body of those who are interested in psychosomatic medicine takes the same view. It is a commonplace for such doctors to hold that there is no sharp difference between mind and body, or that the two are essentially one, and that the dualistic view has done great harm to their understanding of the whole person. The coincidence of opinion of two such groups which have no mutual influence upon one another may suggest that the outlook has some societal root, that is to say, the view may be held for reasons other than strictly rational ones.

This suspicion grows stronger when one examines the position of the mind–body problem in these two groups.

Let us first consider psychosomatic doctors. They have come to the conclusion that certain organic diseases are largely produced by mental conflicts – at least that is the psychosomatic hypothesis. This leads them to be more attentive to people as persons, and not disregard their personality when dealing with diseases of the body. This is very proper, but for some reason it leads doctors to deny the fundamental difference between minds and bodies, a situation that is all the more curious because it abolishes the discoveries they have made; for, if the new psychosomatic hypothesis that the cause of a bodily disorder lies not in the body but in the mind is to have a point, the mind has to be different from the body. Their conclusion is thus not a rational one.

The position with philosophers is somewhat different.

Descartes is commonly regarded as having described mind and body as two utterly disparate and unrelated entities, and to have set the problem for his successors of how these two could be related. This interpretation of Descartes is false; it is clear from his letters to Princess Elizabeth that while the problem was obviously difficult he regarded it as in principle soluble and he did not regard the two domains as utterly disparate and unrelatable; in fact he thought there must be interaction between them though he was very unsure about how this took place. The impact of the problem upon almost all of Descartes' successors was so extreme that they planted upon Descartes a false interpretation of his actual view. The so-called Cartesian problem that they all tried to solve is not the one that is in Descartes. The problem they sought to solve was how to relate utterly disparate unrelated entities. When put thus starkly it is easy to see that the solutions offered were bound to be rather bizarre. I do not propose to go through the fantastic notions of the Occasionalists and of the great intellectualist philosophers who produced various versions of parallelism, which are not so much untenable solutions as non-solutions, that is to say, they left the problem precisely where it was. A version of parallelism has been revived in our own day; it might be called linguistic parallelism, though it is officially called the two-language theory. It suffers from exactly the same defect of leaving the core of the problem untouched. What is so striking about all these attempts is that philosophers have opted for the least serious of all possible solutions. Even the idealistic solution, absurd though it appears to most people, is a more serious contribution because it does not reproduce the problem in exactly the same form as was originally presented. Further, the outlook that denies interaction goes against the daily experience, repeated scores of times, of everybody. Anyone can multiply examples of the sort that if one takes a great deal of alcohol into the body the mind will feel elated, amused, and the like. Similarly, everyone can produce examples in plenty to the effect that a telephone message, which is understood by the mind, gives rise to action by the body. Thus the news of a salary increase is likely to cause the body and its legs to move to a place of celebration. Philosophers seem very ready to overlook the fact that these commonplaces do not cease to exist by being ignored or by being regarded as metaphysically impossible.

Thus the conclusion of philosophers, as with the doctors, is irrational, though in a somewhat different way.

The irrationality of the two points of view suggests that there is something of a societal nature at work. This might be the case even if the conclusions were rational, but some such explanation seems to be more called for if the outlook is in fact highly irrational.

The position of the medical group may be considered first. Medicine owes one of the greatest of its advances to Pasteur, for he invented a great theory that explained a great proportion of the diseases of mankind, that is to say, the explanation of infectious diseases by germs. But medicine continues to live under the shadow of Pasteur; for his very success has had as a consequence the outlook that no other explanation of disorders is possible. But there would seem to be more to it than simply the great success of this theory.

The germ theory of disease made medicine 'scientific'. This was at once its glory and its disaster. For not only was medicine now scientific, but it also became parascientific through misinterpretation of the nature of science. The *Weltanschauung* of all physiological laboratories, since Pasteur, might be expressed by a text written in invisible ink over the walls of all such laboratories: 'For all physiological changes seek only physical causes.' And this would be the spirit of parascientific enquiry. I shall come back later to the question why this restriction is felt to be a part of the scientific outlook.

What is the position as regards philosophers?

The philosophical position must be set against the background of the revival of learning after the Middle Ages. Let us see what this amounts to for present purposes. The Middle Ages had fostered great numbers of occult speculations which suffered reproof from Bacon. This tended to undermine confidence in ideas or in the workings of the mind, at any rate unless some very significant restraint was put upon them. What took the place of medieval speculation or, to put the matter otherwise, what is the intellectual characterization of the Renaissance? It can be epitomized, following

Butterfield, in a word: mechanical explanation. The most advanced of the natural sciences was mechanics, as is evident from the progress made under Galileo, Descartes, and Newton. Under Descartes it was extended into the philosophy of nature in that he tried to explain the physical universe in terms of a theory of push, according to which all matter in the universe moved as a result of being pushed by something. In Newton this was reversed: as Popper puts it, push was replaced by pull, and though gravitation is strictly speaking not mechanical in quite the same sense its effects were all studied under the heading of mechanics – terrestrial mechanics and celestial mechanics. Mechanical explanation was thus extended not only to the world but to the universe, and made into a cosmology. It is of course true that there were other natural sciences or branches of physics; there were some rudimentary notions about magnetism and heat, but these were overshadowed by mechanics, so that it would have been strange indeed if the ideal of mechanics had not dominated the *Weltanschauung*.

Now what does this amount to as a contrast to the speculations of the Middle Ages? I would suggest that it amounts to the principle: 'For all physical changes seek only natural (i.e. in practice mechanical) causes.'

Electrical causes, had they been better known, might have seemed much more magical but they obviously could have had very little influence. Mechanical causes would have seemed natural in a way that no other kind could.

It should be underlined just how revolutionary the idea of seeking natural causes really was. This may be seen by considering what the reverse would be. It would be explanation in terms of non-natural causes, easily identified with witchcraft or anything occult. Thus for the superstitious thoughts might be explained by witchcraft. For the intelligentsia of the Renaissance thoughts would have to be explained by a natural cause. If you got warts, it was no longer a question of *who* willed them on to you but *what* mechanically induced them.

In other words, the transition from the Middle Ages to the Renaissance was no less than a transition, however incompletely carried out, from magical explanation to naturalistic explanation.

Further, the Renaissance was also the age of science, and looked like the birth of science. Small wonder then if science became identified with naturalistic explanation.

And this outlook characterized not only the Renaissance but succeeding centuries right up to the present day. We are surely children of the Renaissance.

But what has all this to do with the mind–body problem? The answer may be put like this. Interaction which allows that mental changes could act upon the body and produce physiological changes is at variance with the principle of naturalistic explanation, of seeking for all physical change only natural causes. To allow the possibility of such interaction would be to incur the risk of allowing magical explanation to reappear through the back door. This contention may be reinforced. In mechanical, physical, or naturalistic explanation a considerable limitation is put upon the power of the causal agency. Mechanical causes are very far from anything that might be called omnipotent. Now by contrast an explanation in terms of witchcraft or anything occult or magical carries at least overtones of omnipotence. Non-naturalistic or non-physical explanation implies that some non-physical occurrence is able at will to produce physical effects. Hence we may put it that the transition from the Middle Ages to the Renaissance may be characterized as a transition from explanation in terms of omnipotence to non-omnipotent, naturalistic explanation. Now to admit that mental changes might produce changes in the body would suggest that a change in the mind could effect changes magically or omnipotently in the natural world. And this would be felt all the more strongly because no mechanism of connection between the two domains has ever been discovered or even found imaginable. We are now in a position to collate the setting for the attitude towards the philosophical problem with the setting for the attitude towards research in physiology, and it is easy to see that both are animated by the same drive: to proceed in accordance with naturalistic science in the sense of the avoidance of magic. In both cases the agent suspected of magical powers is the mind. In the classical mind–body problem it would interact with the body producing changes in it. In the further development of somatic disorder it would be again the mind producing pathological diseases in the body.

Let us now try to put the methodological situation in perspective.

'Sensible' scientists and 'sensible' methodologists naturally would deplore any attempt to frame scientific hypotheses embodying, say, the concept of a witch. How many are there who would not rule such a hypothesis out of order as unscientific? Yet to do so would be parascientific. Suppose for example that a hypothesis were framed embodying the idea of a witch such that, with suitable initial conditions, an observational prediction could be deduced, then the hypothesis embodying the concept of a witch would be testable and, whether we liked it or not, would have to be accepted as scientific even if it in fact were false. A hypothesis has to be removed from the corpus of science simply because it is untestable, not because it smells of the occult.

Now it may very well be that a hypothesis about the power of minds to interact with bodies and produce organic changes in them may be testable. This might entail some risk that some people might be encouraged to regress to a belief in witchcraft; let us not, however, try to resolve all difficulties at once. If we are dealing with the mind–body problem let us refrain from worrying about the scientific morals of those who secretly hanker after the magical.

We may summarize as follows: from the Renaissance to the present day, the world of science has reacted against the intellectual habit of speculation in terms of the occult and magical entities in the Middle Ages. It has done so by going to the opposite extreme of making mechanical explanation its ideal model, and this is a parascientific model in contrast with the scientific model itself, which consists of a hypothesis, however fantastic, that can be subject to empirical testing. Thus a parascientific model leads to a scientific *Weltanschauung* in which only physicalistic explanations are permitted. The world of science is still reacting against the Middle Ages – ghosts and goblins, vampires and witches.

If this is the picture of the past and present, what of the future?

If mankind has achieved a scientific outlook, even if imperfectly, only at enormous cost, the price being the relinquishing of belief in omnipotence and magic, one can readily understand the anxiety that would be aroused in scientific minds at the slightest prospect of having the process reversed. Hence one would expect scientists, or rather those scientists who are animated by the parascientific outlook, to defend physicalistic explanation to the last ditch.

One unfortunate consequence of this situation is that those who are seriously interested in the real power of the mind to effect changes in the world and in particular changes in the body, either from the point of view of philosophy or of psychosomatic medicine, are likely to react against science because of its parascientific form, and thus on the one side there will be naturalistic parascientists who will not investigate certain hypotheses about minds seriously, and on the other humanists doing at best sloppy science and at worst substituting for science a metaphysic, perhaps with scientific trappings, of an untestable kind.

If this diagnosis is correct, then the prognosis is that there will be a struggle between these two cultures, say, over the next twenty-five years. These would not be the two cultures of science and humanities, but the two cultures of parascience and incompetent science.

As regards the philosophy of the social sciences, we have the evident corollary: the influence of the ideology of mechanical explanation inhibits the development of the kind of hypothesis that the problem-situation demands.

M. BODEN: *Interactionism – could experiments decide?*

Dr. Wisdom asks us to treat the dualist theory of mind–body interaction not as a sophisticated superstition, but as a testable scientific theory; if we can deduce observable consequences from a hypothesis, then it is testable – and the only intellectually honest thing to do is to go ahead and test it. But can we deduce observable consequences from an interactionist hypothesis? And can we specify the limits of the hypothesis (the extent and nature of *ad hoc* hypotheses we are prepared to admit) so as to make clear exactly what would count as tests?

Consider the hypothesis in general form: changes in bodily phenomena produce changes in mental phenomena, and vice versa. This implies that specifiable bodily events will be regularly accompanied (followed or preceded, according to the direction of interaction) by specifiable mental events. But – granted that we are prepared to use this language in the first place – we all *know* this to be true from everyday experience; and if we have any doubts there are the experiments of Penfield [1] (electrical stimulation of the temporal cortex is associated with vivid memory-like experiences) and the EEG studies [2] (thinking about subjects which is subjectively emotionally charged is associated with changes in EEG pattern) to persuade us. So, in its general form, it would seem that the hypothesis has been tested already – why, then, do we not all accept it?

Consider some more specific forms of the hypothesis: I shall mention two examples of experiments on imagery, which seem to test the hypothesis that certain behavioural skills are mediated by conscious imagery in a reasonable direct way, i.e. by 'reading-

---

[1] See e.g., Penfield, 'Memory mechanisms', *Arch. Neurol. and Psychol.* **67** (1952), pp. 178–192.

[2] See e.g., Darrow, 'The electroencephalogram and psycho-physiological regulation of the brain', *Amer. J. Psychiat.* **102** (1946), pp. 791–798.

off' from an image. The first [1] showed that subjects who claimed to have formed a definite image of an array of letters formerly presented to them could indeed 'read-off' the letters correctly – but only in the familiar order, *not* from bottom to top, or diagonally. Does this show that the image they claimed to have, and which they described as an essential mediator in their behaviour, was not quite like what they consciously thought it to be, or that it was not there at all, or that it was there merely as an idle epipheno-menon which in no way directed their behaviour? How could any further experiment decide?

Another set of experiments [2] investigated subjects learning to trace a motor pattern by pressing 8 switches in an 8×8 array (only those 8, and in only one order, lighting up the equivalent positions on an adjacent response-board carrying an 8×8 array of bulbs). Some subjects were given no more training after they had learned the task to the criterion of 5 successive errorless trials; others 'overlearned' the task, i.e. they each performed 50 trials *after* having reached the criterion of learning. On later testing, the first group were found to be unable to produce the correct response in the absence of the response-board, while the second group were not only able to do so, but reported visual imagery of the response pattern independent of the visual stimulus of the board, and described their behaviour and method primarily in terms of visual imagery, while the other group claimed to use tactual imagery or cues. In view of the former experiment it is not clear that we should take these claims at their face value; nonetheless it is interesting that descriptions in terms of visual imagery were offered only by those subjects who were able to perform competently in the absence of the physical response-board. However, it is still not clear whether this is or is not a test of the interactionist theory. Would this theory be content to claim that

---

[1] Fernald, M. R., 'The diagnosis of mental imagery', *Ps. Monogr.* **58** (1912).

[2] Mandler, G., 'Transfer of training as a function of degree of response overlearning', *J. Exptl. Psychol.* **47** (1954), pp. 411–417; Mandler, G. and C. K. Kuhlmann, 'Proactive and retroactive effects of overlearning', *J. Exptl. Psychol.* **61** (1961), pp. 76–81.

conscious imagery is an essential mediator in the skilled performance (as the response-board was for the first group of subjects) or does it require that the imagery itself be causally active in the whole behavioural process (as the response-board certainly is not)?

I am, of course, ignoring – as the interactionist must – the supposed difficulty of postulating any causal relation between *things so different* as mind and body, mental and physical events. Let us just ask *whether* there is a causal relation, without getting entangled in the Humean problem of *how* this can be so. But it is still not clear to me whether Dr. Wisdom would be content to take experiments such as those I have cited as tests of his hypothesis; if not, what would he accept as tests? And would we be content to agree with him that certain experiments are – or would be – tests? Is interactionism *really* a scientific theory? Is interaction even as respectable as witches?

R. WOLLHEIM :   *Dr. Wisdom on the mind–body problem : a comment.*

It is, I know, usually thought not correct to criticise a speaker for what he has not said. In general I would agree with this principle. However it seems to me that in the case of Dr. Wisdom's paper the omission is so glaring that it throws a deep shadow over what he *does* say.

The burden of Wisdom's paper is that we should return to the interactionist theory of the relation between mind and body as giving us an account of the matter most in line with the demands of science. So we need to know what interactionism is. From Wisdom's paper one might come away with the impression that the interactionist theory simply consists in the claim that there *is* an interaction between mental events (in the common acceptance of that phrase) and physical events (in the common acceptance of that phrase): conversely, that anti-interactionists, who are Wisdom's enemies, are people who insist that there is not, or even could not be, such interaction. Interpreting the traditional theories in this way, Wisdom has of course no great difficulty in proving that interactionism is true and its contradictory false. For, to take

Wisdom's own example, it can happen that as the result of hearing certain news, my body moves in a certain direction. The hearing of the news would ordinarily be identified as a mental event, the movement of the body would ordinarily be identified as a physical event. So here at any rate is one example of the thesis that the anti-interactionist denies: and such examples could be multiplied indefinitely from the daily experience of mankind.

Unfortunately, Wisdom's account of the interactionist theory is only half the story: or less. For traditionally interactionism does not merely assert that there is an interaction between events of two different kinds, it also has a great deal to say about what these two different kinds of event are. It is indeed only when we take into account what it has to say on this score that we can have any idea of what specific statements of interaction it characteristically asserts: or, to put it the other way round, of what specific statements of interaction the anti-interactionist theory characteristically denies. Wisdom, who overlooks this whole side of the two theories, overlooks this point too: and to the detriment of his thesis. For the point is not purely pedantic. For when in fact we come to look at the accounts supplied by traditional interactionism as to what is a 'mental', and what is a 'physical' event, it is far from clear that these accounts are equivalent, even extensionally, to the ordinary pre-critical notions of the mental and the physical. In other words, we cannot assume – for it may not even be true – that traditional interactionism would be established by the existence of 'an interaction between mental events (in the ordinary acceptance of that phrase) and physical events (in the ordinary acceptance of that phrase)'. Equally we cannot say that traditional anti-interactionism requires the denial of any interaction between events of the kind popularly held to be mental and those of a kind popularly held to be physical respectively. And this disposes of Wisdom's perfunctory proof of one of the traditional theories and disproof of the other: and, for that matter, of his remark that psychosomatic doctors are 'irrational' when they 'deny the fundamental difference between minds and bodies.'

Wisdom might argue that he has not concerned himself with what interactionism says about the kinds of event that interact:

for this is expressed in terms of 'untestable' hypotheses about substance. But such an argument would be misguided. For traditional assertions about substance can be re-expressed in terms of methods of identification. So, for instance, the interactionist theory could be expressed (roughly) as the thesis that there are certain predicates that can be identified without reference to physical predicates but are such that when predicates of both kinds are attributed to the same entity, an empirical correlation between a predicate of each kind is possible. (Of course there are difficulties in this kind of approach which centre round the problem of whether the entity in question can be left, as I have left it, uncharacterised, or whether it has to be characterised in some such way, e.g. as sentient, that presupposes the thesis under definition: such difficulties being notoriously unresolved in Strawson's *Individuals*).

I think that Wisdom might have got a bit further into the problem if he had taken rather more seriously his own suggestion that the resistance to interactionism in part springs from the desire to abandon omnipotent ways of thinking. 'To admit that mental changes' he writes, 'might produce changes in the body would suggest that a change in the mind could effect changes magically or omnipotently in the natural world'. But this looks like a hopeless exaggeration. For taken at its face-value the hypothesis, say, that thinking about topics that are emotionally charged can produce changes in the EEG pattern (Miss Boden's example) surely does nothing to reinforce belief in the omnipotence of thought. For *this* belief is, at least in the first instance, concerned with a narrower or more specific form of interaction, i.e. between wishes or quasi-wishes and the realisation of their objects.

So, if we accept Wisdom's interpretation of the resistance to interactionism, it looks as though what is feared is that we shall have to accept, along with other forms of interaction, *this* form. But then why should we worry about this form of interaction since there is (and I am sure Wisdom would agree with me here) no evidence for it at all?

And the answer seems to be that there is a form of interaction which though not in fact a case of omnipotent thinking, on one interpretation turns out as such. I refer to the power that we have over our own body in voluntary movement, which has been the central issue in the mind–body problem. And the interpretation on which it comes out as, or close to, omnipotent thinking is, of course, that contained in traditional interactionism. For this theory demands that if voluntary movement is a case of interaction, then there must be something mental which is identifiable independently of physical criteria and which is that through which our power over our limbs is exercised. This mental something is postulated as 'a volition': which then approximates itself to a wish or quasi-wish.

I argue, therefore, that if Wisdom had taken more seriously the connection that he suggests between the resistance to interactionism and the transcendence of omnipotent thinking, he would have appreciated rather better the extent to which interaction is not merely a view about the relations into which the mental enters but is also a view about what the mental is.

Wisdom's paper can be seen as a typical instance of one mode of interpreting metaphysical theories: namely, as fundamentally methodological or heuristic. It could also serve to alert us to dangers implicit in this mode of interpretation. For the trouble is that unless we actually rewrite the theories in a methodological form – which of course dispenses with the whole issue of their interpretation – there is no simple route from the general metaphysical theory to the specific scientific theories that on this interpretation characteristically fall under its aegis. For part of what every metaphysical theory does is – for reasons which need to be understood in detail – to advocate a reclassification of scientific theories. So, for instance, it is not clear how many of the empirical hypotheses that Wisdom thinks of as confirming interactionism would be acceptable to a thorough-going interactionist: or for that matter would seem to the anti-interactionist to provide him with any reason for modifying his attitude. If Wisdom were right, philosophy would be much easier than most of us find it. I can readily agree with Hume that the errors of religion are more 'dangerous' than those of philosophy, but I cannot agree with him, though presumably Wisdom can and must, that the latter are 'only ridiculous'.

J. O. WISDOM: *Reply.*

The thesis of my paper concerned a historical-social explanation of a
dominant attitude towards the interactionist theory of the mind–
body relation prevailing for at least a quarter of a millenium. I did
not claim that interactionism is readily testable; in fact the problem
of testing it is a problem of devising a test to discriminate between
it and epiphenomenalism, which I did not discuss. The question
I raised was why it was customary to *dismiss* interactionism,
seeing that this was done by adopting bizarre alternatives (e.g.
parallelism) which denied the evidence of ordinary experience. I
did not claim that this evidence is decisive, only that extraordinary
contortions are needed in order to go against it. (I do not dismiss these contortions; but I could not discuss them in my paper.)

Seen in this light, Miss Boden's striking examples fall in with
the evidence of ordinary experience, but they do not seem to
amplify it or go beyond it in principle (as she herself indicates);
so they are no more effective than the unsophisticated examples
of everyday life to corroborate interactionism against, say, parallelism. The occasionalists could, unfortunately, reply to Miss Boden
that, 'on the occasion' of the imagery she describes occurring in
some subjects, corresponding physical responses also occur. Likewise
the epiphenomenalist could reply that 'overlearning' produces a
physiological abilty to select correctly of which the visual imagery
is but an otiose concomitant. Her examples have punch but are
not decisive.

In short, I was concerned not with the problem of testing interactionism but with that of explaining why philosophers go to
inordinate lengths to avoid being committed to that view.

My introductory remarks in reply to Miss Boden apply also to
Professor Wollheim's comment.

Wollheim makes two main criticisms: (1) that I misreported
the only part of interactionism I referred to, because (2) my account
of it omitted an essential part of that theory. And he makes it
clear that in consequence he regards my treatment of the subject
as highly superficial. I shall discuss the two criticisms, which seem
to be ill-founded, and draw attention to a different one which might

have some force. Wollheim also ascribes certain positions to me, e.g. that I interpret metaphysical views methodologically, and that I must regard the errors of metaphysics as ridiculous. Quite the contrary. But I shall not deal with these points.

1.   Central to Wollheim's comment is that traditional anti-interactionists would not have denied that taking alcohol causes feelings of elation. I took it for granted that they would have denied it. According to Wollheim, these philosophers would have said in effect that of course taking alcohol causes feelings of elation but that our problem is what account (analysis) we can give of the causal relation and of the terms (substances) it relates.

This seems to me to rewrite history in the light of a twentieth century philosophical theory, due to Moore. He held we all agree on the truth of such statements as 'That is a table', the only question being about the proper analysis of them, for various schools of philosophers gave different analyses. But did philosophers accept the truth of such statements? Did they not rather hold, almost to a man, that such statements were a merely popular way of speaking and not really true?

An example from Moore is his discussion of Bradley's view that time (in the character it exhibits) is unreal. Moore considers numerous possible meanings this might have, thinks none fits, and ends puzzled, because it is clear to him that Bradley could not have meant that there are no temporal facts such as that lightning precedes thunder. But that is just what Bradley seems to have meant, or rather that all such statements as 'Lightning precedes thunder' are partially false.

Similarly it seems to me that historically the anti-interactionists held that such statements as 'Taking alcohol causes feelings of elation' do not, from a fundamental/philosophical point of view, refer to a causal relation.

Otherwise expressed, for Wollheim these philosophers were doubtful or disagreed about the nature or meaning of interaction; in my view they took it for granted that interaction had one specific meaning and their problem was whether different substances could interact, or, to put it more sharply, they held that mind and body could not interact because different *substances* could not interact and remain different substances.

Thus Wollheim's comment would seem to stem from reading the philosophers of a quarter of a millenium ago in the light of twentieth century logico-analytical philosophy.

2. Wollheim claims that I omitted an essential part of inter-actionism, to do with the nature of substance, and he objects to the omission because he holds that the meaning of interaction is partly determined by the prevailing view of substance. This claim fails if my reply to (1) succeeds. However I would add that the traditional view of substance was used to disprove the possibility of interaction, not to give it a meaning. Thus the notion of substance did not permeate that of interaction. My omitting to discuss the nature of substance was deliberate.

If, however, instead of dwelling on the notion of substance, a critic were to point to my omitting to discuss the doctrine of 'secondary causes', then, in view of its historical importance, there might be the possibility of uncovering a serious defect in my thesis, for that doctrine would be very relevant to the issue as seen in the Cartesian period. I doubt if it would affect the outcome, but it should certainly be discussed in a full-length treatment of the subject.